human engineering guide

FOR

equipment designers

second edition

by
WESLEY E. WOODSON
General Dynamics/Astronautics   San Diego
and
DONALD W. CONOVER
NASA — Manned Spacecraft Center   Houston

UNIVERSITY OF CALIFORNIA PRESS
Berkeley   Los Angeles   London

UNIVERSITY OF CALIFORNIA PRESS
Berkeley and Los Angeles

UNIVERSITY OF CALIFORNIA PRESS, LTD.
London, England

Copyright, 1954, 1964
by the Regents of the University of California

Second Edition

Library of Congress
Catalog Card Number 54-8698

Printed in the United States of America

ISBN   0-520-01363-8

567890

PREFACE TO THE SECOND EDITION

For those readers who are familiar with the original Guide, it should be noted that this new edition has been expanded considerably. It is hoped that this change has been an improvement, since the additions reflect many of the recommendations submitted by former readers and colleagues over the past ten years.

In addition, it has been the good fortune of the authors to have participated over the past decade in a wide range of human factors problems in industry, the essence of which we have attempted to pass on to you, the reader.

The greatest expansion in this new revision has occurred in the first parts of the Guide. The first chapter, on Design Philosophy, is entirely new, having replaced the former Introductory Section. Chapter 2 is a considerably expanded version of the original material; however, an attempt has been made to retain the original direct format, which seems to have been appreciated by most designers.

The chapter on Body Measurement has been revised appreciably and made more practical from the designer's point of view. This change is a reflection of the application experience of the writers in working very closely with aerospace and weapon system designers since the beginning of the Jet Age. Revisions in the remaining parts of the book are less extensive, but reflect many of the changes brought about by more recent research — especially in the area of man-in-space and in industrial applications.

The authors wish to express their personal appreciation to the many persons who have provided comments, criticism, and encouragement over the past ten years with reference to Guide content and format. Special apprecation must be expressed to the University of California Press for encouraging the senior author to undertake this present revision. Finally, we wish to give special thanks to Dr. John Coyne, of the California Western University, for his contribution on Bionics, Cybernetics, and Neuroengineering Concepts, and to Mr. Clark Hackler, of the NASA, Manned Spacecraft Center, for his critical review and assistance in preparing the section on the Human Transfer Function.
September 1963

WESLEY E. WOODSON
San Diego, California

DONALD W. CONOVER
Houston, Texas

PREFACE TO THE FIRST EDITION

The information in this book was originally compiled at the request of the Sonar Systems Branch of the Electronics Design and Development Division, Bureau of Ships, which has sponsored the work. It was felt that such a compilation would materially aid engineers in designing their equipment from the human-operator standpoint and thus improve the resultant man-machine operation. It is to this end that this book is dedicated.

Grateful appreciation is hereby expressed to the many persons at the U. S. Navy Electronics Laboratory, San Diego; the Medical Research Laboratory, New London; the Aeronautical Medical Equipment Laboratory, Philadelphia; the Aero Medical Equipment Laboratory; Wright-Patterson Air Force Base, and the numerous university and industrial representatives who contributed to the final revision of this book by their constructive comments and criticisms. Special mention is also made of Dr. Paul Fitts, Dr. Douglas Ellson, LCDR Dean Farnsworth, Dr. Arnold Small, and Dr. Max Lund for their personal assistance and critical review of the manuscript.

My sincere thanks also to the NEL publication personnel who so ably prepared in final form for publication the material submitted to them, and to the University of California Press for the care taken in producing this book.

WESLEY E. WOODSON
Human Engineering Branch
Human Factors Division

Special Consultants

M. LICHTENSTEIN, vision and other factors
E. W. DAVENPORT, audition
D. R. CRAIG, equipment design procedure

NEL Publication Personnel

J. L. GORDON, editor
M. MANAR, illustrator
W. GOLDSMITH, cartoonist
H. KIERSTEAD, photographer

contents

HUMAN ENGINEERING—
A DESIGN PHILOSOPHY

The application of human-engineering principles in the design of things which are to be used by people is not an exact science. Rather, it is a philosophy or an approach to problems of designing and constructing things which people are expected to use — so that the user will be more efficient and less likely to make mistakes in the use of the article. In addition, it is an effort to make such articles more convenient, more comfortable, less confusing, and, in the end, less exasperating or fatiguing to the user.

The principles, guides, and recommendations presented here are by no means a law unto themselves. The designer must use initiative and imagination as well as his own good engineering knowledge and judgment to make them work. Two principal factors must be kept in mind in order to provide a well-human-engineered product:

Do not assume that you, as a designer, necessarily represent a Model of People as a Whole in your mental and physical characteristics or likes and dislikes.

Remember that nothing is designed except for the use of or by Man.

YOU DON'T NECESSARILY REPRESENT THE USER

All too often the designer assumes that because he is human, he is typical of all people who may eventually use the equipment he designs. This is why we find tables and chairs too high or too low — or why there isn't enough room in the cockpit of an airplane. Fortunately, designers can design lots of things which will fit a majority of the user population — based on the designer's own good judgment. However, as designs become more complex, as they have in the past few years, and the integration of men and machines into whole operating systems is necessary, we need more than common sense. Besides the engineering sciences and arts, it has now become necessary to bring many new skills and scientific disciplines into the act — in order fully to integrate Man, Machine, and the Environment.

The designer who is successful in human-engineering his product must develop the humility to recognize his need for assistance from these many disciplines. Many specialists are hard at work trying to learn more about how man reacts and behaves — and especially how he interacts in complex man-machine systems. The information they are developing should be understood and used by the designer along with his own important knowledge and skills. Good human engineering is a team effort, and everyone who is part of this team must develop respect for others on the team — recognizing the need for an interdisciplinary approach to design problems.

HUMAN ENGINEERING DRAWS HEAVILY UPON MOST BASIC SCIENCES AND MANY TECHNICAL SPECIALTIES

Psychology	Operations analysis
Medicine	Computer technology
Physiology	Electronics
Anthropology	Thermodynamics
Biology	Industrial design
Neurology	Mechanical engineering
Acoustics	Illumination engineering
Optics	Chemical engineering
Chemistry	Cybernetics
Physics	Industrial hygiene
Mathematics	Time and motion study
Psychiatry	Education

Many designers may find it hard to understand just what these disciplines have in common. One of the first facts a truly interested designer must recognize is how little he really knows about people: i.e., how they see, hear, react, think; how big or small they are; how far they can reach or bend; how strong they are.

The average designer cannot be an expert on all of these factors. In fact, even the experts themselves still don't have a complete picture of the human being — especially as he fits into a complex operational system.

EVERYTHING IS DESIGNED FOR PEOPLE

This categorical statement is invariably questioned at first glance; therefore it is important to understand why we must accept it to develop a sound "human-engineering philosophy." If one were to analyze each and every object designed or constructed (in an objective manner, that is), he could not escape this fact.

A modern lead pencil was designed because people needed a writing tool with readily erasable marks — not because we like to design little sticks of wood with lead in them and rubber erasers on one end. A 90-passenger airplane was designed to transport people, not because we like to design wings and tail sections. Houses were designed to house and protect people and their possessions, not because we like to design walls and roofs. Even a newspaper is designed for people and not for the fun of running a printing press. With the advent of modern technology, especially the development of automatic devices, there has come a mistaken idea that these devices, at least, were not designed for people. Nothing could be further from the truth. Although their operating interfaces leave fewer people to worry about, their maintenance and programming involve people who must make them perform for a human-directed purpose. A complex computer is not built merely for the pleasure "it" gets from running at great speeds. A ballistic missile isn't designed just because we like to see amazingly complex hardware sitting on the launching pads.

All of these things were and are designed and constructed to extend Man's capability in some way — and are therefore built for Man! If we keep man in mind as the central reason for design, we will have learned the first rule for good human engineering. This concept is often referred to as "designing from the man — out." That is, we start with the man and provide what accessories he needs to carry out or reach a prescribed objective. The cave man fashioned a club in much this manner. He realized that he needed to extend his reach and to increase the lethality of a blow for protection from adversaries. Later he recognized the great advantage of attacking his foes or killing animals from a greater distance — thus came the sling and eventually the bow and arrow.

WHO DESIGNS FOR PEOPLE?

Frequently, human engineering is considered to be something which is applied to a very limited list of design problems. Typically we consider human engineering as being applied to such things as aircraft cockpits, electronic consoles, missile-launch control centers, air-traffic control centers, military vehicles, and, now, space vehicles. Unfortunately we have tended (particularly in the United States) to ignore some of the more common, everyday problems — in terms of not applying good human-engineering principles. For example, very little has been done in the design of homes, home appliances, factory layout or factory machinery, schools, hospitals, offices, libraries, automobiles, buses, trains, ships, farm implements, books, toys — or even sporting goods! In Europe, more emphasis has been applied to domestic problems, particularly with reference to industrial-worker efficiency. In America, the emphasis has been primarily on military-equipment problems. In this revised edition of the *Human Engineering Guide* we have made an effort to give attention to more types of problems and thus make the book useful to a larger population of designers, including:

> Architects
> Building contractors
> Electrical-appliance designers
> Farm-implement manufacturers
> Automobile manufacturers
> Illuminating engineers
> Highway engineers
> Commercial-transportation vehicle manufacturers
> Plumbing-fixture manufacturers
> Furniture manufacturers

A special word should be said to the INDUSTRIAL DESIGNER. Industrial designers and stylists play a unique and important role in modern design. They have brought beauty as well as functional utility to many of the things we use in modern society. These people will continue to play an increasingly important role in matching man to machine. Bringing a look of quality and efficiency into product design has a very definite psychological effect on the way we, as buyers, accept and use the final product. People tend to select and buy things which "look better." They also tend to treat the products with more respect, and in many cases operate them and maintain them better, because they are proud of the product. Since the industrial designer and stylist does play such an important role in society, it is perhaps more important for him than any other specialist to understand and apply human-engineering principles.

A stylist can influence a buyer to purchase a poorly human-engineered product over one that is well human-engineered just by the way he styles the package. Therefore, he has a moral responsibility to see that he human-engineers each product, besides making it "pretty." It is easy to find examples of the effect of "style" on products. A single product may go through many style cycles over a period of several years — cycles which have seen good design spoiled for the sake of change. The designer who allows this to happen is negligent, and is a curse to society and to engineering progress. Fortunately, styling can change without abrogating good human engineering — and the public will still buy what is presented to it over the counter. In other words, if a well-designed product also has good looks, the public will choose it. The designer must give the customer a choice (for that is human nature — to compare and choose), but there is no reason that all of the choices cannot be well human-engineered. The important thing to remember is that good human engineering comes first, then style!

MANAGEMENT also has a responsibility to produce products which are representative of good human engineering. More than once, a company president has come into the engineering department and insisted on adding that extra piece of chrome decoration. If management people don't understand the meaning of human engineering, they can very easily destroy an effective design — thinking that they are creating more sales appeal. The chances of a "repeat customer" for a product which is hard to use or difficult to maintain is very slim indeed.

THE SYSTEMS APPROACH TO DESIGN

Wherever people (users) are concerned, we must remember that everything is relative. That is, a light of given intensity will appear brighter at night than it does in daytime. The speed of your automobile will appear greater on a crowded street or a winding, narrow mountain road than it does on a six-lane, straight, and uncrowded freeway. A complex task will seem much easier to perform in the quiet of an office with no outside interruptions than it would if you were in a noisy, crowded room with many other people, telephone interruptions, or with questions being fired at you while you were trying to perform the task at hand. The repair of a radar antenna would be much simpler and faster on a warm sunny day than in the middle of a blizzard.

When approaching a new design, the designer should consider many factors beyond the article itself — e.g., the way the article will be used, the environment in which it will be used, whether or not it may be used by several different types of people, or whether the person who uses this article may be doing something else at the same time. All of these factors will influence its use. Even the intelligence level, manual dexterity, or amount of training of the final user should be considered by the designer.

The United States Air Force recognized the importance of taking a systems approach to weapon-system development, including the "people problem". Several years ago they took steps to put the "people problem" on equal status with the "hardware problem," and established their Personnel Subsystem concept, or PSS as it is referred to sometimes.[30] It became evident that many of their hardware systems were not meeting operational readiness dates because they did not have adequate manning when the systems were delivered. They further realized that many factors were involved in this "people problem" in addition to just numbers of people. Human-engineering considerations were not being sufficiently applied to the product, and no one knew enough about what the new operators and maintenance technicians would have to do to operate the equipment, so the right kinds and numbers of people were not trained for the jobs. Furthermore, they realized that their new systems hadn't been tested with typical Air Force personnel, so, by the time systems were delivered, highly experienced industrial specialists had to remain on to keep the equipment running. It was obvious that much of the equipment was just too complex for the typical G.I. Thus, the PSS concept was adopted and made a mandatory part of new contracts to assure a total systems approach to all future developments. In essence, the concept centered around the idea of concurrent development of both hardware and personnel to support the system. It included nine specific parts: (1) gathering and maintaining an adequate Personnel and Equipment Data file (PED), (2) applying and verifying good human engineering in design (HE), (3) developing systematic Qualitative and Quantitative Personnel Requirements Information (QQPRI), (4) development of Training Concepts in advance (TC), (5) development of adequate Training Plans (TP), (6) providing early Training Equipment Planning Information in order to start procurement early (TEPI), (7) proceeding with a timely Training Equipment Development program (TED), (8) planning and producing Technical Orders and Manuals to support training and eventual equipment support (TOTM), and (9) providing a continuous Personnel Subsystem Test and Evaluation program to assure that the system could, in fact, operate with the types and numbers of people planned for it (PSTE).

PERSONNEL AND EQUIPMENT DATA

Recognizing the need to keep track of all the data developed during a program, the contractor is required to do the same for all data developed relative to human engineering, manning, personnel development, training-equipment development, training, and results of testing men and machines together. This data must be made accessible at all times for monitoring the progress of the development, for adjusting to design changes, etc. Such a collection of data provides a valuable record from which much can be learned and passed on to future developments also.[10]

HUMAN ENGINEERING

It was quite apparent to the Air Force that in many earlier developments human engineering was regularly applied "after the fact"! Since this invariably leads to a mere "fixing up" of design deficiencies, human engineering has been placed at the top of the list of priorities and is required in the earliest phases of design conceptualization — then carried out faithfully through pre-design, detail design, manufacture, and testing of all hardware. Human-engineering principles apply to the prime equipment, the ground support equipment, and training equipment.[21, 23]

QUANTITATIVE AND QUALITATIVE PERSONNEL REQUIREMENTS INFORMATION

In order for the user to be prepared, in terms of numbers and types of trained personnel, on time, it is necessary for each contractor to determine what kinds of tasks people will perform on the new equipment he is developing — what special skills will be needed, and how many people should be prepared to man the new system adequately.[9, 12, 15, 29]

This requires that rough descriptions must be made of each task as soon as any idea of what the new equipment will be like is available. As design firms up, these descriptions are refined. Basic task and job descriptions provide core data from which operational and maintenance procedures, criteria for training planning, and course curricula are developed. Although this particular requirement has been enforced by the Air Force for many years, the PSS concept now requires that this effort be integrated closely with all other aspects of PSS and especially with design.

Training concepts for the new system must be established early. This is done jointly with the Air Force. Development of the overall concept for a system is a natural out-growth of the work done in previous steps. The concept naturally originates with the contractor, since he alone knows exactly what his new equipment will demand of the user.

As soon as training concepts are firmly established, a fully developed training plan must be worked out to insure timely prosecution of the training program. The plan ordinarily includes a step-by-step program of training contractor personnel, then customer cadre, and, finally, military field personnel, who must be ready to take over the equipment when it is delivered.

Major training equipments must have sufficient lead time for development in order to be useful to the training program. Therefore planning must begin early in the development of system concepts. Agreements must be reached with the customer and specifications prepared in time to allow for design and fabrication. Smaller equipments (particularly mobile training-units, part-task trainers, etc.) are proposed and joint Air Force Contractor conferences held to agree to an overall training-equipment plan of development.

Training-equipment development proceeds in the same way as any other hardware development and includes all of the many considerations of design, fabrication, logistics, and maintenance. Human-engineering principles must be applied to training equipment just as they are applied to prime equipment. It must be remembered that training equipment has an earlier delivery-date requirement than prime equipment, since it must be ready for training — which is in advance of prime-equipment delivery.

TRAINING CONCEPT

TRAINING PLANS

TRAINING-EQUIPMENT PLANNING INFORMATION

TRAINING-EQUIPMENT DEVELOPMENT

TECHNICAL ORDERS AND TECHNICAL MANUALS

Like QQPRI, technical orders and manuals were handled formerly as a separately negotiated item, coming under a separate set of regulations, and carried out by an entirely independent group of contractor and customer personnel. Unfortunately, this patchwork approach had been a constant source of confusion, since the inter-relationships between the principal hardware items and the manuals which purported to describe them, and provide guidance for their operation and servicing, were frequently unsuccessful until many revisions were made. The new PSS concept brought this part of the system development into line with the hardware development.[17]

PERSONNEL SUBSYSTEM TEST AND EVALUATION

No one has ever doubted the need for testing a complex piece of hardware to make sure it works. Before PSS, however, little attention was paid to the need for testing the over-all system of men and machines together. This is perhaps the most important part of the PSS concept. PSSTE refers to all man-machine testing, including all of the intermediate as well as the final system tests.[32]

Although the magnitude of a PSS program varies from one system to another, depending on the need, all of the basic elements are generally included. For certain small or less complex systems it is logical for elements of PSS to vary in magnitude and importance. The basic theme of concurrence, however, remains. These principles have been demonstrated as sound and practical through repeated experience in military system-development programs. With modifications to meet unique commercial or industrial demands, they have application to nonmilitary hardware and other types of consumers' goods with complex man-machine interfaces.

Many people are not aware that PSS starts as early as pre-contract studies — or that all of the elements should appear in contract proposals. For more complete information, the reader is referred to Air Force ARDC Manual 80-3.[30] In addition, it is suggested that an adequate organization within a company is necessary to carry out a PSS program or contract. It is not satisfactory to try to accomplish this with PSS specialists spread out in various organizations throughout the company. The Air Force establishes a specific group in its Systems Project Office (SPO) for each project. This group is made up of a specialist from each one of the areas described in the PSS requirement; therefore it is important for a company to do the same in order to "interface" with the customer. This recommendation is in opposition to many company organizations in which some project engineer takes on the PSS responsibility in adidtion to many other duties. This assumption by a single person cannot provide the necessary integration required for so important or complex an operation as PSS, and is to be avoided if possible.

A diagram of a typical PSS–Hardware System Development Cycle is shown on the next page, as a general guide to the relationships and time phasing necessary for successful man-machine system development. Slight modification and possible simplification would make it equally appropriate for a commercial development.

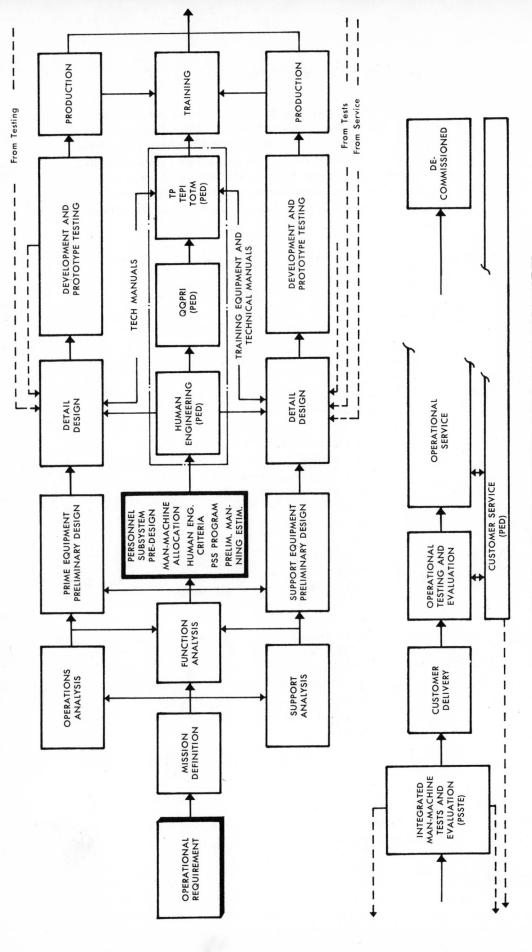

A TYPICAL MANNED WEAPON-SYSTEM DEVELOPMENT MODEL SHOWING THE PSS-CONCEPT INTERACTION WITH EQUIP-MENT DEVELOPMENT

1-9

CATEGORIES OF PERSONNEL-EQUIPMENT DATA

The breadth of coverage required in documenting personnel-equipment data will vary from one system to another. The following comprehensive outline should be useful as a guide for identifying most of the possible interacting data requirements. Inclusion of such a complete outline is meant only to provide a check list, however, and should not be taken to mean that all items would necessarily be required for all systems. (The outline is based on Marks, *A Data Organization Model for the Personnel Subsystem.*[16]

SYSTEM REQUIREMENTS

Effectiveness
1. Accuracy
2. Reliability
3. Reaction time
4. Capability
   a) Destruction*
   b) Pay load
   c) Information handling
      (1) Sensing
         (a) Electromagnetic
         (b) Chemical
         (c) Objects (mass or volume)
         (d) Documentary information
         (e) Atmospheric
         (f) Underwater
         (g) Geological
         (h) Seismological
      (2) Storage
         (a) Capacity
         (b) Access
      (3) Processing
         (a) Internal
         (b) Transfer
      (4) Evaluation
         (a) Identification
         (b) Measurement
         (c) Classification
      (5) Display

Policy
1. Fiscal
2. Scheduling
3. Personnel
   a) Resources
   b) Procurement

        (1) Assessment

        (2) Career-field requirements

        (3) New system requireemnts

    c) Application of force

        (1) Assignment

        (2) Retention-rotation

        (3) Military-civilian*

Vulnerability*

1. Resistance to destruction-ECM
2. Mobility
3. Site nature

*Items marked with an asterisk bear only military significance.

Environment

1. Ambient
   a) Climate
   b) Weather
   c) Temperature–humidity
   d) Light
   e) Safety
2. Geographic

Geographic coverage

1. Range
2. Deployment

Maintenance
Support

1. Installation maintenance
2. Food service
3. Medical
4. Transportation
5. Supply
6. Logistics
7. Security

Personnel (direct requirements or constraints)

1. Manning
2. Training

OPERATIONS

Pictorial descriptions

1. Mission profiles
   a) Ground-support portion
   b) Airborne portion–spaceborne portion
   c) Malfunction profiles

2. Function flow-diagrams
3. Block diagrams
4. Mission segment analyses
5. Work-load time-line analyses
6. Organization charts

Narrative descriptions
1. Operating concept
2. Functions lists
3. Operational plan
   a) Unit organization
   b) Test and check-out procedures
   c) Procedures (task descriptions)
4. Crew performances

Functional performance criteria (time, accuracy, etc.)
Operating conditions
1. Temperature
2. Humidity
3. Shock
4. Acceleration
5. Air flow
6. Toxicity (gaseous or liquid)
7. Acoustic noise–vibration
8. Irradiation
9. Isolation and confinement
10. Pressure
11. Restrictive personal equipment

Auxiliary materials
1. Job aids
2. Manuals
3. Technical orders
4. Handbooks

Position lists
1. Duty descriptions
2. AFSC (Air Force Specialty Classification)*
3. Manning

MAINTENANCE

Reliability goals and data characteristics
1. Program review and considerations
2. System-reliability requirements
   a) Design analysis
   b) Requirement formulations
   c) Parameters
3. Testing program
4. Manufacturing program

Procedures

Crew performance

Preventive-maintenance cycle

Maintainability
    1. Repairability (concepts and specifications)
    2. Availability
      a) Time equipment operating satisfactorily
      b) Down time
        (1) Active maintenance down-time
        (2) Supply down-time
        (2) Waiting or administrative down-time

Materials

Parts lists

Position lists
    1. Duties
    2. AFSC*
    3. Manning

EQUIPMENT CHARACTERISTICS

Includes Operating Equipment, Check-out and Test Equipment, and Special Tools — excludes Maintenance Characteristics and Training Equipment

Descriptions
    1. Photographs
    2. Drawings
    3. Blueprints
    4. Schematics

Theory of operation

Performance characteristics

Reliability characteristics

HUMAN ENGINEERING
(Including biomedical)

Human-engineering plans

Man-machine function allocations

Equipment design
    1. Displays
    2. Controls

Layouts

    1. Work space
        a) Operating consoles
        b) Maintenance consoles
        c) Seats, bunks, lavatories
        d) Hatches, ladders, storage

Design trade-offs

Maintainability Design

    1. Test points
    2. Access points
    3. Trouble-shooting procedures

Life-support functions

    1. Subsistence
        a) Food
        b) Water

    2. Environmental control
        a) Temperature–humidity–ventilation
        b) Protective clothing
        c) Restraint and anti-g protective gear
        d) Noise and vibration attenuation
        e) Radiation detection and protection
        f) Isolation procedures

    3. Waste disposal

Safety

    1. Biomonitoring
    2. Emergency equipment (including escape and survival)
    3. Procedures

TRAINING

Purposes

    1. Knowledges
        a) Job procedures
        b) Other stored information
            (1) Job related
            (2) System related

    2. Skills
        a) Perceptual
            (1) Detection
            (2) Identification
            (3) Instrument and display reading
        b) Psychomotor
            (1) Tool- and test-equipment usage
            (2) Console-equipment operation
            (3) Flight-control operation

       c) Cognitive
         (1) Data interpretation
         (2) Judgments–decisions
         (3) Numerical computations
         (4) Work planning
       d) Communications
         (1) Oral
         (2) Written
         (3) Other (telegraph, signal light, etc.)
       e) Integrated-task performance
         (1) Time-shared tasks in real time
         (2) Crew performance

Curriculums

   1. Formal
      a) Lesson plans
      b) Training schedules
   2. OJT (on-the-job training)
      a) Training plans
      b) Training schedules

Techniques

   1. Lecture
   2. Demonstration
   3. Audio-visual
   4. Practical (performance training)
   5. Automated

Materials

   1. Training equipment
      a) Training functions
         (1) Demonstration
         (2) Practice
         (3) Transition
         (4) Trouble shooting
         (5) Data flow
         (6) Procedures
      b) Assumptions
      c) Special problems
         (1) Unusual skills
         (2) Skill combinations
      d) Existing training equipment
      e) Training-equipment design trade-offs
         (1) Development cost- and time-estimates
         (2) Modifiability estimates
         (3) Maintenance factors
         (4) Installation factors
         (5) Related uses
      f) Applicability of equipment
         (1) Factory training

          (2) Individual training

          (3) Crew and unit training

          (4) Proficiency maintenance training

      g) Recommended training equipment

          (1) Types

              (a) Simulators

              (b) Training devices

              (c) Training aids

              (d) Training attachments

              (e) Training parts

              (f) Training accessories

          (2) Gross description and theory of operation

          (3) Photographs

          (4) Performance specifications

          (5) Drawings

          (6) Schematics

          (7) Features

              (a) Learning

              (b) Transfer

              (c) Programming

              (d) Safety

          (8) Maintainability

          (9) Reliability

      h) Training-parts list

          (1) Nomenclature

          (2) Federal stock number

          (3) Manufacturer's name

          (4) Proposed use of part

          (5) Initial quantity

          (6) GFE or CFE

          (7) USAF Bulletin 507 classification

  2. Instructors

    a) Curricula

    b) Task descriptions

Special problems

  1. Training methods

    a) Unusual skill combinations

    b) Unusual skill demands

  2. Training equipment

    a) Development lead-time

    b) State of the art

    c) Special installations

    d) Power requirements

    e) Climatological modification

Training-equipment design and layout

  1. Instructor station

  2. Trainee station

PERSONNEL SUBSYSTEM TEST AND EVALUATION

Developmental materials

1. Test plans
2. Test outlines
3. Scenarios for performance tests
4. Item pools
5. Pilot forms

Equipment

1. Mock-ups
2. Dynamic simulators
3. Flight or support equipment

Administration materials

1. Administrators' manuals
2. Test booklets
3. Auxiliary test materials
4. Simulation equipment
5. Scoring formulas

Analysis materials

1. Raw-score data
2. Item analyses
3. Reliability studies
4. Validity studies
5. Score diagnosis for training
6. Norms

SELECTION

Test batteries

1. Paper-and-pencil
2. Situational
3. Psychomotor
4. Biographical information
5. Physiological measures
6. Physical measures

Relevant experiences

1. Civilian occupations
2. Military occupations

Other special qualifications

MISCELLANEOUS

Security measures*
Communications nets
Research studies
Housing (ground functions)
Food service (ground functions)

TASK DESCRIPTION

Indicators

1. Visual
    a) Label
    b) Light
    c) Pictorial
    d) Scale–digital
    e) Printed materials
    f) Complex system–environmental relationships

    Challenge each of the above Visual with

Color	Texture	Acceleration
Brightness	Movement	Informational Content
Contrast	Distance	Coding method
Temporal aspects	Noise	Level of abstraction
Configuration	Vibration	

2. Auditory
    a) Pure tones
    b) Speech
    c) Complex non-speech

    Challenge each of the above Auditory with

Frequency	Configuration
Loudness	Timbre
Signal to noise ratio	Movement
Temporal aspects	Direction of source

3. Tactile
    Challenge each Tactile with

Vibration	Configuration
Intensity	Texture
Temporal aspects	Movement

4. Proprioceptive
    a) Static
    b) Dynamic

    Challenge each of the above Proprioceptive with

Pressure	Movement
Tension	Noise
Temporal aspects	

5. Other sense modalities (vestibular, olfactory, etc.)

Responses

    1. Passive

        a) Activity (name of response)

        b) Equipment involved

        c) Behavior

            (1) Decisions

                (a) Selection of response from possible alternatives

                (b) Time aspects of response

                    1) When to initiate

                    2) Pacing or coordinating with other man-machine units

                (c) Determination of response adequacy from feedback data

            (2) Discriminations (other than Indicators; classify as Indicators)

            (3) Memorial

                (a) Access to short-term shortage

                (b) Access to long-term shortage

            (4) Interpretations

            (5) Monitoring (other than Indicators; classify as Indicators)

        d) Nature of procedure

            (1) Fixed

            (2) Variable

    2. Active

        a) Control

            (1) Activity

            (2) Equipment involved

(a) Valves	(e) Wheels
(b) Switches	(f) Pedals–rudder
(c) Levers	(g) Joysticks
(d) Push buttons	

            (3) Behavior

                (a) Discrete adjustment

                (b) Continuous adjustment, undimensional

                (c) Continuous adjustment, multidimensional

               Challenge each of the above Behaviors with:

Force	Temporal aspects	Clothing contraints
Direction	Bodily relations	Environmental conditions

            (4) Nature of procedure

                (a) Fixed

                (b) Variable

                (c) Motor

b) Non-control
  (1) Activity
    (a) Calibrate–adjust
    (b) Remove–install
    (c) Repair–Overhaul
    (d) Clean–Purge–Bleed
    (e) Test–check-out
    (f) Inspect
    (g) Connect–disconnect
    (h) Service–fill–lubricate
    (i) Trouble-shoot–diagnose
    (j) Preserve–package–store
    (k) Communicate–report–record
    (l) Transport–carry–hoist–move–load–unload
  (2) Equipment involved
    (a) Operational
    (b) Test
    (c) Support
  (3) Behavior
    (a) Oral communication
    (b) Other communication
    (c) Manipulation
    (d) Discrimination
  (4) Nature of procedure
    (a) Fixed
    (b) Variable
    (c) Circuit analysis
    (d) System analysis

Feedback
(Same classification as for Indicators)

Performance criteria
  1. Time
  2. Accuracy

Criticality
  1. Level
  2. Probable error factor

Time to perform (hours and fractions)

Place of performance (console, components AGE operation)

Frequency of performance
  s (once a shift)
  d (once a day)
  2w (twice a week)

Task newness

LEVELS OF ANALYSIS AND SOME RELATED TECHNIQUES

LEVEL OF ANALYSIS	PURPOSE	APPLICABLE TECHNIQUE
System	To determine effectiveness of system in performing a specified mission	Operations-research methods[8, 18]
Subsystem	To determine best way of meeting a specified requirement of the mission	System analysis Integration matrix
Function	To determine best combination of components required to make up subsystem	Man-machine system analysis[28] Function analysis
Task	To determine best allocation of man's capabilities to perform required functions	Task analysis Time-line analysis[13] Logic models[23, 27] Information theory[1]
Subtask	To determine best method of utilizing man's capabilities to perform the assigned tasks	Operator load analysis[23] Operator sequence diagrams Decision theory Information-flow analysis
Element	To determine best method of utilizing man's capabilities to perform assigned subtasks	Time-and-motion analysis Elemental task analysis

THE SYSTEMS APPROACH IS APPLICABLE TO ALL PROBLEMS

The Personnel Systems concept just discussed is not necessarily applicable to all problems involving people and equipment. This amount of detail would be entirely too time-consuming and costly for most everyday applications. Frequently, it is not feasible to approach a problem from the very beginning; i.e., major decisions may already have been made in the systems design. In spite of this, the systematic approach inherent in PSS is still applicable to even minor modification of or addition to an older system. Regardless of whether you are designing a man-machine system "from scratch" or merely giving a product a "face lifting," the following general steps are considered vital to successful problem solution:

INFORMATION PHASE — Acquire sufficient information about the operational requirements, constraints, environmental conditions, and type of people who will use the design to be able to state positive and concise objectives for the impending design.

PLANNING PHASE — Explore alternative approaches for meeting your stated objectives, keeping in mind such factors as economy, ease of manufacture, reliability of product, and ease of maintenance or servicing.

SELECTION PHASE — Select the design which seems to optimize all factors listed in Information and Planning phases, above. Proceed with your design, utilizing accepted human-engineering design principles found in other sections of this book.

TEST PHASE — Construct breadboards, models, or mock-ups of your design to evaluate or test it against the stated objectives. In cases where dynamic parameters may be critical to the operation, it may be necessary to provide simulated operational evaluations.

FIELD TEST PHASE — Depending upon the nature of the design, it may be necessary to test your final design under actual operating conditions — utilizing actual personnel who will evenutally use the end item. In many commercial applications, it is desirable to perform follow-up customer surveys to provide feedback information useful to later design improvement.

The designer must have the user (operator) in mind when he designs an equipment. He should be able to describe, verbally, exactly what the operator has to do in operating (or maintaining) the equipment. Too often this task of writing down the job or task has been left to a human-factors specialist. The designer should learn to do this himself, if for no other reason than that it forces him to anticipate difficulties he may have been creating for the user. Both designers and human-factors specialists are also concerned with engineering questions, such as, "Should a function be performed manually by an operator, or should it be made automatic?" This question cannot be answered with a simple statement of "yes" or "no" at the present time. There are, however, certain factors which may be considered in arriving at a fairly sound decision — one that still needs to be tested. Several human-factors experts have prepared tentative lists of statements which compare man vs. machine. The following table is included here as a composite of several such lists:

MAN VS. MACHINE

MAN EXCELS IN	MACHINES EXCEL IN
Detection of certain forms of very low energy levels	Monitoring (both men and machines)
Sensitivity to an extremely wide variety of stimuli	Performing routine, repetitive, or very precise operations
Perceiving patterns and making generalizations about them	Responding very quickly to control signals
Detecting signals in high noise levels	Exerting great force, smoothly and with precision
Ability to store large amounts of information for long periods — and recalling relevant facts at appropriate moments	Storing and recalling large amounts of information in short time-periods
Ability to exercise judgment where events cannot be completely defined	Performing complex and rapid computation with high accuracy
Improvising and adopting flexible procedures	Sensitivity to stimuli beyond the range of human sensitivity (infrared, radio waves, etc.)
Ability to react to unexpected low-probability events	Doing many different things at one time
Applying originality in solving problems: i.e., alternate solutions	Deductive processes
Ability to profit from experience and alter course of action	Insensitivity to extraneous factors
Ability to perform fine manipulation, especially where misalignment appears unexpectedly	Ability to repeat operations very rapidly, continuously, and precisely the same way over a long period
Ability to continue to perform even when overloaded	Operating in environments which are hostile to man or beyond human tolerance
Ability to reason inductively	

In general, if any part of a task cannot be anticipated (in terms of the exact response required — at any given instance or under any given set of conditions), that part of the task should be given to man, to allow him to interpret, assess, and make judgments and decisions as to the best choice of response appropriate to the specific condition, time, and place.

It has often been said that a man in a system provides a means for allowing graceful degradation in system performance. Man is able to assess a complex situation and "save" the system even though the mission is only partly completed. Fully automated systems will "quit" unless previously prescribed conditions are met.

Another important factor to consider in determining whether a man is to be "aboard" the system or should have part in its control is the man's own safety. Man (operator) should have sufficient control over his own destiny to take over in the event his own safety is on the point of being compromised.

With the advent of vehicles and systems such as may be used in space operations, it is generally considered desirable to have man along as a reliability factor. He may be able to repair a subsystem and forestall an aborted mission.

A final guiding principle is that machines should always be considered the servant of man. Automaticity should be applied to relieve man for more important tasks for which he is peculiarly suited — such as exercising judgment, planning and making decisions, etc. Machines should relieve him of such routine tasks as storing informational details, performing calculations, or applying continuous and repetitive or well-defined motions. Do not consider tasks in isolation, however, for man seldom performs a task completely by himself. The choice is really one of "man plus machine vs. machine"!

HUMAN RELIABILITY

Human reliability has important implications not only in the way we design interfaces between man and machine, but also in deciding how to use man in a system. Quantification of human reliability is an extremely difficult and possibly impractical task. It is desirable, however, to consider human reliability from the standpoint of identifying relationships between human characteristics and certain factors which may degrade performance reliability. The primary consideration is to minimize human error potential through proper design.

Let us consider first the broad relationships between task characteristics and probability of error-free performance. Assuming that man can perform best under so-called normal conditions, we may classify types of performance according to their inherent reliability from best to worst.

1. Simple, discrete response to a single discrete signal.
2. Simple but varying response to single, successive signals.

3. Single discrete response to multivariant signals requiring sampling, judgment, and decision.

4. Successive, independent response to multivariant signals requiring sampling, judgment, and decision.

5. Complex concomitant responses to random-variant signals requiring extrapolation, interpretation, and decision.

6. Complex response to complex inputs including concurrence with another operator.

The above list could be described in many ways, but is indicative primarily of the relationship between probability of error and complexity of task. What is more important than the actual list of tasks itself is the effect on such tasks of introducing undesirable environments into the problem. For example:

Reducing the amount of time allowed for performing a task.

Introducing abnormal temperature conditions.

Subjecting the operator to shock, vibration, or severe oscillations.

Failing to provide adequate or proper illumination.

Imposing restrictions to movement through special clothing or other similar constraint.

Failing to provide compatible interface design.

Increasing the work load or introducing "noise" in the task or environment.

Introducing physiological or physical stress (acceleration, weightlessness, Coriolis, muscle strain, etc.).

Imposing general stress (from loss of sleep, confinement, isolation, etc.).

Introducing emotional stresses (fear, anxiety, boredom, etc.).

Designers should create work-task configurations which maximize the operator's response characteristics least prone to error or are least affected by environmental variations. They should consider the effects of motivation; i.e., design tasks which are reasonably challenging, but not discouraging. It is necessary to learn something about the types of users of the product — intelligence, education, skill, etc. — to be successful. One must also beware of the trap which is caused by observing how many times an operator still manages to perform fairly well in spite of poor design or environmental conditions. We would, generally, not design a piece of hardware to operate close to its maximum limit, and so should not force the human to do so either. Special attention should be given to situations where a combination of stresses may degrade the operator's performance even though he is able to overcome any one of the stresses separately.

Unfortunately, too little is known about the effects of combined stress. Designers must assume that good human engineering should be applied across the board in order to maintain human performance reliability at required levels. At best, human variability is such that performance is subject to error from time to time for completely unexplained reasons. Therefore we should not add to this burden by deliberately creating an error-producing design or environment.

An analysis of a proposed system will ordinarily enable one to categorize each subsystem and the associated human tasks according to the functional significance of human error. For example:

FUNCTIONAL SIGNIFICANCE SCORE	CRITICALITY TO MISSION PERFORMANCE
0	No operational effect
1	Degrades performance, but does not abort the mission
2	Results in failed mission
3	Results in loss of man or equipment

By making an error analysis of a system operation and subjecting it to a rating scale as shown above, it is possible to arrive at a gross but valuable indication of what part the operator contributes to over-all system reliability.

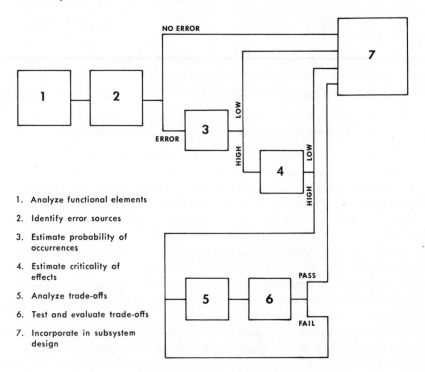

1. Analyze functional elements

2. Identify error sources

3. Estimate probability of occurrences

4. Estimate criticality of effects

5. Analyze trade-offs

6. Test and evaluate trade-offs

7. Incorporate in subsystem design

Basic Analytical Flow-Diagram Showing Human-Error Prediction
and Control Sequence
(after Rabideau[20])

THE HUMAN AS AN INFORMATION PROCESSOR

Consideration of the human operator's capabilities and limitations provides insight into better ways in which he can best be used as a component in a man-machine system.

AS A RECEIVER

Proper inputs to the senses (seeing, hearing, touch, etc.) result in man's being a highly reliable receiver. His time constants are relatively long, 25 to 150 milliseconds, and his sensitivity ranges are limited, approximately 20 to 20,000 cycles per second in the sound spectrum and from 4000 to 7000 angstrom units in the electromagnetic spectrum. His rate of perceived input seems to be not much greater than 10 successive items per second. His input capacity is easily saturated, and care should be taken to avoid messages to him that are overlapping, competing, or visually and aurally incompatible.

AS A TRANSMITTER

Man can utilize the outputs of another man or piece of equipment in a system and transmit these as inputs to other men or other pieces of equipment by voice link, knobs, push buttons, switches, and so on. All of man's outputs are motor responses, and these are relatively slow and low-powered. For steady-state conditions, his output in highly developed skills (typing, or playing a musical instrument) seems to be limited to approximately 25 bits per second (6 or 7 letters or notes per second). Maximum human capacity is about 40 bits; the probable operating rate for typical unskilled tasks may be around 2 bits per second.

AS A COMPUTER OR EVALUATOR

Man is an exceptionally good evaluative computer. From intermittent information on a PPI display he is able to estimate courses, velocities, times, and points of interception with considerable accuracy. Man is able to make decisions based on past experience and patterns of visual or auditory inputs. He is the only available computer able to solve problems by logical induction.

AS A CONTROL MECHANISM

Man's transfer function within a control system is highly dependent upon what is expected of him. In hovering a helicopter he does a remarkable job of maintaining a fixed position which would require the solution of some nine simultaneous equations if done by a computer. In flying an airplane, the pilot is faced with the task of simultaneously responding to several instruments which give him the results of his control movements. Given the usual lag in the system, the likelihood of his anticipating the results of his control movements — so as to pull out exactly on the target — is very remote. If "anticipatory" circuits are used in the system to display the effects of the control movements in advance, his job can be done with extreme precision.

For these and other similar tasks, such as maneuvering a space vehicle, it is desirable to use electronic aids to integrate and differentiate for man — and use him as a simple amplifier in the system. Man's motor output seems to have a band width of about 10 cycles per second and a "natural" periodicity of about $\frac{1}{2}$ to 1 cycle per second. Care should be taken to avoid putting him in a system with a resonant frequency which will be amplified by this $\frac{1}{2}$-to-1-cycle oscillation tendency.

INFORMATION-HANDLING AND DECISION-MAKING CAPABILITIES

Television channel	3×10^7 bits per second
Telephone channel	2×10^4 bits per second
Teletype channel	60 bits per second
Maximum human capacity	40 bits per second
Human operational rate	2 bits per second

Among the characteristics of man which make it possible for him to be used in the functions described above are his sensory capacities, motor responses, memory, flexibility, and computational ability.

SENSORY CAPACITIES

Under proper conditions of illumination, man can see color, brightness, and form. The range or amplitude over which the eye can function covers more than 8 logarithmic units; i.e., taking the lowest intensity at unity, the highest will have a value of about 100 million. The eye responds to as little as 4 or 5 quanta of energy and under ideal conditions can detect the presence of an object which subtends about a half second of visual angle. This is equivalent to seeing a wire, 1/16 inch in diameter, a half mile away. He can hear, touch, taste, and smell with varying degrees of sensitivity. The energy in 1×10^{-10} erg/sec is enough to cause an auditory response. This is only slightly greater than the energy released by the collision of air molecules in random Brownian movement. The loudest sound he hears, without pain, contains roughly 10 billion times as much energy.

The sensitivity of both the eye and the ear is close to theoretical limits for resolution of a physical system. In fact, there is reason to believe that in some cases of hypersensitivity the person actually hears the sounds produced by Brownian movement.

MOTOR RESPONSE

Man can talk, push buttons, use hand cranks or joysticks. He can point, write, push pedals, and so on. All of these outputs are usable and have been used in man-machine systems. It must be remembered that his motor performance characteristics vary considerably, depending upon the mode of response. The design engineer can use these characteristics in two ways: (1) to provide those movement characteristics which are desired as input to the controls, and (2) to eliminate those movement characteristics which are undesirable.

MEMORY

Man has good long-term memory for generalized experience, but rather poor immediate memory for most sensory functions. This is especially so in audition. His access time is slow, compared with that of a computer, but he is able to recall generalized patterns of previous experience to solve immediate problems. As yet, no computer can do this.

FLEXIBILITY

Man is very flexible and can perform well in many different jobs if his limitations are not overlooked. As the requirements placed on him become more complex, however, this same flexibility may result in a decrement to the system's performance. Use the machine to relieve the man of as many routine jobs as possible, but use the man to supply the judgments and flexibility of which machines are incapable.

COMPUTATIONAL ABILITY

Man learns to do numerical computations, but in the main his time constants are such that he is a relatively poor numerical computer when under stress. No computer can match him, however, for the more qualitative, nonnumerical computations.

These characteristics are common to all men in some degree. It must be remembered that men differ widely in their capacities, body sizes, training, and skills. Until "quality control" is utilized in the acceptance of new models of the human being, the engineer should design equipment which can be used adequately by any member of the population likely to use it.

Man's performance usually tends to deteriorate as a function of time on the job. This is seldom a result of physiological tiring per se. It results, rather, from boredom, inattention, and lack of motivation. Care should be taken in designing the man's job so that he is not forced to operate near his maximum load limits for very long. In addition, control over his ambient environment must be exercised. Tolerance to a single stressful condition may be exceeded when several environments interact at the same time. Design for the "normal" whenever possible, and this will allow the operator to perform more nearly to the specifications you expect of him.

STANDARDIZATION AND HUMAN ENGINEERING

The importance of standardization has been recognized in business and industry for many years. It has a special significance in human engineering. Used wisely, standardization will lead to improved human performance. Sometimes, however, the use of standardization as a means of improving human performance is confused with the mere desire to standardize for the sake of "standardizing." Standardization improves human performance in several important ways. For example:

People become accustomed to using a device in one way and can be expected to recognize, understand, and operate it without unnecessary training, explanation, or guidance.

When a device operates in the same way on one equipment as on another, people (once they have learned) will operate the new equipment with less chance for error.

A standard tool will more likely be used properly, thus avoiding possible damage to equipment.

Standard procedures provide less chance for accidents and injuries, since people are familiar with the hazards and are more apt to recognize them — even in a new operation.

Designers should take advantage of certain design characteristics which lead to early familiarity by the user. In other words, people "expect things to operate in a certain way." Sometimes we refer to these expectations as population stereotypes — or the way in which the ordinary person will react to an operation or device. A typical example is in the water faucet. People "expect" the control on the faucet to turn to the left (or counterclockwise) to let the water run and to the right to turn the water off. Wherever such stereotypes exist, it is advisable to follow them!

In other design areas there may not be apparent stereotypes. When one is unsure, it is advisable to perform tests on a sufficient number of "typical" users, to ascertain whether there may be confusion in operating the new design. A number of standards are included in succeeding pages of this Guide. Many of them have been developed by experiment, and others were created by professional committees. Only those standards which appear (in the opinion of the authors) to be compatible with recognized human-engineering principles are included, however, since there are, unfortunately, many standards which contribute to operator problems.

Undesirable effects can result when standards are created without considering the needs of the future. Standards have sometimes become ingrained in the user population — and later been found to be determental to operator efficiency. The typewriter keyboard arrangement is typical.

Although a much improved keyboard was created a few years ago (one which increased typing speed at least twofold), it has been impossible to change to the new keyboard because of the overwhelming number of old machines and the problem of training new typists and, more so, retraining those "wedded" to the old system. Another example of potential standards "failure" occurred with the advent of "shape-coded" control knobs. Codes were good only if the knobs remained in an "upright" position, for their identity was lost when they were miniaturized.

The following list of recognized population stereotypes provides the reader with an idea of the types of human reaction which may be considered "expected or natural."

GENERAL POPULATION STEREOTYPE REACTIONS

- HANDLES USED FOR CONTROLLING LIQUIDS ARE EXPECTED TO TURN CLOCKWISE FOR OFF AND COUNTER-CLOCKWISE FOR ON.

- KNOBS ON ELECTRICAL EQUIPMENT ARE EXPECTED TO TURN CLOCKWISE FOR ON, TO INCREASE CURRENT, AND COUNTER-CLOCKWISE FOR OFF OR DECREASE IN CURRENT. (NOTE: THIS IS OPPOSITE TO THE STEREOTYPE FOR LIQUID.)

- CERTAIN COLORS ARE ASSOCIATED WITH TRAFFIC, OPERATION OF VEHICLES, AND SAFETY.

- FOR CONTROL OF VEHICLES IN WHICH THE OPERATOR IS RIDING, THE OPERATOR EXPECTS A CONTROL MOTION TO THE RIGHT OR CLOCKWISE TO RESULT IN A SIMILAR MOTION OF HIS VEHICLE, AND VICE VERSA.

- SKY-EARTH IMPRESSIONS CARRY OVER INTO COLORS AND SHADINGS: LIGHT SHADES AND BLUISH COLORS ARE RELATED TO THE SKY OR UP, WHEREAS DARK SHADES AND GREENISH OR BROWNISH COLORS ARE RELATED TO THE GROUND OR DOWN.

- THINGS WHICH ARE FURTHER AWAY ARE EXPECTED TO LOOK SMALLER.

- COOLNESS IS ASSOCIATED WITH BLUE AND BLUE-GREEN COLORS, WARMNESS WITH YELLOWS AND REDS.

- VERY LOUD SOUNDS OR SOUNDS REPEATED IN RAPID SUCCESSION, AND VISUAL DISPLAYS WHICH MOVE RAPIDLY OR ARE VERY BRIGHT, IMPLY URGENCY AND EXCITEMENT.

- VERY LARGE OBJECTS OR DARK OBJECTS IMPLY "HEAVINESS." SMALL OBJECTS OR LIGHT-COLORED ONES APPEAR LIGHT IN WEIGHT. LARGE, HEAVY OBJECTS ARE EXPECTED TO BE "AT THE BOTTOM." SMALL LIGHT OBJECTS ARE EXPECTED TO BE "AT THE TOP."

- PEOPLE EXPECT NORMAL SPEECH SOUNDS TO BE IN FRONT OF THEM AND AT APPROXIMATELY HEAD HEIGHT.

- SEAT HEIGHTS ARE EXPECTED TO BE AT A CERTAIN LEVEL WHEN A PERSON SITS DOWN!

SPECIAL TOOLS FOR HUMAN ENGINEERING

Although the typical designer or engineer has his own special set of tools with which he creates drawings, tests concepts, and measures performance of hardware, it is important to recognize that human engineering requires other tools with which the average designer may be unfamiliar. Some of these tools he may have used for purposes other than human engineering. It is important that he understand how to use these tools to help fit the machines to the man.

Drawings with full-scale cutouts are quite useful, for instance, in exploring better arrangements for controls and displays on a panel. If the cutouts can be pasted on a drawing (use rubber cement so that they can be removed easily) and the drawing is placed at the proper angle and position with reference to a seated operator, reach distances and legibility can be checked to make sure that the operator can operate and see controls and displays easily. Relationships between displays and controls can be tested for ease of association or adequacy of the arrangement in terms of sequence of operation.

Miniature scale-models can be used effectively for testing the arrangement of men and equipment to determine proper spacing for clearances, traffic flow, and location of general light fixtures. In fact, such models have been used in selecting colors for room walls, floors, equipment, etc.

Full-scale mock-ups are quite useful for trying out arrangements for console placement, seating, hatches, windows, storage, and many other effects relating to general habitability. Such mock-ups should first be made of the most flexible and easily changed materials possible: e.g., cardboard. Later they can be made of wood and plastic, or Fiberglas, and in some cases of metal. A number of common errors are made by industrial manufacturers in use of full-scale mock-ups. First, they often start out with wood or metal materials and thus reduce the possibility of change. This leads to compromises of the human element for the sake of avoiding expense in changing the mock-up. A second error, which is really a basic error in concept, is that mock-ups are too often thought of only in terms of something to demonstrate the product to the customer; i.e., they are sales tools rather than engineering tools. A mock-up for engineering purposes does not have to be "pretty"!

Simulation of dynamic aspects of a man-machine system is probably the most sophisticated tool that can be applied to human-engineering problems. It usually involves driving displays with computer inputs which are coupled to actual controls so that the operator can be placed in the loop. This allows the designer to test the man-machine system as "a whole," and is very desirable for complex control problems. It is not always necessary to have everything included in such simulations. For instance, the simulation of an aircraft control or instrument system does not need to have an ejection seat, or a canopy over the operator. It's not that these items would interfere with the simulation, but they are costly and do not aid in meeting objectives of the test.

In some cases, total integrated simulation may be necessary. This is especially true in the case of space vehicles — primarily because such a simulation, in actuality, replaces the normal engineering flight-testing phase of the vehicle. In other words, it is not possible to flight-test a space vehicle before delivery to the customer, because of the high cost of launching. Full simulation should strive for as much realism in all its elements as seems necessary to prove that the man (or men) and the machine can and will operate satisfactorily as a total system in the expected environment. Such simulators are suitable also for flight training and familiarization.

Simulation of the type just discussed requires extensive computer facilities. Computers are one of the human engineer's most valuable tools for other reasons also — just as they are for general engineering and research. The implications of the computer for human-engineering research include (1) organization and reduction of statistical data, (2) hypothesis seeking, by finding new relationships, and (3) hypothesis testing, through modeling and simulation.

In addition to the human-engineering tools just discussed, many other smaller instruments and tools are required for measuring purposes. Included are such things as:

Light measuring devices

Sound measuring devices

Temperature and humidity measuring devices

Toxicity measuring devices

Ventilation measuring devices

Force measuring devices

Human-body measuring devices (anthropometric tools)

Visual spectrum analyzers

Radiation measuring devices

Perceptual and motor-performance measuring devices

Obviously such a list could be extended for several pages. One thing which should be apparent, however, is the fact that there are tools for obtaining objective measures of the man-machine factors involved in design, and these should be used wherever possible — in opposition to the "personal-opinion approach" to man-machine design.

It is also important to recognize that certain facilities are necessary to support the use of the tools for human engineering. In other words, human engineering cannot be done entirely at a desk. Even the smallest effort requires reasonably sophisticated facilities for performing typical human-engineering testing. The following list is presented as a guide for those persons wishing to set up a testing facility for the solution of human-engineering problems.

HUMAN ENGINEERING LABORATORY REQUIREMENTS

Function	Facilities
Aerospace medicine and physiology	Medical examination room Biochemistry laboratory Physiology test laboratory Human and small-animal centrifuges Altitude chamber Temperature chamber Small-animal housing
Engineering psychology	Sound test laboratory Visual test laboratory Sensory-motor laboratory
Human engineering design	Mock-up laboratory Simulation laboratory Personal-equipment laboratory
Life support engineering	Atmospheric laboratory Closed-ecology laboratory Toxic test laboratory

NOTE: The above list is not intended to be all-inclusive, or to imply that all of the elements are required in every situation. Rather, it provides some indication (to the uninitiated) of the types of activity and facilities for human-engineering work.

PERSONNEL REQUIREMENTS FOR A HUMAN-ENGINEERING ORGANIZATION

Many industrial organizations, introduced to the need for human-engineering specialists in their organization for the first time, are at a loss as to what types of specialists they should employ. The following are suggested, in order of hiring priority, for a general human-engineering group. It should be noted that these specialists are "in addition" to upper-level ENGINEERS and DESIGNERS who should also be members of a human-engineering group.

ENGINEERING PSYCHOLOGIST — with an advanced degree and/or several years' experience in equipment and man-machine system design, or both.

PHYSIOLOGIST — in many cases physiologists have equally broad experimental experiences as the Engineering psychologist, and are considered of equal priority for initial hiring.

EXPERIMENTAL PSYCHOLOGIST — preferably one who has specialized in human performance measurement, statistics, and laboratory research.

PHYSICIAN — preferably with training as a flight surgeon.

ANTHROPOLOGIST — experienced in human body measurement relative to equipment design.

MANNING AND TRAINING SPECIALIST.

BIOCHEMIST.

RADIOBIOLOGIST.

OTHERS — junior-level scientists representing experimental psychology and physiology; technical support personnel, such as laboratory technicians, personal equipment specialists, mock-up technicians, and draftsmen.

bionics, cybernetics, and neuro-engineering concepts

BY JOHN M. COYNE

Of increasing interest to the human-factors engineer are the numerous researches being conducted on self-organizing, self-regulating, and self-adapting systems. Engineered analogues of these neuro-behavioral functions which characterize the performance of living organisms range from the complex information storage and processing of analogue or digital computers to the facilitory or inhibitory relaying of pulse-coded information by component artificial neurons. The analoguing of these behavioral functions at all levels of complexity has been approximated by a variety of electronic, electrochemical, and electromechanical devices.

BIONICS and CYBERNETICS represent two interactive and inter-related areas of research which have both drawn from and contributed to the design and development of complex man-machine systems. The historically senior partner of this cooperative, cybernetics, was formalized and named by Norbert Wiener, a professor of mathematics at the Massachusetts Institute of Technology, in a 1948 introduction and subsequent 1954 and 1961 elaborations.* The junior (in time) partner, bionics, was both titled and launched by Major Jack Steele, MC, USAF, in an Air Force–sponsored symposium at Dayton, Ohio, in 1959.†

To identify and differentiate these closely related areas of investigation, we might review the definitions formulated by a principal investigator in each of the areas. Wiener, who identifies cybernetics as the study of communication and control functions common to both living and engineered systems, elaborately states:

"It is my thesis that the physical functioning of the living individual and the operation of the newer communication machines are precisely parallel in their analogous attempts to control entropy through feed-back. Both have sensory receptors as one stage in their cycle of operation: i.e., in both of them there exists a special apparatus for collecting information from the outer world at low energy levels, and for making it available in the operation of the individual or of the machine. In both cases these external messages are not taken *neat*, but through the internal transforming powers of the apparatus, whether it be alive or dead. The information is then turned into a new form available for the further stages of performance. In both the animal and the machine, this performance

---

*N. Wiener, The Human Use of Human Beings, Doubleday, 1954, and Cybernetics, or Control and Communication in the Animal and the Machine, 2d ed., Massachusetts Institute of Technology Press and Wiley, 1961.

†J. E. Steel, et al., Bionics Symposium: Living Prototypes, the Key to New Technology, Air Force, Wright Air Development Division, Technical Report No. 60-600, 1960.

is made to be effective on the outer world. In both of them, their *performed* action on the outer world, and not merely their *intended* action, is reported back to the central regulatory apparatus." (The Human Use of Human Beings, p. 26)

By way of contrast and comparison, McCulloch, in his own cryptic style, offers his definition of bionics:

". . . Jack Steele coined legitimately the word Bionics from *Bion,* a living thing, and *ics,* the science of. Being born as an integration of science and art it is clearly illegitimate, with no official past but a promising future enlivened by hybrid vigour. The integral is definite from a scalpel to a soldering iron. It seeks, from an intimate knowledge of biological systems for communication and control, to improve the design and performance of artifacts, chiefly electronics, to match the reliability, and flexibility, the adaptability and the economy of nature's prototype."*

Essentially, the focus of cybernetics and that of bionics converge on the same phenomena from different perspectives. The phenomena are those of developing engineered analogues of adaptive and regulatory behaviors characteristic of living organisms, and the perspective differences are in the levels of abstraction and complexity at which these neurobehaviors are modeled. Cybernetics might be described as focusing on the *macro*-modeling of the *processes* involved in self-communicating information-feedback and adaptive performance-modification which characterize the more complex behaviors of animals and machines, whereas bionics concentrates more on the *micro*-modeling of *component* functions of artificial neurons and simulated nerve networks, building more complex function analogues of such processes as visual or auditory pattern-recognition from these basic components. The cybernetics approach derives the components in terms of the funtcion. The bionics approach reproduces the function by an expedient assembly of determined components.

Underlying the concept of both cybernetics and bionics is the principle of differential information-feedback loops which permits the responding system to modify selectively its subsequent responses in terms of goal approximations attained by its previous responses. Thus described, such an adaptive system requires (1) a capability for holding some criterion representation of a postulated goal condition, (2) an effector mechanism for adaptively seeking that goal condition, and (3) a feedback sensor circuit for the detection and correction of the system's approximation of that goal condition. To permit such a purposive search, the information feedback from the system's responses must provide for an iterative differential analysis between its *actual* status and the postulated *desired* (goal) state. This, of course, constitutes negative feedback, which permits the progressive damping of search oscillations around the specified goal. Positive

---

*W. A. McCulloch, "Syllabus on Biotechnology Course," University of California Extension, 1962.

feedback would provide information only to the effect that change is occurring, and, lacking data on goal approximation, it would amplify the search oscillations, producing excursions progressively farther away from the specified goal-state. In the case of a *progressively adaptive* homeostatic system, the process is appreciably more complex. In this situation the goal itself, rather than being a determinable *state,* is more likely to be a non-stable oscillating status. (The terms "state" and "status" are being used differentially: state — a static, determined condition; status — a dynamic, varying process.) This condition introduces Heisenberg's "uncertainty principle" and requires that we convert our sensor system from a fixed-threshold comparitor circuit to a variable-threshold goal-tracking detector. That such on-line, covariable, self-stabilizing computational systems exist is repeatedly demonstrated in a variety of living organisms. That engineering analogues of these complex integrative functions are realizable will require considerably more "software" research on these regulatory functions as they operate in living organisms. But that such analogues would have valuable application in the engineering development of complex systems scarcely needs justification.

The living prototype of this homeostatic regulating system is postulated to involve (1) selectively sensitive areas of the ventricular surfaces of the hypothalamus, (2) the activating reticulum of the brain stem, and (3) the sequential programming functions of the limbic end-brain.* The periventricular membrane of the hypothalamus which borders the third ventricle has been shown to contain a series of stimulus-specific sensor areas which are presumed to be arranged in an intercoupled system for the integrative, on-line monitoring of vital body parameters such as O_2/CO_2 ratio, pH ratio, H_2O balance, metabolic rates, body temperature, toxicity levels, osmotic pressures, etc., which covariantly affect the behavioral efficiency of the total organism. A critical deviation from the tolerance envelope in any parameter disturbs the homeostatic equilibrium of the entire system and introduces *directional* compensatory searches in the accommodation limits of other, related parameters. These compensatory changes in threshold seem to be effected through the activating mechanisms of the reticular formations in the brain stem, which, in turn, are "programmed" by the intrinsic functions of the frontal aspects of the limbic endbrain.

---

*W. R. Ashby, *Design for a Brain*, Wiley, 1952; W. B. Cannon, *The Wisdom of the Body*, Norton, 1932; J. M. Coyne, *Neuro-Engineering*, Proceedings of San Diego Bio-Medical Symposium, April 1963; E. Fonberg and J. Delgado, "Inhibition of Food and Defense Conditioned Reflexes," *Acta Physiol. Pol.*, vol. 11, 1960, pp. 696-698; K. H. Pribram, "A Review of Theory in Physiological Psychology, in *Annual Review of Psychology* (Palo Alto, Calif.) vol. 11, 1960.

A simplified physical-system analogue of the covariable functioning of this living homeostatic system might be conceptualized as a sophisticated environmental-control process. This environmental-control system would include a bidirectional thermostatic regulation of heating and cooling, a hygrometer-controlled device for humidifying or dehumidifying the atmosphere, and a sensing flow-meter which variably regulates the circulation of air. If we now intercouple each of these separately controlled subsystems with information feedback loops which permit each device to evaluate its own function in relation to the ongoing functions of each of the other component devices, and if we provide each subsystem with a representation of some optimal output for the total system, the contributory functions of each of the participating subsystems can covariably modulate to attain this optimum total system output (see the accompanying figure). A similar construct has been developed for the on-line management of a variable-expenditure fuel system for ballistic missiles.

A more recent dimension of life-sciences research which holds significance for the human-factors engineer is that of neuro-engineering. The principal focus of this area is on the application of physical-science theory and technology to assist, improve, or replace biological and psychological functions essential to living organisms. In this pursuit, the behavioral and biological scientists intervene in the "normal" behavioral functions of their system components, the living organism, to improve its efficiency in much the same way that the physical scientist modifies and upgrades the performance efficiency of his system component, the machine. Included in this neuro-engineering area would be (1) the activity of the prosthetics design engineer, who is concerned with the replacement of both the sensory and motor control of lost behavioral capabilities, as well as the improvement of faulty behavioral functions, and (2) that of the neuro-psychologist, the physiologist, and the biochemist, who are concerned with maximizing the behavioral efficiency of the organism's sensory acuities, cognitive functioning, and motor responses through techniques such as: intensive responsive conditioning, the developing of relatively unused sensory intake channels (e.g., tactile), and the extending of sensory, cognitive, and motor thresholds and asymptotes chemically with psychopharmacological agents, and even the modulating of sensory and motor activity through controlled electro-stimulation of the cortex and deeper brain regions.

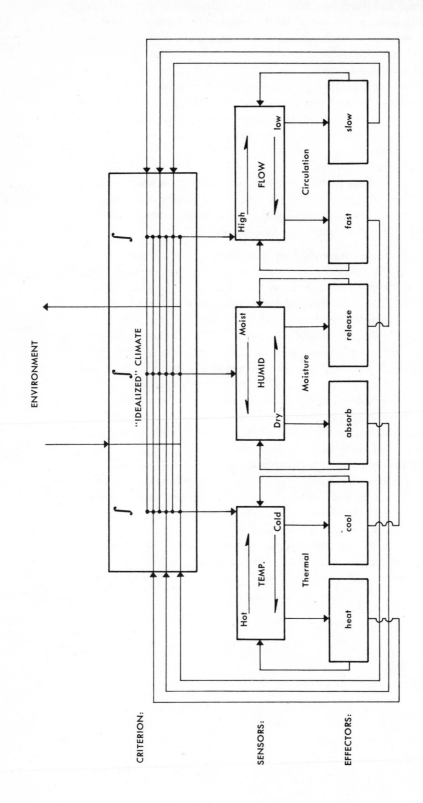

A SCHEMATIC CLIMATE-CONTROL ANALOGUE OF THE
THERMAL HOMEOSTATIC REGULATION SYSTEM
FOUND IN MAMMALIAN ORGANISMS

references

1.   Attreave, F. *Applications of Information Theory to Psychology: Summary of Basic Concepts, Methods and Results* Holt, 1959.

2.   Chapanis, A. *The Design and Conduct of Human Engineering Studies* (Office of Naval Research, Technical Report no. 14, NR 145-075) San Diego State College Foundation, July 1956.

3.   Chapanis, A. *Research Techniques in Human Engineering* Johns Hopkins Press, 1959.

4.   Churchman, C. W., Ackott, R. L., and Arrott, E. L. *Introduction to Operations Research* Wiley, 1958.

5.   Eckman, D. P. *Systems: Research and Design* Wiley, 1961.

6.   Erickson, C. J., and Rabideau, G. F. *Function and Task Analysis as a Weapon System Development Tool* (Northrop Aircraft, Inc., Hawthorne, Calif., Report no. 59-1148) October 1957.

7.   Fitts, P. M. "Functions of Man in Complex Systems" *Aerospace Engineering* vol. 21, no. 1, January 1962.

8.   Flagle, C. D. et al. *Operations Research and Systems Engineering* Johns Hopkins Press, 1960.

9.   Folley, J. E., Fairman, J. B., and Jones, E. M. *A Survey of the Literature on Prediction of Air Force Personnel Requirements* (Air Force. Wright Air Development Division, Technical Report no. 60-493) July 1960.

10.   Gael, S., and Reed, L. E. *Personnel Equipment Data: Concept and Content* (Air Force. Aerospace Systems Division, Technical Report no. 61-739) December 1961.

11.   Goode, H. H., and Machol, R. E. *Systems Engineering* McGraw-Hill, 1957.

12.   Heuston, M. C. *Concepts for Estimating Air Force Manpower Requirements for Planning Purposes* (The RAND Corporation, Santa Monica, Calif., Research Memorandum no. 2611) 1 December 1960.

13.   Kurke, M. I. "Operational Sequence Diagrams in Systems Design" *Human Factors Journal* vol. 3, no. 1, March 1961.

14.   Lindquist, O. H., and Gross, R. L. *Human Engineering Man-Machine Study of a Weapon System* (Minneapolis-Honeywell Regulator Co. Research-Engineering Department, Aero Report no. 6094) October 1958.

15.   Losee, J. E. et. al. *Methods for Computing Manpower Requirements for Weapon Systems under Development* (Air Force. Aerospace Systems Division, Technical Report no. 61-361) August 1961.

16.   Marks, M. R. *A Data Organization Model for the Personnel Subsystem* (Air Force. Aerospace Systems Division, Technical Report no. 61-447) September 1961.

17.   Miller, R. B. *Manual for Man-Machine Job-Task Description* American Institute for Research, Pittsburgh, Penna., June 1955.

18.   Morse, P. M., and Kimball, G. G. *Methods of Operations Research* Wiley 1956.

19.   Quastler, H. (ed.) *Information Theory in Psychology: Problems and Methods* Free Press, Glencoe, Ill., 1955.

20.   Rabideau, G. F. "Human Factors in Engineering" unpublished paper presented at Special Student Program, Society of Automotive Engineers, National Aeronautic and Space Engineering and Manufacturing Meetings, Los Angeles, 10 October 1962.

21.   Shapero, A., and Bates, C. *A Method for Performing Human Engineering Analysis of Weapon Systems* (Air Force. Wright Air Development Division, Technical Report no. 59-784) September 1959.

22.   Shapero, A. et al. *Human Engineering Testing and Malfunction Data Collection in Weapon System Test Programs* (Air Force. Wright Air Development Division, Technical Report no. 60-26) February 1960.

23.   Siegel, A. I., Wolf, J. J., and Crain, K. *Techniques for Evaluating Operator Loading in Man-Machine Systems: A Model for Digital Simulation of One and Two-Operator Man-Machine Systems* Applied Psychological Services, Wayne, Penna., March 1961.

24.   Sinaiko, H. W., and Buckley, E. P. *Human Factors in the Design of Systems* (Naval Research Laboratory, Report no. 4996) 1957.

25.   Van Cott, H. P., and Folley, J. D. *Human Factors Methods for Systems Design* American Institute for Research, Pittsburgh, Penna., 1959.

26.   Wilson, C. L. (ed.) *Project Mercury Candidate Evaluation Program* (Air Force. Wright Air Development Division, Technical note no. 59-505) December 1959.

27.   Wortz, E. C. *Use of Logic Symbols in Man-Machine Task Analysis* (Proceedings of Midwest Human Factors Society Symposium, General Motors Corp., Milwaukee) 19 May 1961.

28.   Wright, G. O. *A General Procedure for Systems Study* (Air Force. Wright Air Development Division, Technical Note no. 60-18) January 1960.

29.   Wright, G. O. *Development of Qualitative and Quantitative Personnel Requirements Information: Final Report* (Aerospace Medical Division, Report no. MRL-TDR 62-4) 6570th Aerospace Medical Research Laboratories, Wright-Patterson Air Force Base, Ohio, December 1962.

30.   Wright, G. O. *Handbook of Instructions for Aerospace Personnel Subsystem Designers* (Air Force Systems, Command Manual no. 80-3) Headquarters, Air Force Systems Command, Andrews Air Force Base, Washington 25, D.C., 15 January 1963.

31.   Wright, G. O. *Mathematical Theories in Performance, Decision Making, and Learning: A Literature Review. Final Report* Aerospace Medical Division, 6570th Aerospace Medical Research Laboratories, Wright-Patterson Air Force Base, Ohio, July 1962.

32.   Wright, G. O. *Personnel Subsystem Testing for Ballistic Missile and Space Systems* (Air Force. Ballistic Missile Division, Exhibit no. 60-1) Air Force Ballistic Division (ARDC), Air Force Unit Post Office, Los Angeles 45, 22 April 1960.

page 2–1 **design of equipment and work space**

EQUIPMENT DESIGN PRACTICES

visual displays

Design or selection of visual displays is one of the most important problems to face the designer in developing an efficient man-machine system. Since the human eye is the medium through which man receives the greater share of his information about the world in which he lives, effective transfer of this information is vital to his operational efficiency. The following general recommendations are presented as an aid in the selection of the most suitable type of indicator for a given purpose.

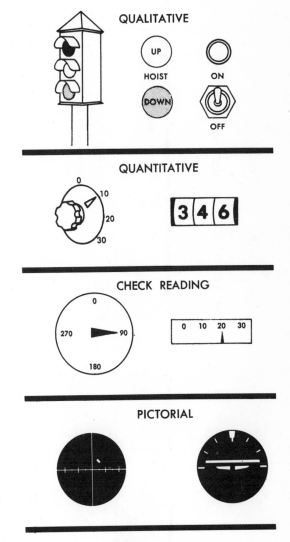

For a few, discrete conditions, use an indicator which presents large differences in position, brightness, or color. Use of two or more variables together normally increases operator reliability — e.g., color plus position.

For precise numerical values, with no need for interpolation between numbers, or for rate or directional indication, use a digital or counter indicator. Use a scalar indicator, however, when values are to be set into the equipment.

For numerical value plus orientation in time, space, magnitude, or rate, use a scalar indicator. Avoid multiple pointers or moving scales whenever possible. A pointer plus an adjacent counter is best when scale expansion is necessary.

For multidimensional information, use combinations of single-value indicators or composite graphic or pictorial representations.

For qualitative check reading, use a moving pointer against a fixed scale. If several dials are to be scanned rapidly, orient pointers so the "normal" position of the pointer is at 9 o'clock.

2-1

GUIDE TO VISUAL DISPLAY SELECTION

To Display	Select	Because	Example
Go, No Go, Start, Stop On, Off	Light	Normally easy to tell if it is on or off	
Identification	Light	Easy to see (may be coded by spacing, color, location, or flashing rate; may also have label for panel applications)	
Warning or Caution	Light	Attracts attention and can be seen at great distance if bright enough (may flash intermittently to increase conspicuity)	
Verbal instruction (operating sequence)	Enunciator light	Simple "action instruction" reduces time required for decision making	RELEASE / EJECT
Exact quantity	Digital counter	Only one number can be seen, thus reducing chance of reading error	5 2 9 0 0
Approximate quantity	Moving pointer against fixed scale	General position of pointer gives rapid clue to the quantity plus relative rate of change	
Set-in quantity	Moving pointer against fixed scale	Natural relationship between control and display motions	

To Display	Select	Because	Example
Data pick-off	Electronic "Hook" or electromechanical pantograph over CRT target presentation; Coördinates transferred to a digital counter automatically	Provides simple means for "pointing" at the position without interpreting or calculating actual values	
Tracking	Single pointer or cross pointers against fixed index	Provides error information for easy correction	
Vehicle attitude	Either mechanical or electronic display of position of vehicle against established reference (may be graphic or pictorial)	Provides direct comparison of "own position" against known reference or base line	
Geographical position	Plan-position analogue	Shows direct relationship to natural geographical features	
Command guidance	Analogue of "predicted" position or path	Allows observer to see or anticipate what is going to happen in advance	
Equipment-performance analysis	Meter CRT (wave form) Pen recording	Single parameter simple to interpret Multiple parameter shows interrelationship Provides permanent record for later analysis	

NOTE: Combinations of any of the above are possible and often desirable. Care should be taken not to introduce ambiguities, extreme complexity, or crowding, since these will increase operator-response time.

CHECK LIST FOR A GOOD VISUAL DISPLAY

CAN THE DISPLAY BE READ QUICKLY IN THE MANNER REQUIRED (THAT IS, QUANTITATIVE, QUALITATIVE, OR CHECK READING)?

CAN THE DISPLAY BE READ ACCURATELY WITHIN THE NEEDS OF THE OPERATOR (PREFERABLY NO MORE ACCURATELY)?

IS THE INSTRUMENT DESIGN FREE OF FEATURES WHICH MIGHT PRODUCE AMBIGUITY OR INVITE GROSS READING ERRORS?

ARE THE CHANGES IN INDICATION EASY TO DETECT?

IS THE INFORMATION PRESENTED IN THE MOST MEANINGFUL FORM REQUIRING THE MINIMUM OF MENTAL TRANSLATION TO OTHER UNITS?

IS THE RELATIONSHIP OF THE REQUIRED CONTROL MOVEMENTS NATURAL TO THE EXPECTED INSTRUMENT MOVEMENT?

IS THE INFORMATION UP TO DATE WITH RELATION TO THE NEED?

IS THE INSTRUMENT DISTINGUISHABLE FROM OTHER DISPLAYS?

WILL THE OPERATOR BE AWARE OF AN INOPERATIVE CONDITION?

IS ILLUMINATION SATISFACTORY UNDER ALL CONDITIONS OF EXPECTED OPERATION?

IS THE DISPLAY FREE OF PARALLAX OR OTHER POTENTIALLY DISTORTING CHARACTERISTICS?

Once the type of indicator has been selected and the amount and accuracy of the information to be displayed have been determined, then it is necessary to consider the factors which contribute to the legibility of the display. The efficiency with which an operator uses the display will be affected by the size of detail, the form of numerals, pointers, or other markings, and the illumination, reflections or glare. On the following pages you will find recommendations for design which will assure an optimum display. Ingenuity is still required of the designer, however, since there may be conflicts between some recommendations, depending on how the elements of the display are combined into new forms. It is recommended that mock-ups be made of all new displays so that they can be tested — particularly under the conditions of actual use: e.g., position on the panel, potential illumination, vibration or other typically degrading environment.

SCALE-POINTER INDICATORS

Scale-pointer indicators provide qualitative as well as quantitative information. Normally they display information symbolically. That is, they present an abstract representation of various conditions such as time, distance, speed, direction, rate, altitude, and temperature. This information is identified in terms of minutes, miles, knots, degrees, feet per second, etc. In addition to these absolute values, qualitative information is available in terms of the relative rate at which a pointer moves, or its position along a finite scale.

Some indicators have been made more useful by incorporating pictorial elements into the display. This adds an aspect of realism which enhances the interpretability of the information. Many authors have emphasized the difference between symbolic and pictorial displays. It is felt, however, that the continuum between symbolic and pictorial concepts is actually only a matter of degree, and therefore the differences will not be stressed.

To help identify the principles which will be presented on the following pages, a series of indicator types is illustrated below. It must be realized that these are general in nature and that an almost unlimited number of combinations is possible.

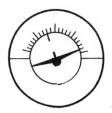

CONTINUOUS SCALE   FINITE SCALE   FINITE POSITION   CONTINUOUS POSITION

SYMBOLIC   PICTORIAL

FIXED-SCALE, MOVING-POINTER DIALS

EXPOSED SCALE   OPEN WINDOW   COMBINATION

MOVING-SCALE DIALS

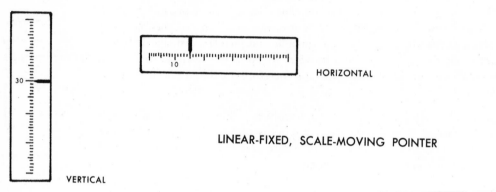

HORIZONTAL

LINEAR-FIXED, SCALE-MOVING POINTER

VERTICAL

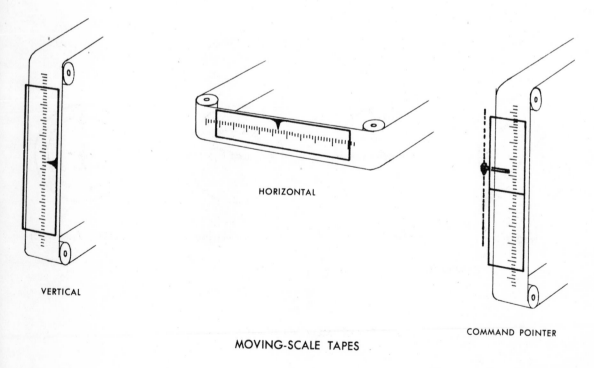

HORIZONTAL

VERTICAL   COMMAND POINTER

MOVING-SCALE TAPES

MULTIPLE POINTER

SUB-DIAL

PARTIAL SUB-DIAL

TO EXPAND SCALE

SUB-COUNTER

COMPONENT POSITION

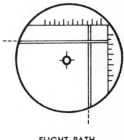

FLIGHT PATH
(CROSS-POINTER)

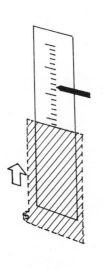

MECHANICAL MASK

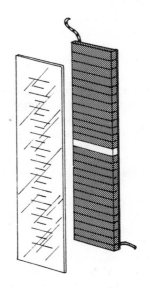

ELECTROLUMINESCENT POINTER

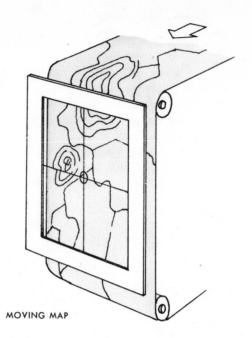

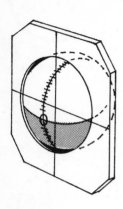

ROLLING BALL

MOVING MAP

FACTORS TO CONSIDER IN DECIDING WHETHER THE SCALE OR POINTER (INDEX) SHOULD BE THE MOVING ELEMENT IN YOUR DISPLAY

In general, a pointer moving against a fixed scale is preferred.

If you wish to have a numerical value readily available, however, a moving scale appearing in an open window can be read more quickly.

If numerical increase is typically related to some other natural interpretation, such as *more* or *less,* or *up* or *down,* it is easier to interpret a straight-line or thermometer scale with a moving pointer because of the added cue of pointer position relative to the zero or null condition.

Normally you should not mix types of pointer-scale (moving element) indica- when they are used for related functions — to avoid reversal errors in reading.

If a manual control over the moving element is expected, there is less am-biguity between the direction of motion of the control and the display if the control moves the pointer rather than the scale.

If slight, variable movements or changes in quantity are important to the observer, these will be more apparent if a moving pointer is used.

INDICATOR DETAIL

Many seemingly minor details can affect the ease with which a visual display will be seen, read, and interpreted. Even the best choice of presentation type will suffer if the principles on the following pages are neglected. Frequently the designer feels that he has finished his job after specifying the general characteristics of the indicator face — leaving the details to a draftsman, artist, silk-screen specialist, or photo-lab technician. These details are extremely important to the designer, however, and he must see that they are recognized and followed if the results of his initial design are to be really effective.

IMPORTANT GENERAL CONSIDERATIONS

● Distance of the observer from the display.

● Position of the observer relative to the display.

● Type, color, and amount of illumination available to the display.

DESIGN OF NUMERALS, LETTERS, AND INDICES

In general, the larger the size of letters and numerals, the less we have to worry about backgrounds and illumination.

Capital letters are recommended for most panel labels although upper- and lower-case letters are suggested for extended instructional material. (See p. 2-207.)

All labels should be normally oriented so that they can be read from left to right. Special cases of vertical orientation are permissible when the label is generally ignored and confusion might arise if it were adjacent to more critical labels.

If instruments or observers are subject to vibration, dials and markings must be larger than they would be otherwise. Dial detail should also be simplified.

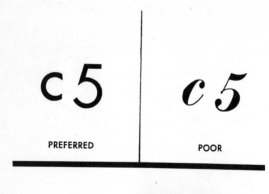

PREFERRED | POOR

For panel use, the design of letters and numerals should be without flourishes. Such details are confusing, especially under threshold conditions. The critical details of the figures should be simple but prominent. Diagonal portions of the characters should be as near 45 degrees as possible and such characteristic features as openings and breaks should be readily apparent. (See pp. 2-206, 2-207.)

The stroke width of black characters on white background should be about one-sixth of the character height. Stroke width of white figures on black background should be about one-seventh to one-eighth of the character height; the narrower stroke is necessary since the light figure tends to spread or irradiate.

The height-to-width ratio of the normal character should be about three to two. Although there are exceptions to this rule, a close approximation to this ratio is recommended, especially for panel and scale design.

LETTER HEIGHT VS VIEWING DISTANCE AND ILLUMINATION LEVEL

(MINIMUM SPACE BETWEEN CHARACTERS, 1 STROKE WIDTH;
BETWEEN WORDS, 6 STROKE WIDTHS)

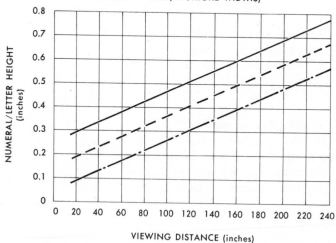

NUMERAL/LETTER HEIGHT (inches)

VIEWING DISTANCE (inches)

—— For instruments where the position of the numerals may vary and the illumination is between 0.03 and 1.0 ft-l.

- - - For instruments where the position of the numerals is fixed and the illumination is 0.3-1.0 ft-l, or where position of the numerals may vary and the illumination exceeds 1.0 ft-l.

—·— For instruments where the position of the numerals is fixed and the illumination is above 1.0 ft-l.

LETTER-STROKE WIDTH VS DISTANCE VIEWED

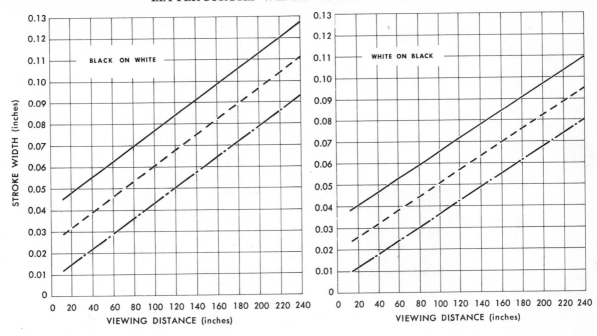

Scale indices should be limited in number to the accuracy required and no more. The smallest readable division should never be finer than the probable error in the metering device. Indices may be spaced as close together as 0.04 inch, although the distance should not be less than twice the stroke width of a "light" index mark on a dark background nor less than one stroke width when the index is darker than the background. A minimum of ½ inch is recommended for the distance between "major" indices. These figures are for the normal instrument-panel reading distances, 14 to 28 inches. The number of graduation marks between numbered scale points should not exceed nine.

MINIMUM INDEX DIMENSIONS (28-INCH VIEWING)

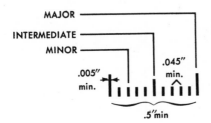

RECOMMENDED FOR AIRCRAFT INSTRUMENTS

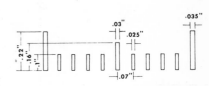

VIEWING DISTANCE (feet)	INDEX HEIGHT		
	MAJOR	INTERMEDIATE	MINOR
	(inches)		
1 2/3 or less	0.22	0.16	0.09
1 2/3 to 3	0.40	0.28	0.17
3 to 6	0.78	0.56	0.34
6 to 12	1.57	1.12	0.68
12 to 20	2.63	1.87	1.13

DIAL DIAMETER VS NUMBER OF INDICES REQUIRED

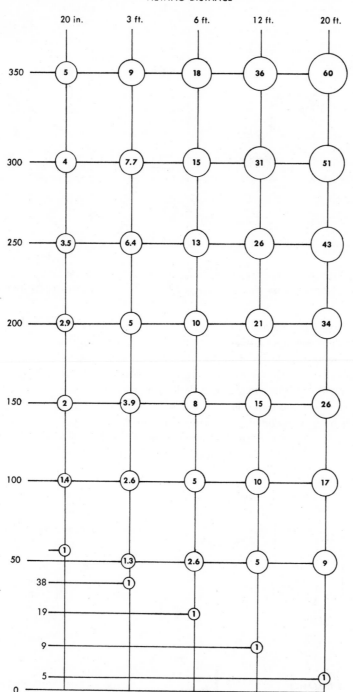

VIEWING DISTANCE

MINIMUM DIAMETER
IN INCHES

Example: If viewing distance is 12 feet and 50 graduation marks are required, the diameter of the inner annulus of the dial should be at least 5 inches.

Given a desired number of indices (left column) and the expected maximum viewing distance, the required diameter for a circular indicator may be determined from the chart above. It is neither practical nor desirable to use a dial diameter of less than 1 inch.

For ease in reading, figures should be oriented according to the type of scale or dial used:

Orient figures vertically on dials which have a fixed scale and moving pointer.

When the scale is of finite length there should be a break between the end and the beginning of the scale. The break should be equal to or greater than a major scale division. Place break as shown.

Orient figures radially on dials which have a fixed pointer and moving scale. When possible, orient the index at the 12-o'clock position.

When the figures of a dial move past an open window, they should be oriented so that they appear vertically at the window opening. Two or more figures should appear in the window simultaneously.

Numbers should appear to increase in a clockwise direction, left to right, or bottom to top.

Avoid the use of irregular scales whenever possible. Some machine and slide-rule type scales are considered as exceptions to this rule. Logarithmic scales may be used where tolerance is a constant percentage of the indication or where critical or often used settings appear in the low end of the scale and it is desirable to minimize average error in scale units.

When two or more similar scales appear on the same panel, they should have compatible numerical progression and scale organization.

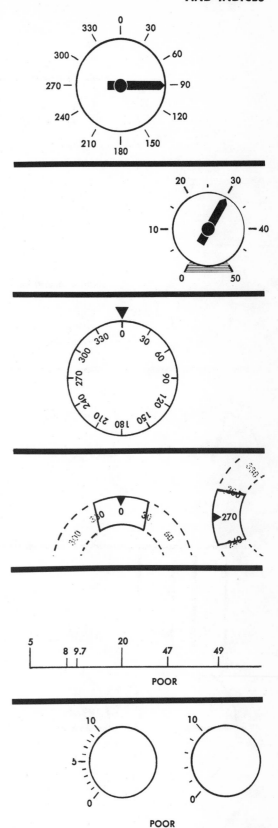

RECOMMENDED NUMERICAL PROGRESSION

GOOD					FAIR					POOR			
1	2	3	4	5	2	4	6	8	10	3	6	9	12*
5	10	15	20	25	20	40	60	80	100	4	8	12	16
10	20	30	40	50						1.25	2.5	5	7.5

* Except for bearing dials where cardinal directions are standard orienting points or where operating doctrine specifies conditions of time scales, or turn rates.

RECOMMENDED SCALE BREAKDOWN[1]

** Studies of this design showed less variability in time when setting-in than did usual dial markings.[1]

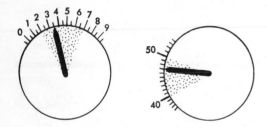

Whenever possible, orient a dial scale so that the critical range to be read will appear as left to right or bottom to top, to avoid confusion as to direction of increase. This is especially important for check-reading instruments.

For multirevolution dials, orient zero at the 12-o'clock position.

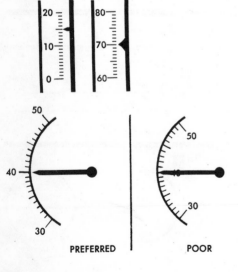

Pointers and scale indices should be oriented so that the pointer, either moving or fixed, is close to the index and yet does not cover the number.

Multiple-range meters: Ordinarily, multiple scales should not appear on the same display. When such a compromise is necessary, color coding should be used to help the observer associate the right scale with the proper selector-switch position.

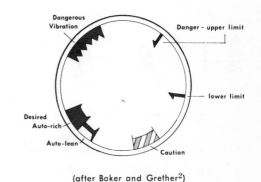

Color-coded zone or operating ranges are useful in helping the observer recognize conditions quickly. Standard colors for general conditions are:

RED: Danger
YELLOW: Caution
GREEN: Normal

Shape-coded zone markings are also useful to indicate various operating conditions. These may be the only alternative under certain monochromatic lighting conditions, such as red instrument-light for night flying.

(after Baker and Grether[2])

If a number of related meters with different ranges are required on the same panel, zero-deviation meters can be used to facilitate interpolation. This can be accomplished by reducing normal values to percentages so that a constant frame of reference obtains regardless of the original values.

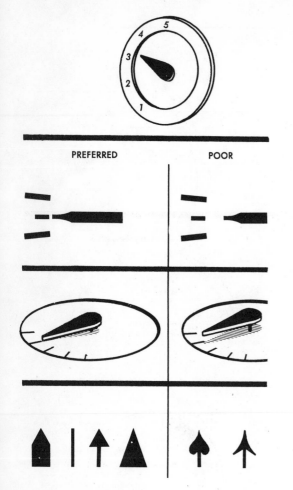

PREFERRED   POOR

When the dial diameter must be too small for adequate pointer and index design, it is possible to utilize bezel or panel space for engraving the numbers. (This method should be used only when gross pointer position is all that is needed.)

The pointer tip should be the same width as the smallest index.

The pointer should be designed so that there is a minimum distance between tip and index — 1/16 inch maximum.

Avoid use of pointers which overlap index marks.

The pointer should be mounted so that visual parallax is minimized.

The pointer should be painted the same color as numbers and indices when possible.

When reciprocal readings are necessary, the two ends of the pointer must be identifiable.

Simplicity in pointer-tip design is important for reading speed and accuracy.

CHECK LIST FOR DIAL AND SCALE DESIGN

- HAVE I MAINTAINED MAXIMUM SIMPLICITY COMMENSURATE WITH IN-FORMATIONAL REQUIREMENTS?

- CAN THE DIAL OR SCALE BE INTERPRETED EASILY (NO SPECIAL COM-PUTATONS OR MULTIPLIERS REQUIRED)?

- HAVE I PROVIDED MAXIMUM CONTRAST BETWEEN FIGURES AND BACK-GROUND AS RELATED TO EXPECTED ILLUMINATION?

- DO I HAVE OPTIMAL DIAL SIZE BASED ON BEST FIGURE AND INDEX SIZE AND SPACING?

- DO I HAVE AN APPROPRIATE NUMERICAL PROGRESSION (OPTIMUM NUMBER PROGRESSION; SCALE BREAKDOWN; RELATIONSHIP BETWEEN NUMERICAL INCREASE, POINTER MOVEMENT, AND RELATED CONTROL MANIPULATION)?

Evolution in the solution of a parallax problem: In example one, the use of a flat cover on the dial forced the dial face to be inset so deeply that numerals can't be seen owing to shadow and actual interference from the bezel.

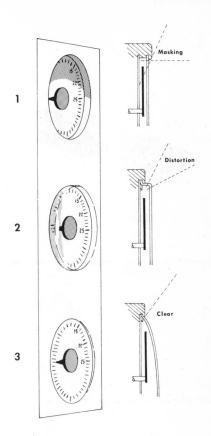

An improvement was brought about in example two because the dial face was brought forward — with the glass cover being reshaped to fall outside the bezel. Note, however, that this cover configuration created optical distortion in the bend of the glass, thus blocking out some of the numerals even yet.

The third solution removes the optical distortion by changing the form factor of the glass, and now no distortion is apparent.

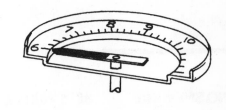

Maximum reduction of parallax may be obtained by insetting the pointer as shown in the illustration at the right. Although this approach is more expensive in terms of original preparation of the instrument dial dies, the benefits over the long run are worth the effort.

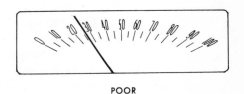

Avoid distortion of scale layouts such as shown in the illustration at the right. This type of error is brought about by designers who try to introduce style idiosyncrasies into an instrument panel.

POOR

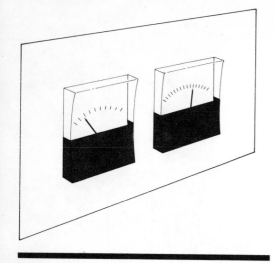

In a great number of applications, commercially available instruments will be used. Careful selection should be made of those instruments which have good human-engineering attributes — such as the type shown at the left — which simplify illumination by using extended transparent covers.

Stock instruments can also be reorienated to cause the pointers to be more compatible with direction of motion. In such cases, the dial face should be modified so that the numerals are upright to the reader.

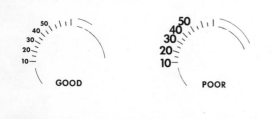

Although optimum numeral size and shape is usually desirable, this sometimes causes crowding and poor legibility. It is better to compromise the proportions or size of the numerals — leaving sufficient space between numerals for better legibility as shown in the illustration at the left.

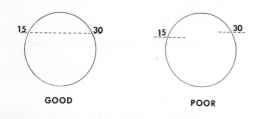

An effort should be made to maintain a certain amount of symmetry in laying out numerals around a dial. If the layout is slightly skewed, it becomes difficult to read, and errors will be made.

NO SMOKING   **NO SMOKING**

Avoid crowding of lettering on signs or labels just because of the desire to use optimum letter size and proportion. Sufficient spacing between letters is necessary for good readability. This can be obtained by using a condensed type-style as shown in the illustration at the left.

NOTE: Instrument faces and labels or signs should be laid out and inspected for legibility in much the same way that a mock-up is fabricated for, say, a console. Avoid taking recommended sizes and proportions at face value regardless of the many other factors of space, arrangement, balance, symmetry, etc., which also contribute to the final effectiveness of the layout and eventual proficiency of the user. Whenever possible, test a layout on a number of your colleagues to discover if some apparently insignificant element is out of place, or is likely to introduce confusion or error.

PICTORIAL INDICATORS

Pictorial indicators are useful for clarifying spatial relationships. They are miniature representations of the world outside the cockpit or control room. They may be either electronic or mechanical in design.

The design of mechanical as well as electronic pictorial displays poses the difficult question of which parts are to be fixed and which parts are to move. The problem is further complicated by the fact that natural visual-motor relationships enter into the picture if the operator affects the display by his own manipulative efforts. In general it can be said that, as an operator's vehicle moves about in space, he can best comprehend a display that gives a representation of his movement with the fixed portions of the instrument representing the space within which he has moved. Conversely, it is generally true that, when an operator is interested in the movement of some other object that is moving about him, he will best comprehend the display that gives his own representation as the fixed portion of the instrument, and the moving portions representing objects moving about him. Special care should be taken in the choice of these opposing points of view. It is especially important that the two opposing conditions do not appear on the same panel.

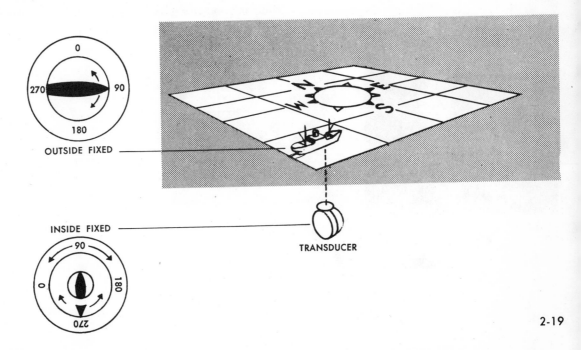

OUTSIDE FIXED

INSIDE FIXED

TRANSDUCER

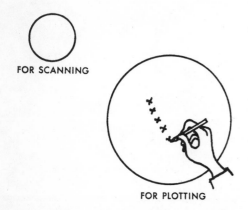

FOR SCANNING

FOR PLOTTING

Electronic displays are usually presented on cathode-ray tubes in rectangular- or polar-coordinate form. Display considerations that affect operator performance are presented as follows:

SIZE — When plotting or simultaneous viewing by several operators is not important, there is no significant advantage between large or small tubes. More time is required to scan the whole scope of an extremely large tube, but such a tube will allow use of a more adequate grid overlay and thus improve accuracy. Scopes of 5- to 7-inch diameter are quite adequate when plotting is not required.

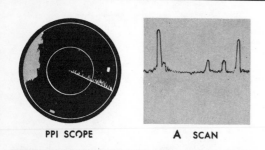

PPI SCOPE   A SCAN

SHAPE — The bezel or frame around a CRT display should conform to the general configuration of the type of presentation — round for a PPI or rectangular for an A-scan.

MOUNTING POSITION — CRT's should be mounted so that the visual axis of the operator is perpendicular to the face of the tube at its center. Recommendations for various operator positions and tube mounting angles may be found on page 2-128. Normal viewing distance is 14 to 18 inches.

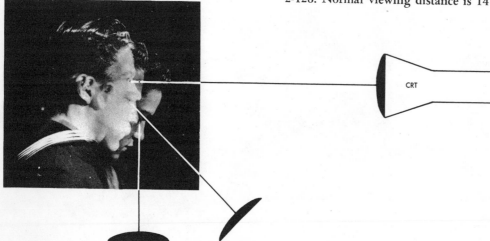

CRT

CURSORS — Electronic cursors which are continuously printed are superior to mechanical cursors from the operator's point of view, since parallax can be eliminated and accuracy improved. The addition of a scale is essential for bearing accuracy; the addition of a counter which presents the exact numerical values found by the cursor manipulation improves accuracy still more. When bearing accuracies of 5 degrees or more may be tolerated there is no real need for the cursor since the operator can interpolate bearing position to that degree of accuracy. (See pp. 2-9 to 2-16 for scale design.)

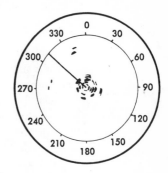

GRIDS — Accuracy of interpolating target position is improved by adding grid markings. The more accurate the reading requirements, the more elaborate the grid structure should be. To minimize confusion caused by many fine grid lines, it is important to increase scope size. The size compromise cannot be predicted, but certain design suggestions can be made.

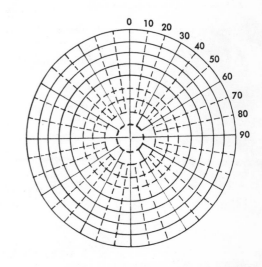

The minimum spacing between range rings on a polar display should be of the order of 1 degree 36 minutes visual angle subtended at the eye, or about ½ inch at 18-inch viewing distance. For bearing, a solid line each 30 degrees and dotted lines for each 10 degrees are recommended for maximum accuracy. If more than four range rings are necessary to cover the scale it is wise to divide the rings into subgroups by making half of them dotted and half solid lines. Use of separate colors per subgroup is also satisfactory. Range rings may also be designed to act as unnumbered bearing aids on very large grid systems (30-inch diameters or larger).

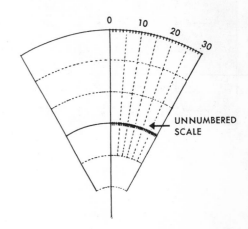

UNNUMBERED
SCALE

WRITING SYMBOLS ON RADAR DISPLAYS

Conventional radar equipments are not designed primarily to write symbols, but to display target and environment information. Special circuits have been designed specifically for displaying symbols, however, and synthetic radars and devices such as xerographic equipments and charactron tubes have been created primarily for this purpose. Alpha-numeric symbols are obviously useful, used in conjunction with target pip position to provide means for adding other information about the target (its identification, altitude, etc.). CRT characteristics such as beam focus, phosphor graininess, and persistence, as well as ambient illumination, all interact to enhance or degrade legibility. Sixteen minutes of visual angle, which is roughly equivalent to 5-point type (at a 16-inch viewing distance), is the minimum size required for the characters to be reasonably legible. The optimum is 27 minutes of visual angle of letter height.

Geometric symbols are also useful as a symbolic code. It is desirable to have shape elements which require relatively simple circuits to write them. In general, the requirements for perceptual simplicity are compatible with engineering requirements for simple elements.

MINIMUM SATISFACTORY SIZES FOR SYMBOL ELEMENTS

Element	Description	Dimension (inches)
Dots and circles	Diameter	0.02
Squares and rectangles	Length of short side	0.02
Lines	Width	0.005 (light on dark)
		0.01 (dark on light)

A SET OF DISCRIMINABLE SYMBOL CONFIGURATIONS[3]

NOTE: Don't use 11 and 3 together, 12 with 5 or 7, or 13 with 8.

It is often required that primary symbols have auxiliary symbols added onto them. When combining auxiliary symbols with the primary symbol, consider the following:

- Primary symbols should be large and enclose a space.

- No auxiliary symbol should cross, distort, interfere with, or in any way obscure the primary symbol.

- Symbol complexes normally should not exceed two, possibly three geometric symbols — e.g., a location dot, a speed, and a direction vector.

- When other information is required, use alpha-numeric or one, two, or three parallel marks to indicate magnitude.

- The geometric center of the symbol or a "clear dot" should indicate location.

- Auxiliary marks should be "solid figures."

ILLUMINATION (See also pp. 2-176ff.) — Brightness contrasts between signal and background and between target and "noise" vary to such a degree that exact optimum levels cannot be stated. Contrast ratios may be improved by minimizing background brightness and surface reflections. By proper filtering the trace-to-background ratio can be maximized. A cross-polarization filter technique has proven quite adequate. The technique utilizes a polarized light source and a second polaroid filter over the scope face. With this technique it is not necessary to work in completely darkened rooms. Scope hoods are recommended for a single operator when ambient illumination cannot be adequately controlled.

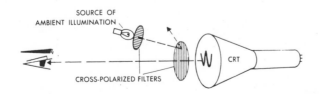

COMBINED DISPLAYS

The combination of different types of visual displays within one instrument, or of several instruments into an array or within a single frame such as a projection or television screen, should be governed by the following principles:

Combine only those forms of information which bear a common relationship.

Keep the common factor of interpretation (fixed and moving parts, scale values, etc.) the same.

Minimize parallax between successive layers of overlays.

Do not confuse the operator by unnecessary information.

SINGLE-INSTRUMENT COMBINATIONS

The single frame of one instrument for more than one item of information saves the operator time which would be taken in locating parts of a total picture.

Scale range may be increased by combining pointers and counters. The total range may be increased by extension (pointer plus counter) or the range may be given with more precision (pointer plus sub-dial and pointer).

NOTE: This type of scale expansion is to be used only when some qualitative information relative to rate or normal operating range is needed. The counter is best when only quantitative information is needed.

Do not use multiple-pointer displays with more than two pointers.

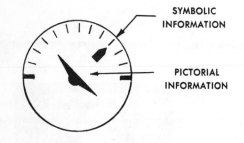

SYMBOLIC INFORMATION

PICTORIAL INFORMATION

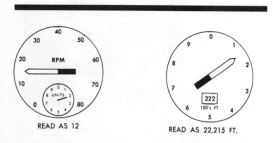

READ AS 12

READ AS 22,215 FT.

POOR

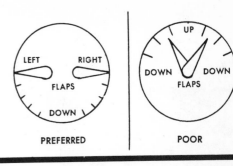

PREFERRED   POOR

Proper orientation of two pointers or. the same dial face will make check reading easier.

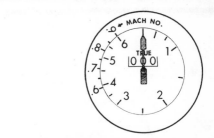

Avoid use of unrelated information combinations (aircraft attitude plus engine condition, or compass heading plus speed). In the example at the right, indicated air-speed, true air-speed, and Mach number are closely related.

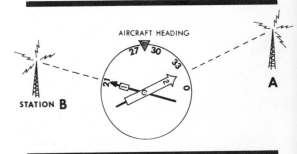

In the Radio Magnetic Indicator, two radio-compass needles are superimposed over a magnetically slaved rotating compass card — magnetic heading to a station can be read directly under the compass needle tuned to that station. From the angles formed by the two radio-compass needles the pilot can estimate ground position and course in relation to the two ground stations.

It is sometimes possible to use one pointer as a moving reference for alignment of a second pointer. In the illustration, the relative-heading pointer is kept aligned with the localizer needle, making the aircraft approach the desired localizer track in an asymptotic path. Matching the two pointers is easier than integrating readings on separate indicators. In the example shown, the localizer pointer shows aircraft position relative to a radio beam. The relative heading indicator defines the rate at which the aircraft approaches or leaves the localizer track. Relative heading is the first derivative of position, as shown by the localizer pointer. Rate (in this case heading) is more easily controlled by the pilot than position, although the goal of the pilot is aircraft position. But, this is accomplished by controlling heading, which is under more direct control and responds with much shorter lag. In applications of this type, the pointer being controlled directly by the operator should present the first derivative of the data indicated by the moving reference.

(after Baker and Grether[2])

2-25

RIGHT TURN

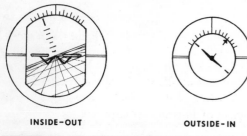

INSIDE-OUT   OUTSIDE-IN

KINALOG

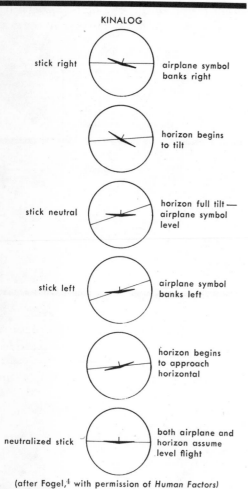

stick right — airplane symbol banks right

horizon begins to tilt

stick neutral — horizon full tilt — airplane symbol level

stick left — airplane symbol banks left

horizon begins to approach horizontal

neutralized stick — both airplane and horizon assume level flight

(after Fogel,[4] with permission of *Human Factors*)

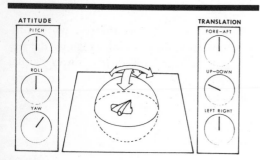

Inside-out and outside-in pictorial displays have been the subject of controversy for many years. Although the controversy has never been completely resolved, there are important considerations which should be kept in mind in arriving at the proper choice between these two opposing points of view. The more realistic the details are in the display, the less chance there is for confusion in using the inside-out concept. If, however, the realism is omitted (i.e., the pictorial elements are definitely abstract), the Outside-in concept is recommended.

A more recent innovation has been suggested which combines both concepts. This is called Kinalog. It presents the maneuver first as an outside-in presentation, but then as time proceeds, becomes altered gradually until the presentation appears inside-out. The unique feature of this concept is that it attempts to account for the pilot's "feeling" about the maneuver. The first thing he feels in beginning a right turn, for instance, is that the airplane is actually turning right. Looking at the airplane symbol, he sees the symbol bank to the right gradually, which reinforces his original "feeling" about the maneuver. As the airplane banks into a coordinated turn, his feeling adapts to the tilted position and he references the outside horizon, while Kinalog in turn performs the same adaptation on the panel, further strengthening the compatibility between display and pilot feeling. Although this display concept has been tested only in the laboratory, it is representative of the type of truly integrated man-machine design that should be considered in complex displays.

With the advent of space vehicles, attitude displays have become even more complex — introducing besides pitch, roll, and yaw, lateral displacements right, left, up, and down. Pictorial representations of multiple-dimensional factors have led to many ambiguities in displays. Studies so far have not produced an optimum configuration; it has been shown, however, that rate information is a critical parameter in any such display. One of the most promising solutions to this problem is in the use of a three-dimensional model which can be manipulated for gross positioning and later corrected for final alignment, using quantitative readouts.

THE WHOLE-PANEL CONCEPT

The instrument panel should always be considered as a whole. In many cases this can be accomplished by simple analysis of the operational sequence and arrangement of available instruments to reduce scanning distances and "backtracking." The ideal approach, however, is to analyze the functions to be accomplished and develop an integrated instrumentation layout. This approach quite often leads to entirely new displays and usually reduces the actual number of instruments required.

Integration around a vertical-horizontal reference may be used to reduce the over-all scanning profile.

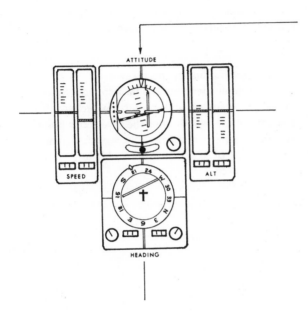

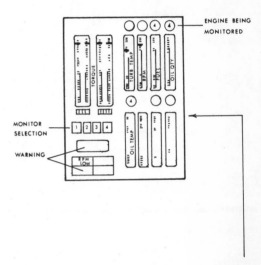

Ten vertical-scale indicators replace 32 round-dial indicators formerly used for control of a propulsion system through the use of advanced digital computing techniques (After Wright[5] and and the Bendix Corporation.[6])

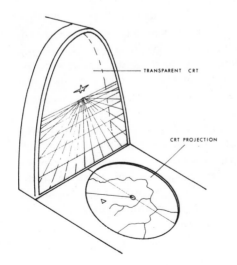

A contact analogue of the real world provides a transparent display which permits the operator to "see through" the display during visual flight without transferring his eyes from an instrument panel to the outside of the cockpit.

2-27

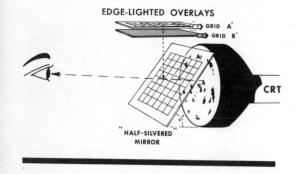

EDGE-LIGHTED OVERLAYS

GRID A'
GRID B'

CRT

"HALF-SILVERED" MIRROR

Frequently it is desirable to provide semi-permanent overlays with scales or quantitative symbology to be referenced to a CRT display. Owing to the disparity between the plane of the CRT and the overlay, extreme parallax can become a severe problem for the observer. This can be overcome by the use of an arrangement of independently lighted plates which are reflected in a half-silvered plate mounted 45 degrees to the line of sight. This makes the image from the edge-lighted overlay appear at the same plane as the surface of the CRT.

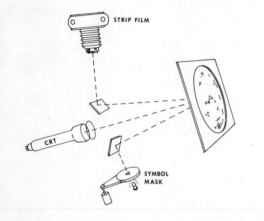

STRIP FILM

CRT

SYMBOL MASK

A combination of permanent, semipermanent, and dynamic elements can be displayed simultaneously by means of back-projection techniques. This is particularly good from the observer's point of view since there is no parallax between elements. Careful control of contrasts and ambient glare is required, however.

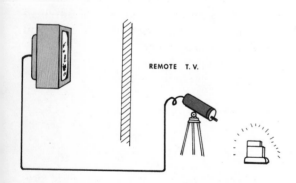

REMOTE T. V.

Closed-circuit television systems are an excellent solution to the problem of bringing a picture of a remote operation into the crew work-area. When operator panel space is limited, and certain instruments are referred to only intermittently, these instruments can be mounted elsewhere and called into view on the TV screen as required. The closed-loop TV technique is especially useful for observing remote hazard-areas, such as may occur with nuclear engines, or for control of "slave" manipulators in atomic research laboratories.

A principal consideration in all of the above types of display techniques is proper control of ambient lighting conditions at the operator's viewing screen. Since the brightness of these indirectly viewed images is not high, ambient light should be filtered or blocked from the screen wherever possible.

DESIGN CONSIDERATIONS ASSOCIATED WITH COMBINED DISPLAYS

Most of the combination displays discussed in this section have a serious problem with reflected light because of the necessity for large areas of glass which cover the faces of the instruments.

Hoods may be used to prevent direct ambient light rays from falling on the display cover glass. Such hoods should be painted dull black on the inner side.

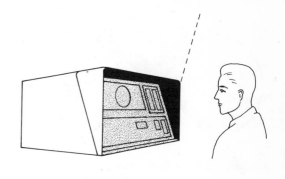

Panels which have a great amount of glass are prone to reflect the operator's face, and if he is wearing light-colored clothing, this too will interfere with his seeing the display. Although we emphasize mounting instruments normal to the line of sight, this actually creates the worst condition for "self reflection." Therefore, instruments should be mounted at angles slightly off the normal line of sight. (See p. 2-135.)

Integrally lighted instruments, because of the differences in amount of reflecting or energized markings, tend to appear unevenly bright to the observer. This, in addition to large glass-covered areas suggests use of other than black instrument-face backgrounds. Medium gray tends to help maintain an over-all balance in the brightness emitted from the several displays.

Some integrated displays have the problem of symbols appearing over more than one shade or color of background. It is important to recognize this and take steps to create a symbol that is equally visible under all conditions. In the illustration to the right, note that the airplane symbol has been outlined so that it can be seen in either the dark or light background.

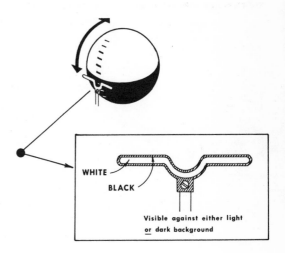

WHITE
BLACK

Visible against either light
or dark background

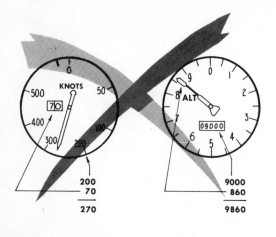

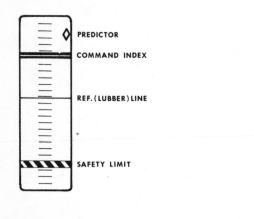

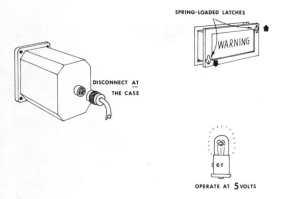

When using off-the-shelf instruments from different manufacturers on the same panel, be sure there are no inconsistencies between them. A good case in point occurs with combination instruments which use a pointer with digital-counter insert. In the example illustrated, on one instrument the counter presents gross value with vernier on the scale, while on the other the arrangement is reversed.

Integrated instrument designs usually involve more than one type of pointer, and these are generally coded by shape, size, color, or other special scheme of marking. Care must be taken to maintain a constant code throughout the panel. In other words, a command marker should appear in the same configuration on each instrument.

The importance of pointers, index markers, and lubber lines varies with different instruments. Care should be taken to make this difference apparent. Variation in size and stroke width are the most acceptable methods for accomplishing this.

There is a tendency when combining or integrating instruments to create a severe maintenance problem owing to the necessity for miniaturization and dense packaging. Modularizing techniques are recommended to alleviate this problem. Avoid use of large numbers of screws if possible. Special fasteners for quick release are desirable — as are quick-disconnect cable connectors.

Integrally lighted instruments are fine when they are operating. However, special care must be taken in the design of the instrument for lamp replacement. Proper selection of long-life lamps operated slightly below rated voltage often provides sufficient lamp reliability to outlast the required life of the instrument. Electroluminescent materials are suggested also. This approach reduces the problem of uneven illumination, and will not be subject to "all at once" loss of light.

GRAPHIC PANELS

A graphic representation of a complex control system can be made to convey operational status to an operator more clearly than the typical array of abstract meters and controls. The graphic panel, as it is called, pictorializes the salient features of system directly on the panel, so that the operator has a better appreciation for the parts, direction of flow, and subsystem relationships. The extent to which the elements of the display are static or dynamic will depend, of course, upon how much the designer has to spend on the panel. In the simplest case, elements of the system can merely be painted on the panel. For more complex or exotic renditions, the elements, including flow lines, can be made to appear dynamic by means of illuminated indicators, edge- or back-lighted lines, or by use of electroluminescent panels and strip elements. Color coding is quite useful in segregating various subsystems or for emphasizing certain critical elements of the display. Another technique which is useful is the flashing light for attracting attention to important elements of the display — especially when it is important for the operator to react to the signal quickly.

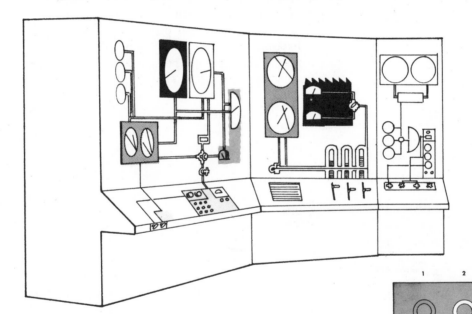

A typical application used aboard submarines is the panel which displays open or closed hatch conditions. In the first display to the right, the circles (when illuminated) indicate that a particular hatch is still open. Not until all bars are illuminated can the command be given to submerge.

In the second illustration, missile tubes are pictorialized, showing when the hatch is open and also when a missile tube is being flooded. Electroluminescent panels are very useful in making up displays of this type.

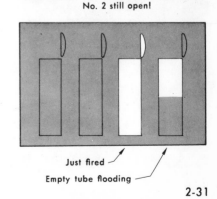

No. 2 still open!

Just fired

Empty tube flooding

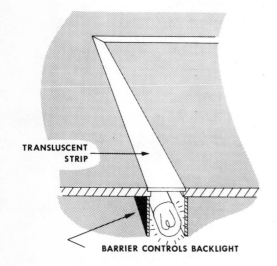

TRANSLUSCENT STRIP

BARRIER CONTROLS BACKLIGHT

Combinations of edge-lighted lines, areas, symbol and indicator lights, annunciators, or illuminated instruments are useful in developing a graphic layout of complex systems.

In the design of graphic panels using edge-lighting techniques, it is important to control the spread of light in the plastic transilluminating medium. Barriers must be provided between elements to avoid having stray light from one part of the graphic affect another. Also, it is important to position the lamps in such a way that there is a good balance among various parts of the display. If it is impossible to locate the lamps in an optimum position, it is sometimes possible to balance the illumination by means of filters.

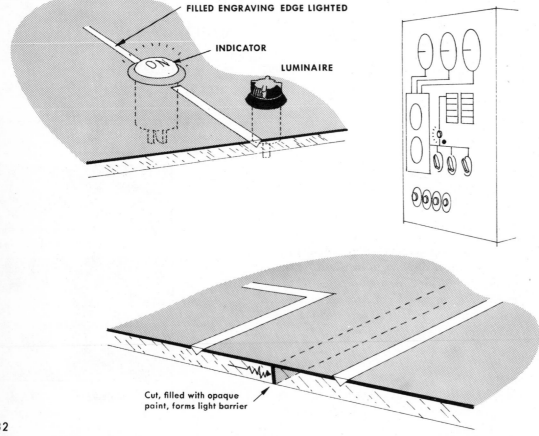

FILLED ENGRAVING EDGE LIGHTED

INDICATOR

LUMINAIRE

Cut, filled with opaque paint, forms light barrier

DIGITAL READ-OUT DISPLAYS

Digital read-out displays are recommended when strict quantitative information is all that is needed. Such displays require no searching interpretation of pointer-scale relationships or decisions about display-motion ambiguities that are often inherent in more complex displays. They can be read accurately and rapidly if certain principles of design are observed.

Digital read-out devices are available in a wide variety of types, a few of which are illustrated for reference in discussing good design practice.

COUNTER WHEELS — These indicators are economical and reliable, and they can be made extremely legible. They may be mechanically driven or electrically pulsed. Character size is small, owing to practical considerations, so that viewing distance is limited. (Character height = approximately $\frac{1}{4}$ inch.) Response rate is up to 500 cycles per second for mechanical counters or 50 pulses per second for electrically pulsed counters. Illumination is normally from reflected light, although it is possible to light them internally if the counter wheels are made from clear plastic materials.

DESIGN CONSIDERATIONS

Digits should "snap into place" and should not follow each other faster than about two per second if the observer is expected to read numbers consecutively.

An "upward" movement of the counter drum should indicate a numerical increase. If a manual control is associated with the counter, the clockwise rotation of the control should result in numerical increase. Control-display ratio should be such that one revolution of the control knob = approximately 50 counts on the counter.

Counters should be mounted as close as possible to the panel surface to provide maximum viewing angle and reduce possible shadow from ambient illumination.

Minimize space between digits.

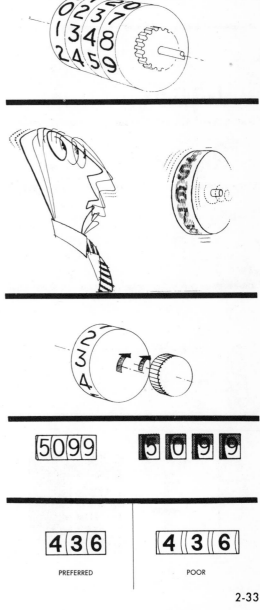

PREFERRED   POOR

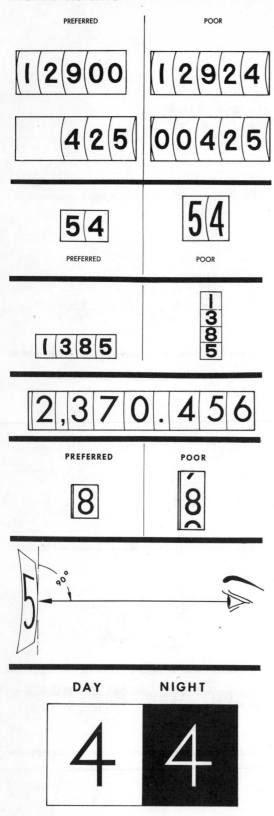

When final digits have no significant value (i.e., the accuracy implied does not actually exist), these digits should be replaced with stationary zeros. Similar treatment is recommended for preceding digits which are not required; in this case, the space should be blanked out.

The height-to-width ratio of numerals for counter-wheel read-outs should be 1:1 rather than the 3:2 recommended for other displays. This is because of the distortion from the curved drum surface.

Counters should always be oriented to read from left to right. Spacing between digits should be limited to no more than half the digit height.

If more than four digits are required, it is easier to read and recall groups of digits if they are separated by slightly greater space or by a decimal symbol or commas.

No more than one digit should appear in the open window at one time.

Because of the limited viewing angle of drum-type counters, they should be mounted normal to the observer's line of sight.

Contrast between characters and the immediate background should always be maximized. Black on white provides maximum visibility under normal illumination conditions. The reverse combination is desirable, however, when the situation calls for maintaining the dark adaptation of the observer.

OTHER DIGITAL READOUT DISPLAYS

REAR-PROJECTION TYPE — Character configuration can be optimized and in viewing distance and angle this type is superior to most other indicators. Character heights to about 3¾ inches are available; larger ones could easily be devised. Response rate depends on switching. A singular drawback is the necessity for bulb replacement. Average bulb life is about 3000 hours.

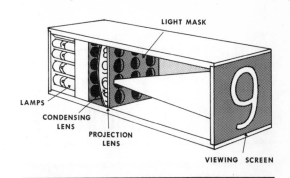

EDGE-LIGHTED TYPE — Character configuration is reasonably good; viewing angle is limited, however, owing to the tunnel effect of the stacked plates. Primary disadvantages are: ambient illumination should be relatively low to maintain good contrast, and it is necessary to replace bulbs. Viewing distance is good to about 30 feet, although greater distances could be obtained with special engraving techniques.

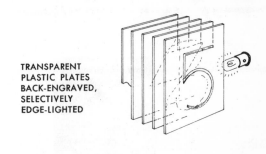

TRANSPARENT PLASTIC PLATES BACK-ENGRAVED, SELECTIVELY EDGE-LIGHTED

ELECTRONIC REGISTER-TUBES — Human-engineering characteristics are similar to the edge-lighted displays. These neon-glow displays are good to 60,000 hours and can be read up to 30 feet and 120 degrees. A response rate as low as 10 microseconds is possible. Care must be taken to shield the tube from ambient light to avoid spectral reflection from the curved surface of the tube.

MATRIX DISPLAYS — A variety of displays are available which form characters from prepared matrices. Some use lamps banked in mosaic patterns; others use electroluminescent sections to build up a given character. In general, all such displays suffer in terms of character legibility and are not recommended from a human-engineering standpoint.

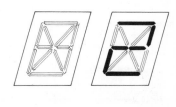

DECIMAL ARRAYS — Not generally recommended, owing to reading difficulty and potential transposition error by the observer.

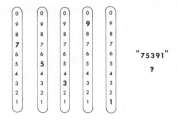

"75391"
?

PILOT LIGHT

ANNUNCIATOR

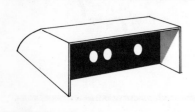

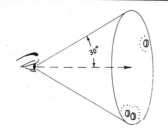

INDICATOR LIGHTS

Simple panel lights may be used for indicating certain types of operating conditions. For example:

GO, NO-GO condition
CAUTION
WARNING

In addition, indicator lights with engraved nomenclature may be used to give visual commands or identify conditions. These are often referred to as annunciator displays.

Brightness factors are of prime concern in light displays. Lights which must attract immediate attention should be at least twice as bright as the immediate background. The background should be dark in contrast to the display and should be in a dull finish. When a major panel area is light in color, it is possible to improve the effectiveness of the display by painting the immediate area around the display a dark matte finish. If dark adaptation must be maintained, variable control over the light intensity is necessary.

Simple pilot lights need not be large to be effective. Color and brightness are the important variables. Standard colors for aircraft indicators are:

NORMAL : green
CAUTION : amber
WARNING : red

As a general rule, avoid combining colors which can be easily confused, such as red and orange, purple and blue, etc.

Even the brightest pilot light cannot compete with direct sunlight. Therefore the display should be located in a shady spot or be hooded.

Flashing lights are good attention-getters. Flash rates of 3 to 10 per second with "on duration" of at least 0.05 second are recommended.

Important light indicators should be located within 30 degrees of the normal visual axis to insure that the observer will see the light when it comes on.

Identification should normally be provided with light displays. If the ambient conditions of illumination are sufficient, the identification does not have to be printed directly on the light. If, on the other hand, the display is in darkness, it will be necessary to have identifications printed on the face of the indicator. If the indicator is of the Warning type, the print should be dark and the background bright in order to maximize the brightness of the indicator. On the other hand, bright print on a dark background is recommended for those indicators used to communicate routine messages.

DEFINITIONS

WARNING: Dangerous condition requiring immediate attention!

CAUTION: Abnormal condition not necessarily requiring immediate action.

Frequently, there is insufficient panel space for all of the system-malfunction indicators required. In such cases it is recommended that single master Warning and/or master Caution lights be located in a conspicuous position on the panel close to the normal visual axis — with separate system-malfunction indicators grouped in another, less critical area.

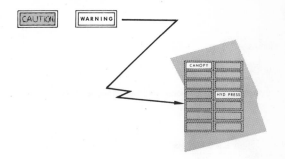

GENERAL PRECAUTIONARY NOTES

Don't use more lights than are necessary. The attention value of indicator and warning lights is reduced if there are too many of them, especially when they serve little purpose. For example, if a normal condition of "on" is indicated by sounds or the movement of a meter, etc., it is not necessary to have a pilot light indicating "on." On the other hand, when a pilot looks at a radio console containing several channels, he will find it helpful if lighted indicators show which channels are activated.

Dual-lamp assemblies should always be used in critical indicators, and there should be a means for checking for burned-out lamps.

LABELS

The lack of, or misinterpretation of a label will not only delay an operation, but in some cases can lead to serious human error. Many of the considerations which are given here will appear obvious to the reader. Experience, however, has demonstrated that these factors or principles are regularly ignored in many modern-day equipments. A special word of advice is offered to the designer of commercial equipment: "Don't consider labels as an eyesore to be eliminated or camouflaged for the sake of beauty."

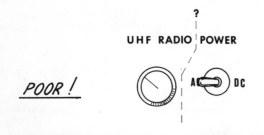

POOR !

Place labels where they can be seen. Think ahead and anticipate what possible obstructions may occur in the final installation.

Arrange labels close to the component being identified and make sure two different labels aren't so close together that they appear to be "one a continuation of the other."

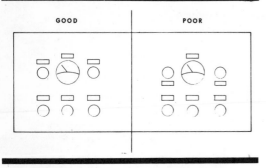

Place labels consistently either below or above each component identified. (Above is preferred.) If a new equipment is to be used later with an older piece of gear, make the new panel consistent with the old, unless it is too poorly labeled. In the latter case, the old equipment labels should be modified.

Vertical orientations may be used in rare cases where the label is needed only for initial familiarization purposes, and not as part of the regular operational routine. Avoid use of curved patterns of labeling.

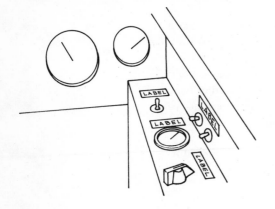

All labels should be oriented horizontally to the expected line of sight. If labels are to be placed on low side consoles, check the placement with reference to the eventual operator position. For example, as a pilot turns his head to the side, there will be an obvious point where the choice of label orientation shifts to a "side view" orientation.

Plan labeling for electrical cabling so that numerals and letters will appear upright "after" the installation. It too often happens that, although they

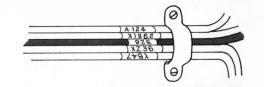

are mounted right side up for the bench technician, they appear in an "upside-down" position after they are installed and viewed by the field technician.

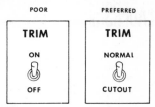

AVOID   BETTER

When labels are used on an instrument face, they should not obscure or detract from the important figures or scales which must be read by the operator. Avoid use of manufacturer's labels placed directly on the instrument face.

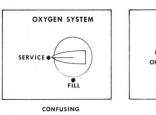

Labels should be as brief as possible, consistent with clarity. They should identify what is being measured rather than indicate an instrument title: e.g., ALTITUDE, not ALTIMETER. Switch position labels should identify the positions clearly (see example at right).

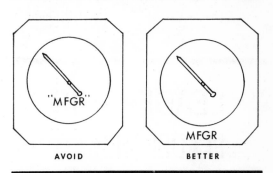

CONFUSING   BETTER

Avoid the use of similar words if these could lead to an error in interpretation.

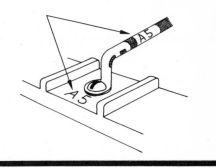

Labels used on electrical wires should be coded to match the terminal they connect to — and the terminal label should also be compatible with the wire code. The same principle applies to mechanical cables and liquid- or fuel-carrying pipes or hose.

GOOD   **POOR**

All labels should be capitalized, generally. Use simple, unadorned letter styles. Although several different letter heights may be desirable on the same label for emphasis, the smallest letter size must be compatible with viewing distance and anticipated illumination level.

QUANTITY   **QTY**   **QY**

(Best)   (Ok)   (Poor*!*)

LEADERSHIP
LEADERSHIP
LEADERSHIP

Abbreviations should be avoided wherever practical. They may be necessary, however, to avoid crowding. When this is required, consult standard abbreviation lists. If these are not available and new ones have to be made up, follow a plan of experimental testing; i.e., try them out on a number of naive subjects to see if they interpret the abbreviation as you intended.

Height-to-width ratios for label lettering may vary — and in many cases is desirable for emphasis. Variation should be limited to approximately 5:3 to 1:1, and stroke width from one-eighth to one-sixth of the letter height (narrower stroke widths associated with narrower letters).

RECOMMENDED SIZE FOR LETTERING ON LABELS

	Viewing Distance	Critical Labels	Routine Labels
For illumination less than 1 ft-l	28 in.	0.15 to 0.30 in.	0.10 to 0.20 in.
	3 ft	.19 to .39 in.	.13 to .26 in.
	6 ft	.39 to . 77 in.	.26 to .51 in.
	20 ft	1.29 to 2.57 in.	.86 to 1.71 in.
For illumination greater than 1 ft-l	28 in.	.10 to .20 in.	.05 to .15 in.
	3 ft	.13 to .26 in.	.06 to .19 in.
	6 ft	.26 to .51 in.	.13 to .39 in.
	*20 ft	.86 to 1.71 in.	.43 to 1.29 in.

Critical labels refer to key control or component identifiers and to position markings on such controls.

Routine labels refer to over-all instrument identifiers, routine instructions, or any marking required only for initial familiarization.

*For greater viewing distances: $\text{Letter height} = \dfrac{\text{Viewing distance (") } \times 0.15"}{28}$

LABELS FOR CONTROLS

Whenever possible, labels should appear on the control itself. Labels or directions should appear "upright" to the observer. The label or direction should be brief but "clear" in its meaning. If you have any doubt, test it with persons who are unfamiliar with the operation. If abbreviations are necessary because of limited space, use only standard abbreviations.

Numerical key-set arrays should be arranged and numbered according to expected direction of numerical increase. An effective arrangement is illustrated at the right.

Frequently designers require assemblies of push buttons, but forget to call out the proper orientation for labeling the array. As indicated in the illustration, labels should appear upright even though the assembly array changes from a horizontal to a vertical position.

Avoid the use of "abstract" symbols on controls, for these usually require special training.

Engraved controls, such as push buttons, will become filled with dirt and thus reduce the legibility of the printing. Such engravings should be filled with paint pigment or covered with clear plastic covers.

Special two-position controls should be labeled according to rules of compatibility: i.e., "up or to the right for ON, down or to the left for OFF."

For controls too small to accommodate labels, place the label as close to the control as is practicable and make sure the position is standardized for all controls on the same panel — e.g., all above, or all below.

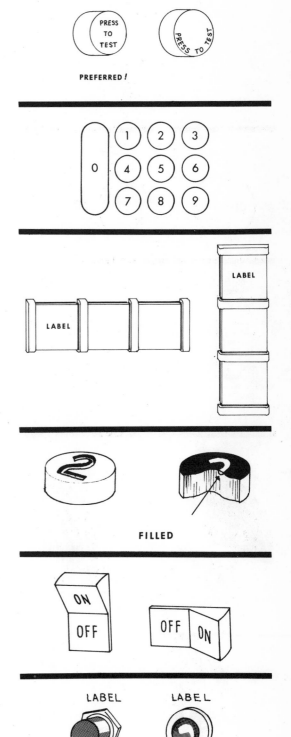

2-41

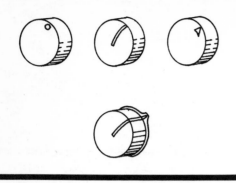

Even though some controls don't require exact setting (dimmers, etc.), some indication of the position is desirable. The pointer configurations shown are all equally good. Where more accuracy is required, engrave (and fill with contrasting pigment) a line both on top and down the side as shown in the bottom example.

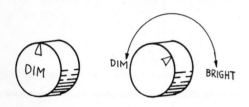

Either of the two methods shown to the left is good for marking a continuous-function control, although the one on the right is preferred if space permits.

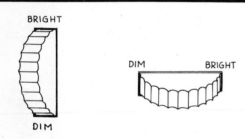

Certain types of controls, such as the thumb control, are not designed for putting labels or directions right on the control. Lettering should be oriented as shown.

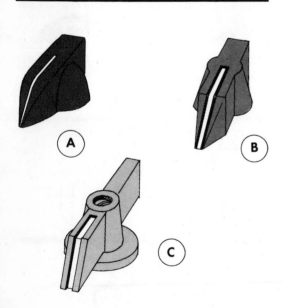

Pointers which are black or of a dark color (A) should have a contrasting white mark showing the pointer axis. The mark should not extend more than halfway down the top surface of the knob however.

Pointers which are of a light color (B) should have a white marker outlined in black to provide sufficient contrast between the basic (light) color of the knob and the white marker.

Some special knobs created for military use (C) have insets which are painted white or filled with phosphorescent pigment. If the inset is too deep, the marker may not be seen because of parallax. Care should be taken to fill the inset completely or reduce the depth of the inset.

SEQUENTIAL INSTRUCTIONS

When a sequence of operations is required, as in the example to the right, directions may be required at the starting point which refer to the remaining control devices. Many factors must be considered in deciding the best manner for labeling. Above all, remember the necessity for illumination. In the example shown, the handle under the cover was painted bright yellow since there would be little light to see printing on the handle. Construct a mock-up of the arrangement and test the operation under realistic conditions of illumination and time before you decide.

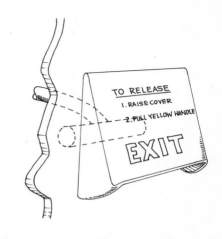

Some controls must of necessity be located where they are not normally seen by the operator. Provide instruction decals where they can be seen. Avoid the temptation to ignore the problem or excuse it for so-called esthetic reasons!

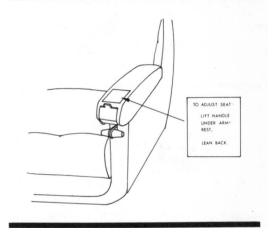

COMMON ERRORS TO AVOID:

Control handles which turn (A), allowing the label to end up "upside down."

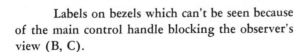

Labels on bezels which can't be seen because of the main control handle blocking the observer's view (B, C).

Labels whose positions are incompatible with the direction of motion and position of the control (D).

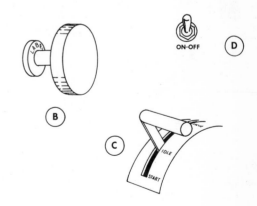

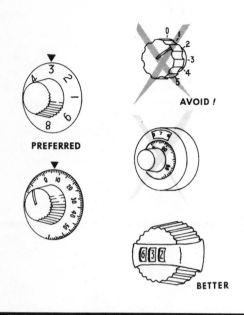

PREFERRED

AVOID !

BETTER

Although moving-scale displays are generally to be avoided, they will undoubtedly be used at times. If the control is a gross approximator of position and is detented (i.e., it steps mechanically from one position to another), the numbers should increase from right to left. This will be compatible with the natural inclination to turn the knob "right" for an increase in value.

If more exact setting is required (as shown at the left), the numbers should increase from left to right, making the interpretation of the unmarked scale indices easier.

Note that numbers are oriented normal to the index pointer. Although the 12 o'clock index position is preferred, other cardinal positions may be used in special cases. When other index positions are used, remember to change number orientation.

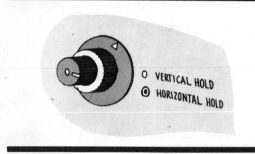

O VERTICAL HOLD

◎ HORIZONTAL HOLD

Special stacked-control knobs are difficult to mark because of lack of space. To avoid confusion, paint a "dot" on the smaller knob and the rim of the larger knob. A similar set of symbols on the panel identifies the function of each knob. Use of different colors will increase the code-symbol reliability even more.

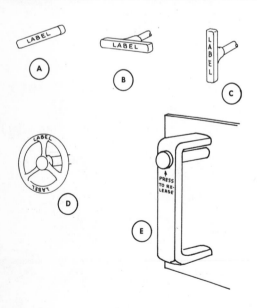

Pull handles are sometimes difficult to label. Handle A would probably be positioned to the left of the operator. The 45-degree position makes it easier to grasp. If the same handle were on the right at 45 degrees, the label would be reversed (i.e., from top to bottom). Handle B is the preferred case. Handle C is a last resort which might be necessitated by lack of horizontal space on the panel.

When labels are put on controls which turn, it is desirable to repeat the label on opposite sides, as shown in D.

Directions for special assemblies should be oriented "upright" relative to the observer, as in E.

Labels or signs used on curved surfaces, such as piping, must be designed so that part of the lettering is not lost owing to the curvature.

LETTER SIZE FOR USE IN LABELING PIPES OF VARIOUS SIZES

Outside Diameter of Pipe Surface (inches)	Recommended Letter Height (inches)
0.75	0.50
1.50	0.75
2.50	0.875
3.50	1.25
4.50	1.50
6.0	1.75
7.0	2.0
8.0	2.50
10.0	3.0
12.0	3.50

(From American Standards Association.)

Tools or control devices requiring engraving on curved metal surfaces should have the surface anodized to reduce spectral glare. Shiny surfaces under typical lighting conditions will completely obscure scales or lettering.

"A" SIZE OF ROUND (INCHES)	"B" CHARACTER SIZE (INCHES)	DEPTH AT "X" = 0.003, DEPTHS AT POINTS "B"
1/8	1/64	0.0030
	1/32	0.0070
3/16	1/32	0.0057
	3/64	0.0091
	1/16	0.0139
1/4	1/32	0.00496
	3/64	0.0074
	1/16	0.0113
	5/64	0.0161
5/16	3/64	0.0065
	1/16	0.0093
	5/64	0.0132
3/8	1/16	0.0081
	5/64	0.0113
7/16	3/64	0.0055
	1/16	0.0075
	5/64	0.0101
	3/32	0.0129
1/2	1/16	0.0069
	5/64	0.0091
	3/32	0.0116
5/8	5/64	0.0079
	3/32	0.0099
	7/64	0.0125
3/4	3/32	0.0087
	7/64	0.0122
7/8	7/64	0.0099
	1/8	0.0119
1	7/64	0.0091
	1/8	0.0107
1 1/8	1/8	0.0099
	5/32	0.0139
1 1/4	1/8	0.0091
	5/32	0.0127
1 3/8	1/8	0.0086
	5/32	0.0119
1 1/2	1/8	0.0081
	5/32	0.0111
1 5/8	1/8	0.0077
	5/32	0.0105
1 3/4	1/8	0.0084
	3/16	0.0129
1 7/8	1/8	0.0071
	3/16	0.0122
2	1/8	0.0068
	3/16	0.0117
	1/4	0.0187

On machined, ground, or polished surfaces, a marking depth of 0.003 inch is clearly legible, but maintaining this minimum depth is dependent upon the ratio of the diameter of the surface to the size of the character to be stamped.

As a guide in determining when a curved surface should be marked with a concave die, and when a flat marking die can be used, the adjacent chart has been prepared by the Steel Marking Tool Institute.

Black lettering on white background makes for the most legible labels. Other combinations, however, may be desirable for other reasons (for example, red lettering on white for a "FIRE" label or sign). There may also be other reasons for having a lighter color for lettering (for example, when a dark background would help maintain the dark-adaptation level of the observer).

RELATIVE LEGIBILITY OF COLOR COMBINATIONS UNDER REFLECTED LIGHT

Legibility Rating	Color Combination
Very good	Black letters on white background
Good	Black on yellow Dark blue on white Grass green on white
Fair	Red on white Red on yellow
Poor	Green on red Red on green Orange on black Orange on white

Back-lighted, edge-lighted, or self-illuminated labels (as with electroluminescent devices) are exceptions to the foregoing color/legibility rating scale. In most cases all colors will be equally legible. Care must be taken, however, to adjust the intensity of the illumination to the ambient condition. It is possible to get the intensity of the lighter colors so high that a halo effect occurs — which decreases legibility. Also, it is important to balance the brightness of labels on any one panel or within, say, the immediate cockpit area of an aircraft or other vehicle, since the pilot or operator who requires dark adaptation will dim the entire lighting system to a level sufficient to keep the brightest unit from bothering him. In the meantime, if labels or instruments do not have balanced light intensity, he may inadvertently dim some indications below this visibility threshold!

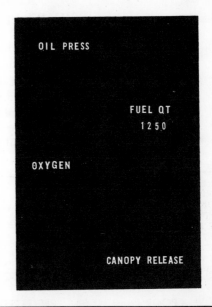

Distinctive borders may be placed around critical labels to make them more conspicuous than other, routine labels. Care should be taken not to overdo this. Each succeeding embellishment on the same panel reduces the over-all effectiveness of any single one.

Utilize labeling methods which are resistant to abrasion and wear. Avoid use of stencils, silk-screen processes, or stamping. Engraved letters should be filled with pigment or otherwise protected from dirt. Even ordinary maintenance cleaning will fill open engravings and reduce legibility of the label.

Because of the importance of proper labeling, the designer should practice testing each and every design. The test is for the purpose of making sure that the eventual user will interpret the label as intended. In addition, if there may be any anticipated problem with illumination or visibility, it is recommended that a mock-up be devised and examined under the expected illumination conditions. This is particularly important for labels to be used by maintenance technicians where supplementary lighting is not optimum.

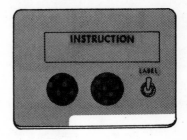

SIGNS, PLACARDS, AND INSTRUCTION PLATES

Recommended practices for legibility of Labels are equally applicable to signs, placards, and instruction plates. Too frequently, however, the designer does not recognize the need for applying these practices to this type of informational display. The recommendations which follow are based on typical and frequent discrepancies found in signs and placards produced for use not only on equipment, but in industrial and public buildings and highways.

FOR EMERGENCY EJECTION IN FLIGHT, JETTISON CANOPY BY PULLING THE CANOPY-JETTISON HANDLE, HOOK HEELS IN FOOTREST, RAISE BOTH ARMRESTS TO HORIZONTAL POSITION, ASSUME ERECT POSTURE, ACTUATE EJECTION TRIGGER FOR SEAT EJECTION.	**TO EJECT** • Jettison canopy • Feet in stirrups • Raise arm rests • Sit erect • Squeeze trigger
POOR	**PREFERRED**
SERVICE WITH MIL–H–5606	SERVICE WITH MIL–H–5606 (HYD FLUID—RED)
DANGER DO NOT REMOVE VALVE UNTIL ALL AIR HAS ESCAPED.	DANGER Do not remove valve until all air has escaped, or valve will blow — with possible injury to personnel.

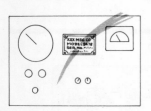

EQUIPMENT

Instruction plates should be as concise as possible without distorting the intended information or meaning. Avoid use of abbreviations wherever possible. If they must be used to save space, use standard abbreviations where available. If new abbreviations must be created, test them on a sample of typical users.

Add nomenclature with a specification. Don't rely on the reader's memory or force him to waste time looking it up in an instruction manual.

Consider the effect of your instructions. Qualify Warning or Danger when the results of disregarding the instruction are not obvious.

Placards used to identify equipment should be mounted in a position where they will not be confused with operating labels or functions. Manufacturing serial or identification numbers should be placed where the supply, shipping, or maintenance man can find them quickly and easily. Don't put them under or behind panels which must be removed.

Instruction plates are read more easily if they are printed in "caps-and-lower-case" lettering. The identifying heading, however, should be "all caps."

Signs to indicate alternate status (Lavatory Occupied, Seat Belts, No Smoking, etc.) should not be covered up during the nonapplicable condition. This is frequently done for aesthetic reasons. There is considerable value in letting the observer know what the sign is about before it comes on. Naturally the difference between "on" and "off" must be clearly distinguishable.

OPERATOR CHECK LISTS

Operators of complex equipment can easily forget to perform certain parts of their task and therefore need to be prompted. A typical example is the aircraft pilot's procedural check-list normally provided in the cockpit. In addition to the check list's being located conveniently and being visible and legible, a method should be provided for making sure that the operator has considered all the steps listed. A typical solution shown in the illustration reminds the pilot which steps he has or has not completed by the position of the manual slides (which he operates himself). This type of device also provides means for performing steps out of order, such as not lowering flaps and landing lights when air speed is too high. These items, held over because of operational limitations, require special emphasis in the list.

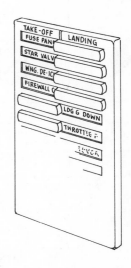

ROAD AND TRAFFIC SIGNS

Special attention should be given to the location of signs — anticipating the possibility of obstructions such as other signs, poles, parked vehicles, etc. Another hazard often encountered is the advertising sign in close proximity to the road sign or traffic signal. In many cases the advertising sign commands more of the observer's attention and must be offset by sufficient spacing or provision of a protective shield to isolate the road sign.

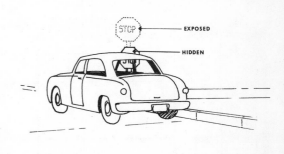

Frequently an industrial facility must create local road signs within its own area. It is desirable that these signs be made compatible with local municipal designs, since the vehicle operator will be more subject to traffic error if he is confronted with two different sets of sign configurations.

Size of lettering and location of road signs must be related to the point of expected action and the expected approach-speed to that point of action. A vehicle operator must have time to react and maintain adequate control of his vehicle based upon seeing the sign far enough ahead of the action point.

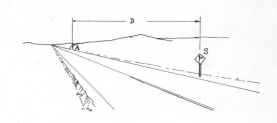

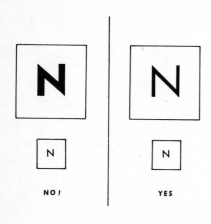

NO!   YES

It is a common failing in the design of signs to believe that "the bigger the sign, the bolder the letters." In addition, there is no room for artistic license in sign design. The same rules of legibility which apply to instruments and labels should be applied here: i.e., simple character style, proper height-to-width ratio and stroke width, optimum spacing, good contrast between letters and background, and adequate illumination.

Minimum letter height for 10-foot viewing distance = 0.3 inches. Letter height for longer viewing distances may be computed as follows:

$$\text{Desired letter height} = \frac{\text{Viewing distance (ft)} \times 0.3''}{10}$$

MINIMUM LETTER SIZE RECOMMENDED FOR HIGHWAY SIGNS

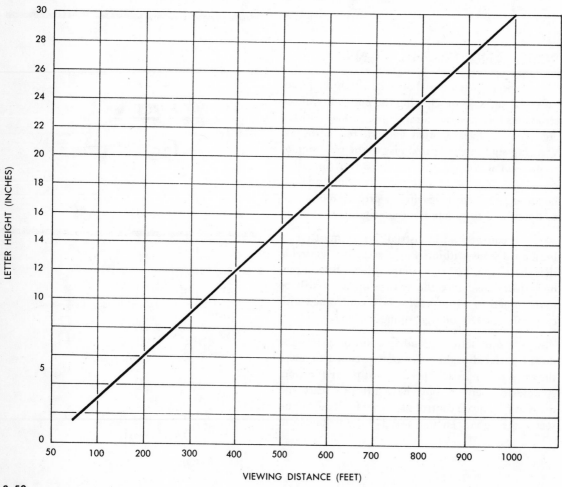

Lettering size for signs on main thoroughfares should be increased, since the speed of traffic affects the amount of time motorists have for seeing and reading the signs. The values in the table at the right are recommended for various average traffic-speeds considering the time necessary for the motorist to see and react before a typical maneuver such as turning off the highway onto a side road.

Street signs should be located so that motorists can find them easily. They should be on the corner nearest the approaching auto, and should be mounted so that the sign cannot be obscured, as shown in the illustration. The name of the street should be printed on both sides of the sign, which should be mounted at a height above the ground compatible with headlight beams so that the sign can be seen easily at night.

Letter Height vs. Road Speed

Speed (mph)	Letter Height (inches)
15	4
25	6
40	10
60	20
70	30

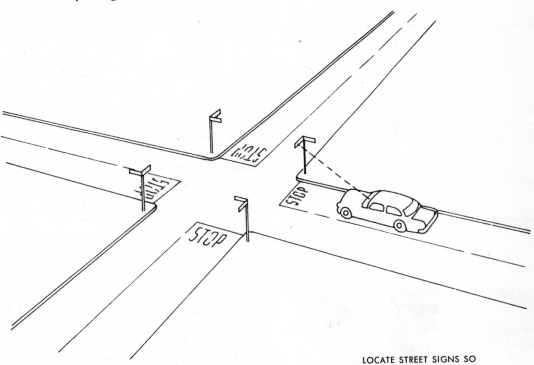

LOCATE STREET SIGNS SO MOTORISTS CAN FIND THEM!

Use black letters on white background. White background should be self-luminous.

ROADWAY SURFACE SIGNS

Elongated lettering improves readability from a moving vehicle. Doubling the height of the letters is about right. Further distortion reduces recognition time.

The addition of an irregular line which ends in an arrow-head pointing directly to the word "STOP" attracts attention and warns the approaching driver of the printed warning. The length of the "wavy arrow" line should be 20 to 30 feet for normal approaches. For freeways, expressways and other high-speed roads, such signs as these should be supplemented by a flashing amber light approximately 300 yards in advance of the stopping point.

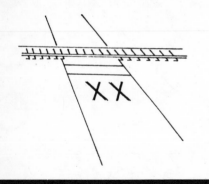

Special codes such as the one at the left are recommended for hazardous railroad crossings. Refer to road and highway marking standards for federal and state roads.

STANDARDIZED ROAD SIGNS

In addition to visibility and legibility factors, it is important that road signs be standardized. Unfortunately, there is still disagreement as to what such standards should be. Among the factors which should be considered are: differentiating color and shape codes for (1) regulatory, (2) directional, (3) instructional, and (4) cautionary road signs.

Roadway signs which cannot be illuminated should be painted with reflecting pigments, or the letters should be constructed with reflector buttons which reflect the headlights of oncoming automobiles.

In recent years an attempt has been made to standardize road signs on an international basis. Common symbology has been developed which is designed to overcome the language barrier. A sample of these is shown at the bottom of the page.

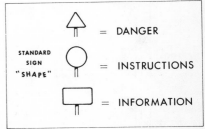

INTERNATIONAL ROAD SIGNS

I Danger Signs

UNEVEN ROAD

DANGEROUS CURVE (Curves)

RIGHT (LEFT) CURVE

LEVEL CROSSING WITH GATES

LEVEL CROSSING WITHOUT GATES

LEVEL CROSSING WITHOUT GATES

ROAD WORKS

SLIPPERY ROAD

PEDESTRIAN CROSSING

BEWARE OF ANIMALS

UNSPECIFIED DANGER

Double Curve, First to Right (Left)

ROAD INTERSECTION

TRAFFIC CIRCLE

DANGEROUS HILL

ROAD NARROWS

OPENING BRIDGE

WATCH OUT FOR CHILDREN

BEWARE OF ANIMALS

Intersection With A Non-Priority Road

PRIORITY ROAD AHEAD

TWO-WAY TRAFFIC ON ONE WAY ROAD

II Signs Giving Definite Instructions

ROAD CLOSED

NO ENTRY

NO LEFT (RIGHT) TURN

No Entry All Motor Vehicles

NO ENTRY Pedal Cyclists

MAXIMUM WIDTH

END OF SPEED LIMIT

STOP AT INTERSECTION

CUSTOMS. STOP

NO OVERTAKING

No Entry Except MOTORCYCLES

NO ENTRY MOTORCYCLES

MAXIMUM HEIGHT

MAXIMUM WEIGHT

SPEED LIMIT

Restricted Stopping Or Waiting

DON'T BLOW YOUR HORN

Give Way To Approaching Traffic

No Parking Fig. 1 Side Uneven Dotes, Fig. 2 Even Dotes

END OF SPEED LIMIT

End of Prohibition to Overtake

III Informative Signs

FIRST AID STATION

FIRST AID STATION

MECHANICAL HELP

TELEPHONE

FILLING STATION

PRIORITY ROAD

END OF PRIORITY ROAD

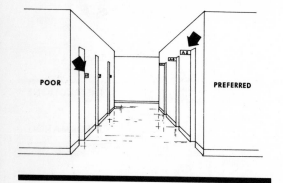

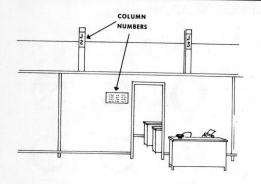

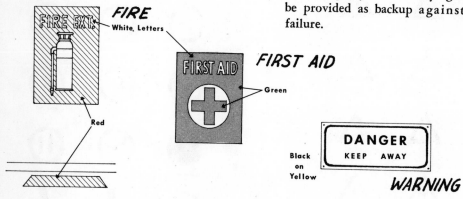

BUILDING-IDENTIFICATION SIGNS

Signs used in corridors of multi-office buildings should be mounted so as to be seen by the observer long before he gets to the office door. Considerable time is often lost because the observer can't see the sign until he is directly in front of the door. Remember, the door may be open, so it is important to mark the doorway, not the door.

Many large industrial plants use the "column numbering system" to identify areas. Too frequently, however, the numbers are covered by temporary walls or obstructions after the column numbers were first applied. Time can be saved if all column numbers within a given area are displayed at the entrance to the area. Floor-plan placards are useful in orienting the person hunting for a certain column number.

Critical signs — Exits, Danger, Caution, Fire Extinguisher, First Aid, etc. — should follow standard safety rules for location, color, special borders, etc. Emergency or secondary lighting systems should be provided as backup against bulb or power failure.

OPTICAL AIDS

Optical aids are used primarily to offset reduction in visibility owing to extreme viewing distance. Telescopes and binoculars are available in a wide variety of configurations and magnifications. In general, viewing with both eyes (binocular) is preferred to one-eyed viewing since it preserves a certain amount of depth perception.

Because of the limited field of view through optical aids, they are more appropriate for examination and target recognition than for detection. This is owing to such optical characteristics as magnification, contrast rendition, light transmission, and the size of exit pupil. One must recognize that the magnification of size is accompanied by a magnification of relative motion, making it very difficult to maintain line of sight with the object being viewed.

For identification of objects the size of an airplane, up to distances of 3000 yards, a $2\times$ magnification is appropriate. Increases in magnification make it difficult to shift from naked-eye to optically aided viewing. It is recommended that for magnifications higher than $2\times$, suitable means for steadying both the device and the observer be provided.

Visibility through an optical aid depends on the amount of light transmitted. The more glass surfaces in the optical system, the greater the light loss. All glass surfaces should be anti-reflection coated.

Hand-held optical aids are easier to use than permanently mounted devices because of the criticality of eye–optic axis alignment. Hand-held devices should not exceed 2 pounds in weight to avoid severe arm fatigue.

A short eye-relief is recommended where possible. In certain cases (jostling in a moving vehicle, etc.,) this may be a hazard however. A Fresnel lens design can be used to reduce the criticality of the eye-relief and eye alignment. Ambient illumination control is necessary, however, to maintain brightness control which is lost through the Fresnel system.

SUGGESTED MAGNIFICATION CRITERIA

DISTANCE	MAGNIFICATION
1000 yards	$1 - 1.5 \times$
3000 yards	$2 - 3 \times$
5000 yards	$3 - 4 \times$
*Beyond 5000 yards	$6 - 8 \times$

*SHOULD BE MOUNTED ON VEHICLE OR TRIPOD.

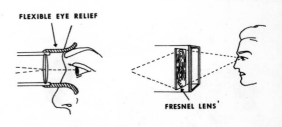

FLEXIBLE EYE RELIEF

FRESNEL LENS

Reticles for optical aids are fine lines or markings superimposed on the focal plane of the system. These serve as references against which to compare the size or position of the object being viewed. Care should be taken in the design of reticles to:

- Make sure they are visible both night and day.

- Reduce interference with view of the target.

- Minimize apparent distraction from the task of target viewing.

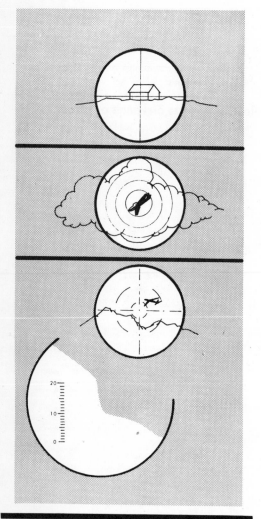

A vertical and (or) horizontal cross-hair reticle provides a stable frame of reference for the field of view.

Concentric circles provide complete two-dimensional reference without the observer having to rotate the optical aid.

Broken lines permit reasonable reference with minimum obstruction of the target.

Numbers are appropriate only where extreme accuracy is required. Numerals should always be placed "outside" the scale so that the scale marks can be brought in juxtaposition with the target.

Provision for reticle illumination is desirable for night viewing. The level of illumination should be maintained below about 0.02 ft-l. A variable-intensity control is desirable. Red light is preferred in order to maintain dark adaptation and also to help differentiate reticle marks from objects or lights being viewed.

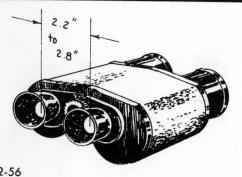

Binocular devices should be designed with adjustable interocular distance and independently adjustable focal distance for each eye. Optic aids used where there is a possibility of flash blindness should be provided with automatic filtering since the hazard is magnified through the optic system.

EXTERIOR LIGHT DISPLAYS FOR VEHICLES

Lights are extremely helpful in conveying information about a vehicle being observed at night — particularly aircraft, ships, trucks, etc. Such lights can be used to convey the following kinds of information:

Presence and location

Identification

Heading

Intended maneuver

Distance or range

Altitude

Speed

Attitude

Needs help

Size or road clearance

Certain standard light signals have been developed for aircraft, shipping, railroads, and for commercial road vehicles. It is not the purpose of this section to discuss the pros and cons of these standards, but rather to present recommendations for making these light displays readily observable. Unbelievable as it may seem, many such light displays are poorly located on the vehicles in question and therefore do not serve the purpose for which they were installed.

Regardless of the vehicle in question, it is important to analyse the configuration with respect to all possible viewing angles in order that (1) the light will not be blocked from view, and (2) the light or series of lights do not give a false impression of the position or direction of motion of the vehicle being observed.

TYPICAL AIRCRAFT EXTERIOR LIGHTING INSTALLATION

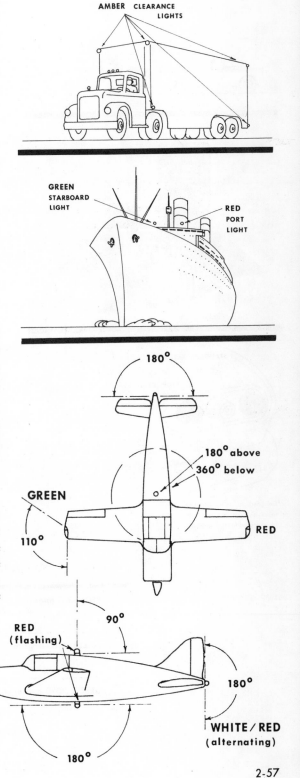

TAIL LIGHTS on commercial road vehicles should be mounted high enough that they can be seen by the driver of the automobile approaching from the rear. Remember that this driver has to look over the hood of his automobile!

In addition, it is recommended that normal tail lights be designed so that they can be seen from the side also.

Very wide vehicles, such as trucks, should be provided with clearance lights indicating the extremities of the truck to the passing or approaching driver.

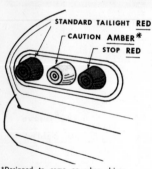

STANDARD TAILLIGHT RED
CAUTION AMBER*
STOP RED

*Designed to come on when driver takes his foot off accelerator. Can also be used for turn indication.

TURN INDICATORS should be made to flash automatically between 3 and 10 times per second, with flash duration of 0.05 second. Preferably such lights should be mounted in fixtures separate from regular tail light.

It is further recommended that a *Caution* light indicator be added to the array of lights for the rear of vehicles. Each light should be in separate fixtures similar to the illustration at the left.

Colors for Vehicle Signal Lights

RED (6300 angstrom)	Danger	Used for regular tail lights and stop lights, port position lights for ships and aircraft
AMBER (5900 angstrom)	Caution	Used for clearance warnings, fuselage identification, anticipatory signals
GREEN (5000 angstrom)	Safe	Used for starboard position for ships and aircraft, etc.

Other colors are permissible for a variety of uses. These colors, however, tend to wash out with increase in viewing distance and cannot be differentiated easily from a white light.

ANTICOLLISION LIGHTS

The primary purpose of anticollision lights is to make aircraft conspicuous to other aircraft pilots at night. Although there is disagreement as to the best type of light for this purpose, it is obvious that the one most important factor is intensity. The visual range R, of a light of intensity I, is given by Allard's law,

$$R^2 = \frac{IT^R}{E_0}$$

where T is the transmittance of the atmosphere for unit distance and E_0 is the threshold illuminance at the observer's eye. To obtain the required intensities compatible with warning times for modern aircraft would be prohibitive in terms of practicable power considerations. Therefore it can only be recommended that the highest intensity practicable within the state of the art be provided. It is also generally agreed that anticollision devices other than lights are the only real solution to the problem. In the meantime anticollision lights are still useful in a limited sense. A flashing red light is recommended (80 to 90 flashes per minute with on-off ratio about 2:1 to 3:1).

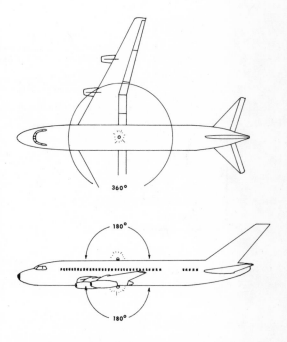

"All lights must be designed or positioned such that they do not shine directly in the pilots' eyes."

FORMATION FLYING LIGHTS

A minimum of three simultaneously visible reference lights is recommended; (a) at the juncture of wing and fuselage, (b) at the wing tip, and (c) at the trailing edge of tail surfaces. They should be located so that at least three of the lights are visible from any viewing position. A three-position dimmer control should be provided to prevent glare. Since the pilot cannot usually see his own formation lights, the control must be suitably coded so that he can find the correct positions readily.

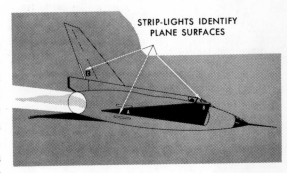

STRIP-LIGHTS IDENTIFY PLANE SURFACES

SIGNAL LIGHTS FOR AIRPORT OPERATIONS

The greatest problem in providing signal lights for airport operations stems from the fact that the pilot observer must be able to interpret their meaning and arrangement and his relative position under varying viewing positions and under different atmospheric and illumination environmental conditions. The following recommendations are provided with the caution to the designer to consult current federal and international standards for specific applications.

General Considerations

Consider the pilot's "point of view" in locating lights to avoid ambiguity with surrounding community lights.

Upon "touch down," the pilot is in a very difficult position to observe the layout of runway and taxiway lights, particularly with reference to "turn-off" points.

The pilot landing at night is highly susceptible to glare.

Ground-mounted light fixtures can be a serious obstruction hazard.

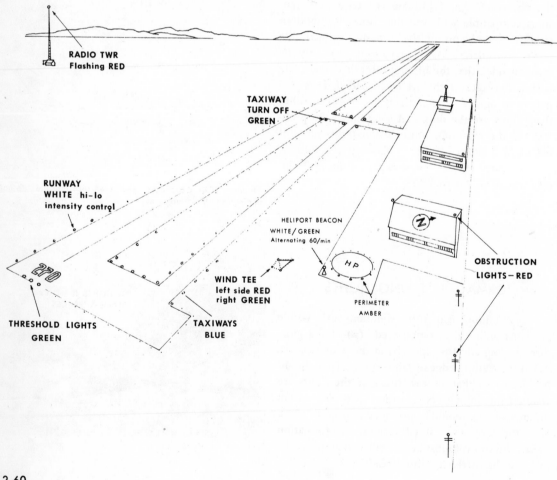

RADIO TWR
Flashing RED

TAXIWAY
TURN OFF
GREEN

RUNWAY
WHITE hi–lo
intensity control

HELIPORT BEACON
WHITE/ GREEN
Alternating 60/min

OBSTRUCTION
LIGHTS – RED

WIND TEE
left side RED
right GREEN

PERIMETER
AMBER

THRESHOLD LIGHTS
GREEN

TAXIWAYS
BLUE

Direction signs are quite useful for guiding the pilot who is trying to taxi — especially at night. Such signs must have lettering heights commensurate with the distance they will have to be viewed — and this must be related to the landing touch-down point and expected aircraft rolling speed. A good rule of thumb is letters 15 inches high. The signs should have white letters on black background for daytime viewing — the letters showing up as yellow-amber at night.

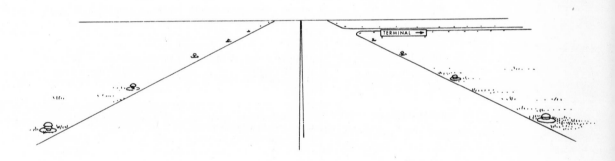

All critical ground-signal lights should be provided with an automatic system for turning them on and off, since manual systems are subject to human failure or oversight. It is also desirable to provide a method for indicating to a central control station when individual lights are burned out, so that maintenance crews can be dispatched to the scene to replace the failed luminaire. All lighting fixtures should be designed for ease of maintenance, to reduce the time required for performing replacement of bulbs.

PRINTED MATTER

DETAIL RECOMMENDATIONS FOR DESIGN OF PRINTED MATTER

	Books and Pamphlets	Labels, Check Lists, Signs, License Plates, Instruments, and Technical Manuals
PRINT STYLE Vertical (roman) print is recommended for normal use. Italics are permissible for special emphasis, but should be used sparingly.	Bookman Old Style Garamond Cheltenham Antique Scotch Roman (Styles under *Labels*, etc., can also be used for headings, graphs, tables, etc.)	Gothic Spartan Copperplate Futura (For instruments see also p. 2-10.) Note: Condensed, medium, and some demi-bold versions of the above are permissible. Avoid bold or extra-bold versions.
PRINT FORM	Combinations of capital and lower-case letters	All "caps" for instruments and labels. Others: combination of caps and lower case, depending on length of material.
PRINT SIZE	10-point type preferred; 9 to 12 points permissible. (1 point = 0.0138 inch.)	Depends on viewing distance (see p. 2-10).
LINE LENGTH	19 picas preferred; 14 to 28 picas permissible. (1 pica = 0.166 inch)	For manuals see *Books and Pamphlets*. For others, as required or dictated by space and balance.
LINE SPACING	With 10-point type, space between lines should not be less than 2 points.	Minimum = 3 points
CONTRAST	Dark print on light background. Black print on highly reflecting but non-glossy white paper is recommended for general use. Paper weight must be sufficient to avoid bleed-through of print from the opposite side of page.	For manuals see *Books and Pamphlets*. For others see special instructions under appropriate sections of Guide.

NOTE: For more detailed instructions on preparation of printed materials consult style guides of specific publishers. In cddition, refer to the following: American Standards Association, Z15.1 — *Engineering and Scientific Charts for Lantern Slides*; Z15.2 — *Time-Series Charts: A Manual of Design and Construction*; Z15.3 — *Engineering and Scientific Graphs for Publications*. American Standards Association documents are published by the American Society of Mechanical Engineers, 29 West 39th Street, New York 18, N. Y.

Graphs, Tables, Charts, and Scales	Lantern Slides
See *Labels, etc.*	See *Labels, etc.*
All "caps" preferred. Combinations are permissible for extended printed text inserts.	See *Graphs, etc.*
For use in books and manuals, size depends on page proportions. For other uses, size depends on viewing distance (see p. 2-50).	Minimum letter at least 0.04 inch high — stroke width about 0.006 inch.
As required	As required
Graphs, as required. Tables, 0.2 of letter height is recommended minimum separation.	As required (see recommendations for *Books and Pamphlets* and for *Graphs, etc.*).
Dark print on light background (exception, see Slides, pp. 2-69, 2-70).	Either way, depending on ambient lighting conditions (see discussion on Slides, pp. 2-69, 2-70).

GENERAL CONSIDERATIONS FOR PREPARATION OF PRINTED MATERIALS

The primary purpose of printed material is to communicate thoughts, ideas, and detailed information from one person to another. The most important objective should be to get this information across in the simplest, quickest, and most understandable manner possible. In order to do this effectively, it is important to know the background of the audience and the manner in which they expect to use the material. Materials which are instructional in nature should not be prepared in exactly the same manner as, for instance, reference materials. It is particularly important not to make assumptions about these things without a thorough analysis of the user problem. From the human-engineering standpoint, every effort should be made to save the user's time and to design the material to insure his reliable understanding. A common failing of authors, publishers, illustrators, and designers is to design their product with the objective of making their own job easier — thus causing many problems for the final user of the material. Typical examples of this are; word abbreviations, refusal to use illustrations because of cost, poor layout because it is easier for the typesetter, elaborate and complex cross-referencing to save repeating and duplicating pages, poor type-style because a better style isn't immediately available in the typesetter's standard type-tray, poor-quality paper because it's cheaper. In addition, such factors as outmoded publishing standards, contemporary illustration fads imposed under the guise of aesthetic principle, or unfounded opinions about writing "down" to the intended audience quite frequently make the finished product difficult to use.

FLAT /

BOOKS AND OTHER BOUND MATERIALS — The size of such materials is related to the environment in which they will be used and stored. If the bound volume is too large or thick, it is difficult to handle and store. On the other hand, if it is too small, the reader may spend most of his time turning pages. In general, the following size-to-thickness relationships are reasonable:

$7\frac{1}{8}$ x $10\frac{1}{2}$" page — up to 2" thick

$5\frac{3}{8}$ x 7-5/16" page — up to 1" thick

Such sizes are easy to handle and store. Larger volumes are, of course, to be found; owing to their size and weight, the user needs something to support the book.

Books should be bound so that the pages will lie flat when the book is spread open.

Books used for reference are more effective if some method of indexing is provided. If tabs are provided, these should be designed so that they cannot tear out with normal usage.

Labeling the bindings of books presents an awkward problem which is related to the peculiarities of storage. Standard labeling (American publishers) for books stored vertically is shown at the right. The advantage of this orientation is that when the book is lying horizontally on a table, the label is easily read from both the binding and the front cover of the book.

PAGE LAYOUT — The principal point to keep in mind is that the reader normally enters the page (visually, that is) at the upper left-hand corner. Layout concepts proceed from that point on. Many hypotheses have been developed as to the merits of one concept or another: location of critical reader-interest point on the page, balance of print versus pictorial material, etc. Consultation with an experienced publisher is advised on this point. The pages of the present book are laid out with a different principle in mind — indicative of consideration for the user's point of view. Since the average designer is expected to use this book as a ready reference, the layout was designed primarily with a "thumbing through" behavior in mind. Illustrations and headings are placed at the outer portions of each page so that they are readily available as the user thumbs through the book, from either direction.

At least ½-inch outer margins should be provided for book printed-matter. Inner margins must be large enough to prevent obscuring printed matter by the method of binding.

If more than one column per page is used, there should be at least one pica of space between columns. Use of ruled lines to separate columns is not recommended.

Tables are preferable to graphs or scales for numerical data — except where the general shape of a function is important and is more easily understood from a graph. Graphs, scales, and charts, are about equal in terms of readability and should be used to show trends or relationships between quantitative values.

Tables should be reduced to the simplest form consistent with the degree of sensitivity required — avoid making the reader interpolate between steps.

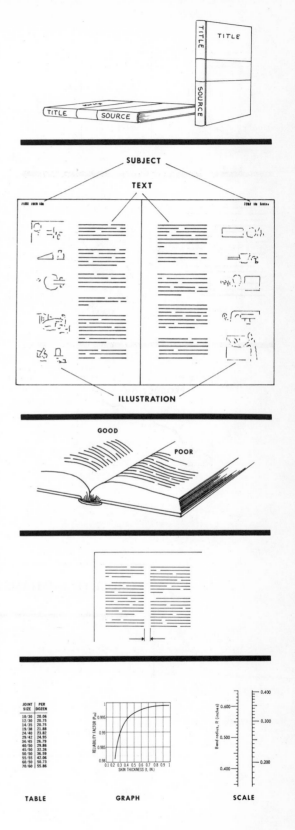

i Observation Number	Y_i Measured Diameter	i Observation Number	Y_i Measured Diameter	i Observation Number	Y_i Measured Diameter
1	0.992	11	0.998	21	1.001
2	0.992	12	0.998	22	1.002
3	0.993	13	0.998	23	1.002
4	0.994	14	0.998	24	1.003
5	0.995	15	0.999	25	1.003
6	0.995	16	0.999	26	1.004
7	0.996	17	1.000	27	1.005
8	0.996	18	1.000	28	1.005
9	0.996	19	1.000	29	1.006
10	0.997	20	1.001	30	1.008

Use of vertical lines in design of a table is recommended to clarify the column separation. Horizontal lines should be used only for separation of major sections of the table. When columns run to numerous items, however, they become difficult to read, and separation should be provided after every fifth item.

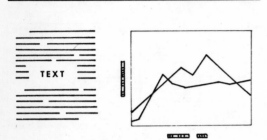

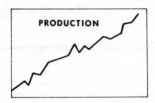

Graphs should be used when over-all general impressions are to be communicated. They should include all necessary notations to make them self-explanatory. They should also be mutually supplementary with any associated written text.

Graphs should be designed with the idea of minimizing reader effort. They should be free of all lines and lettering which are not absolutely essential to clear understanding. Viewed as "a whole," a graph should give a quick and obvious impression of the features of major importance, with subsidiary parts suggestive of the meaning of the whole.

ORDER OF EMPHASIS IN THE DESIGN OF CHARTS AND GRAPHS

Title

Curve(s)

Curve captions

Scales and their captions

Subtitles and notes

Grid rulings

The number of curves for a single graph should be limited to four to avoid an appearance of clutter.

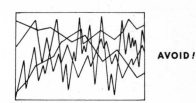

Lettering for graph labels and notations should be oriented to be read along the bottom and on the left.

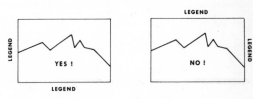

The "weight" (or thickness) of various lines on the graph should vary with the order of importance; i.e., the principal curve should be the most prominent. Coordinate lines should never be as bold as the curve. Numbered lines should be heavier than unnumbered lines. When ten-line intervals are used, the fifth or intermediate line should be less bold than numbered lines, but may be bolder than other unnumbered lines.

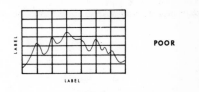

Limit the number of coordinate lines on "non-arithmetic scales" by the use of "tick marks."

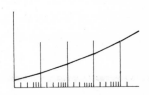

Graph scale, captions, etc., should be arranged to give a sense of balance around vertical and horizontal axes. The center of the mass should be slightly above the halfway point to appear balanced. Horizontal (independent variable) values progress normally from left to right, vertical (dependent variable) from bottom to top. Captions should indicate "Quantity and Unit of Measurement."

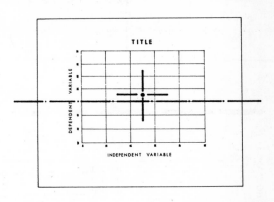

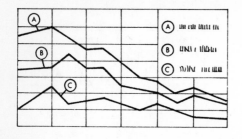

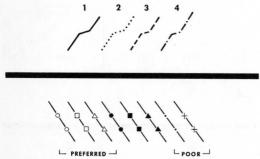

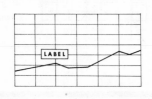

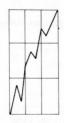

Graph titles should be as concise as possible. A subtitle can be used to augment the title for clarity. Titles should not appear within the grid area. Don't use abbreviations in titles. Only standard abbreviations should be used elsewhere on graphs or charts.

Circled numbers or letters are preferred to printer's symbols (*, †, etc.) for use in reference legends.

Abbreviations — Use Sun, Mon, Tue, etc. Maintain the three-letter balance. Space can be saved by the following: 1940, '41, '42, '43, etc.

Curves — Use different types in order of importance and preference. (But it is not always necessary to make all curve lines different.)

Open circles, squares, or triangles are preferred for indicating observed points on a curve.

Brief labels close to curves are preferable to letters or numbers requiring a "key." Remove grid lines around these labels. When legends or keys are required, they should appear within the grid system.

Grids — A grid system "wider than high" should be used:
>   For data extending over a long time-period
>   For a series requiring frequent observed points
>   When actual rate of growth is slow

A grid "higher than wide" should be used:
>   For data over a short period of time
>   When it is desirable to accentuate minor fluctuations
>   When actual rate of growth is rapid
>   For separating overlapping curves
>   For showing series which differ greatly in magnitude

When two scales are required on the same graph, it is desirable to convert both scales to a common base: index numbers, per cent of average, etc.

Scale numbers may require shortening to avoid making the scale difficult to read. Sometimes common symbols can be used rather than word captions to identify scale numbers.

THOUSANDS			HUNDRED THOUSAND	
500	500,000		5	
400	400,000		4	
300	300,000		3	
200	200,000		2	
100	100,000		1	
0	0		0	
PREFERRED	POOR			

USE TIME-SERIES CHARTS:

- For close reading or interpolation
- For emphasis on movement rather than amounts
- When several series are to be compared

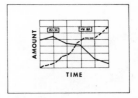

- To add emphasis to a line chart
- To emphasize amount as against ratio
- To picture point data, as distinguished from period data
- To present general picture as against exact measure unsuitable for irregular chart

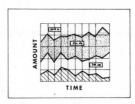

- To emphasize comparisons of amounts
- To picture period data as against point data
- For showing range of values or deviations from a normal or base line

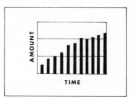

PREPARATION OF MATERIAL

An original graph 8½ by 5½ inches will reduce to one-third lantern-slide size or one-half size for publication. A graph 8½ by 13 inches (including captions) will, after reduction by one half, approximate a full page in the average single-column magazine or journal. Graphs for publication should be kept within the limits of a type column or page in terms of width and within limits of the type-page height.

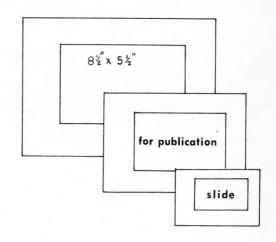

SLIDES

Proportions for lantern slides should be about 7 to 10. Negative slides (white lines on black background) are less fatiguing to the audience than "positives," but should be used only in a thoroughly darkened room. If there is any doubt, it is safer to use "positives."

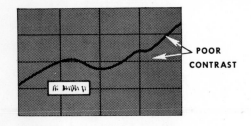

POOR
CONTRAST

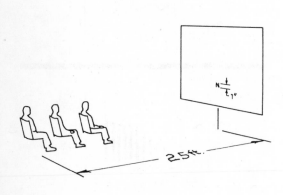

Appropriate use of color on slides (and on other graphics) can increase the effectiveness of the presentation. Care, however, must be exercised not to degrade visibility or legibility through poor selection of color combinations. The greatest hazard comes in reduction of figure and ground contrast.

Where possible, limit lettering to one size. Do not use more than three curves to a slide unless they are similarly shaped and well separated.

Recommended practice:
Curves — $1\frac{1}{2}$ to 2 points in thickness.
Reference lines — 1 point.
Grid rulings — $\frac{1}{2}$ point.
Ratio of letter height on screen to distance viewed by farthest observer — 1-inch letter for 25-foot distance (or 1:300). In general, the smallest letter on a slide should be at least 0.040 to 0.045 inches high, with a stroke width of 0.006 inches. In preparing chart, enlarge the copy about three times — the letters should then be about $\frac{1}{8}$ inch high.

HUMAN-ENGINEERING A DOCUMENT

Printed documents such as handbooks, library accession brochures, and training and technical manuals are frequently not designed with the user in mind. For example, librarians frequently prepare accession lists for the use of technical personnel to inform them of new materials acquired by the library. The librarian naturally looks for means to simplify the process of making the lists by combining the process of printing the catalogue file cards with the printing of the accession lists. In a sense, there are two users to consider, the librarian and the technical man who wishes to scan the accession list quickly. Unfortunately the technical user suffers and finds the job of scanning the accession list confusing and time-consuming, since the list is actually laid out more for the simplifying of the librarian's task. For instance, the technical man is interested in finding subject matter first, then topic titles, then authors or source, and finally when he finds a report of interest he will then, and only then, be interested in the report number for purposes of ordering the report to read. Although this example is biased toward the technical user, it demonstrates the difference in form of a simple layout problem when approached and designed with a particular user in mind. Note that the things the technical user needs are emphasized in the order he uses for scanning the list:

Subject category
Report title
Author
Source
Source or accession number

Another example of human-engineered format is a check list. In this case, the same check list is a standard item used many times. Since the user actually doesn't need a bulky repetition of the answer part of the list, the question part of the list is designed so that an answer card can be inserted in the questionnaire booklet, aligned properly, and, when the questions are answered, removed for further analysis or filing.

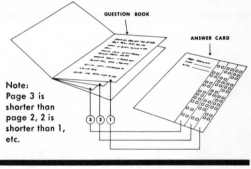

Fold-out pages facilitate the user's task with certain types of printed matter. They are an excellent means for providing a particular reference page on a continuous basis for reference while the reader proceeds through several related pages of material. The fold-out page, however, should never fold into the lap of the reader. It should fold to the top, right, or left.

Transparent overlays are an effective means for successively combining or exposing parts of an illustration. They are particularly useful for analyzing a technical illustration of complex objects or collections of objects. Use of color coding with the successive layers will further enhance the display.

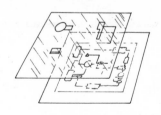

HUMAN ENGINEERING A MAINTENANCE HANDBOOK

A handbook, through the adoption of recognized learning techniques, should succeed in adapting the man to the job required of him. To accomplish this, it must incorporate the typical elements of the learning process: acquisition, retention, and transfer. It must take the reader through the basic acquisition steps, taking into account experience and actual abilities. This must be followed by a logical sequence of procedures for applying the new information — with frequent check points which test each step or segment of the learning process.

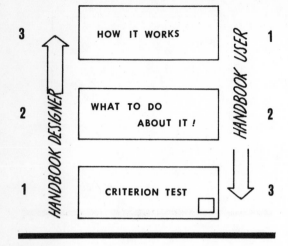

The information presented in a good maintenance handbook should perform three basic functions:

Instruct
Direct
Measure

The handbook writer must start with the last function and work backwards — i.e., determine what he wants the technician to learn, and to what level of proficiency. This provides the objectives for the other two functions. The next critical consideration is the symbolic interface: printed numbers, words, pictures, or other schematic markings. Although it is often said that "one picture is worth ten thousand words," all forms of symbology have their place in the development of a handbook. Some of the hazards in their use are presented as a guide in determining the proper symbolic mode:

- WORDS IMPROPERLY CHOSEN MAY EVOKE AN ERRONEOUS MENTAL PICTURE OF AN IDEA OR RELATIONSHIP.

- PICTURES (PARTICULARLY PHOTOGRAPHS) MAY INADVERTENTLY HIDE A CRITICAL FACTOR IN SHOWING ALL THE REQUIRED RELATIONSHIPS.

- SCHEMATICS ARE A SHORTHAND THAT MUST BE LEARNED — SELDOM APPARENT TO THE NOVICE.

- ILLUSTRATIONS DRAWN TO EMPHASIZE MAY PRESENT A POINT OF VIEW THE TECHNICIAN WILL NEVER ACTUALLY SEE.

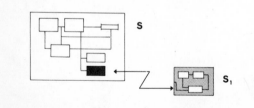

DESIGN SUGGESTIONS:

When discussing or illustrating a subsystem, always show its relationship to the larger system first.

Pictures or illustrations should be oriented in the way that the technician expects to see the actual equipment. If he sees the back of a chassis when he pulls it out of a cabinet for inspection, don't picture that chassis from the front in the handbook!

If a succession of pictures is used to illustrate a sequence of steps, the pictures should proceed from left to right.

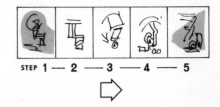

Borders around text materials of critical content are useful for emphasis. They should be consistent throughout a single book or series of related books.

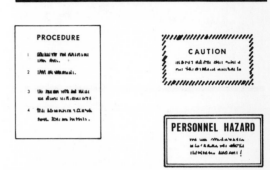

The "exploded view" illustration is useful for conveying relationships of a complex assembly.

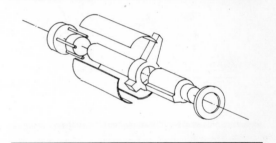

Avoid the use of "gimmicks" to dress up the handbook. Cartoons are useful if they actually convey an important point; they should not be used just for amusement. Avoid such distortions as the typical "through the magnifying glass" approach.

Whenever possible, plan the layout of text materials so that page turning is minimized — i.e., an associated text is on the same page as the illustrations it discusses, and a topic is not split at a critical point, forcing the technician to turn back and forth between pages.

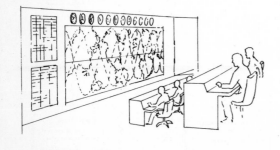

MAPS, NAVIGATIONAL CHARTS, AND TOPOGRAPHIC PLOTS

It is not the purpose of this section to cover completely the topic of map making. The purpose is to discuss a number of human-engineering considerations which will increase the readability or effectiveness of such charts from the user's standpoint.

Three basic questions should be considered before designing or selecting a map or chart. (1) How is it to be used? (2) Where will it be used? (3) What is it to be used for? The order in which these questions are considered depends on the situation, for in a great many cases it is customary to select maps which are already available.

HOW THE MAP IS TO BE USED — In general, a map or chart which has a more or less permanent location can be larger and contain a greater amount of fine detail than one which must be portable. If the viewing distance of the observer is relatively fixed — i.e., if he cannot get close to the map or doesn't have time to scrutinize the map for a length of time — details of the map must be designed for the specific viewing distance (see legibility recommendations for letters and numerals). In addition, care must be taken not to put too much detail on the map or to crowd the detail — causing an increase in reading time.

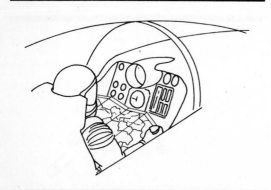

WHERE THE MAP WILL BE USED — Maps which are to be used in confined quarters become difficult to handle. Attention should be given to the size, method of folding, or possibility of developing special multiple-map series. Other approaches include use of maps reduced to film strips or slides which can be projected on a single screen at the discretion of the user.

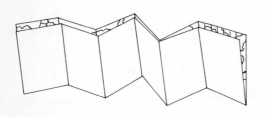

WHAT THE MAP WILL BE USED FOR — Frequently maps are designed or selected with the idea of getting every bit of information possible on them. Theoretically this is to be avoided. Maps should be as simple as the required need will allow. A case in point occurred with the advent of high-speed jet aircraft. It was found that standard aeronautical charts contained much more information than was actually needed for the rapid progress of the jet across the country. The great detail on the map made it very difficult for the jet pilot to find the important information in time — before he had already passed a significant check-point. Original charts were also too large and cumbersome for the small space within which the pilot had to work. Consequently, it became obvious that the map should be made much smaller and simpler for this specific operational situation.

ENVIRONMENTAL FACTORS WHICH INFLUENCE DESIGN OF MAPS AND CHARTS

AMBIENT ILLUMINATION — When ambient illuminations are normal (daylight equivalent), use of colors is very helpful to the map user. When the map must be used at night or under special monochromatic lighting conditions such as the red-lighted cockpit, it is suggested that alternate techniques are more appropriate. A "black map" technique is recommended for certain conditions. This type of map is essentially "reversed" in terms of light and dark areas. In addition to the reversal, however, it should be greatly simplified also. For example, the pilot flying at night cannot see many of the things outside his cockpit which are visible in the daytime; therefore these items should not be included on the "black map" to crowd or confuse the important "seeable" items. An added advantage to be gained by the reversed contrast map is that dark adaptation of the pilot is preserved, owing to the reduction of reflected light in his eyes.

The same rules for legibility of printed materials is applicable to maps and charts; e.g., paper and print colors should provide maximum contrast and minimize glare. Printing styles for letters and numbers should be simple and should follow the rules given for maximum legibility at the expected viewing distance.

Coded symbols should be limited to standard devices wherever these are available — aeronautical, meteorlogical, military, railroad, etc.

STORAGE — Wherever possible, maps or charts which are used for plotting should be designed so that they do not have to be folded. It is best if they can be stored flat — second best is to roll them up.

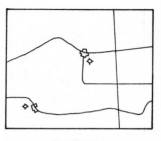

DAY TIME

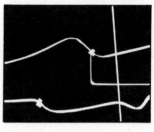

NIGHT

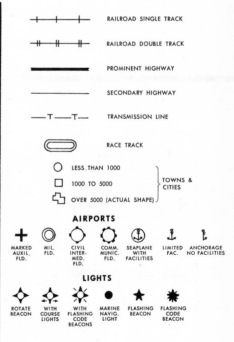

RAILROAD SINGLE TRACK

RAILROAD DOUBLE TRACK

PROMINENT HIGHWAY

SECONDARY HIGHWAY

TRANSMISSION LINE

RACE TRACK

LESS.THAN 1000

1000 TO 5000   } TOWNS & CITIES

OVER 5000 (ACTUAL SHAPE)

AIRPORTS

MARKED AUXIL. FLD.　MIL. FLD.　CIVIL INTER-MED. FLD.　COMM. MUNIC. FLD.　SEAPLANE WITH FACILITIES　LIMITED FAC.　ANCHORAGE NO FACILITIES

LIGHTS

ROTATE BEACON　WITH COURSE LIGHTS　WITH FLASHING CODE BEACONS　MARINE NAVIG. LIGHT　FLASHING BEACON　FLASHING CODE BEACON

RIVER AND STREAM　　INTERMITTENT STREAM　　INTERMITTENT LAKE　　DRY LAKE　　MARSH　　GLACIER ON CONTOURED PEAK　　HACHURED PEAK　　SAND DUNES

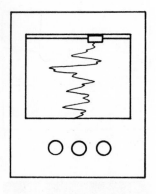

AUTOMATIC PRINTERS AND GRAPHIC RECORDERS

Design of chart paper to be used in automatic pen-recording equipment should consider visibility and legibility. Under normal lighting conditions, the paper should be white, graph lines black, and pen tracing red, green, or some other color which shows up well against the black graph lines.

Pen-recording devices should be designed so that the pen assembly covers no more of the chart than is absolutely necessary.

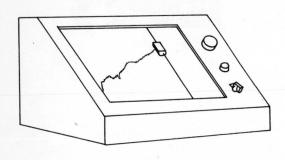

Captive-paper storage should be povided so that the operator isn't required to provide some make-shift method for collecting the paper as it comes from the machine. The method for reloading chart paper should be made as simple as possible.

Pen assemblies should be designed so that they are easy to refill and do not leak or lead to spillage because the operator did not adjust the assembly properly.

Recording devices should be designed so that it is possible for the operator to make notes directly on the chart. Continuously variable paper-speed control is recommended. Manual controls should be placed so that the operator does not cover the tracing as he adjusts the control knobs.

Provide a simple, sure method for tearing or cutting off finished chart-paper segments.

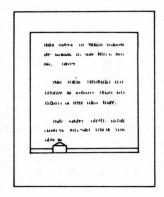

For single-sheet chart systems, the pen should always move from left to right. For moving-chart systems, the paper should move from right to left. For printers (e.g., teletype), the paper should move from bottom to top.

VISUAL DISPLAY REINFORCEMENT

Sometimes it is not only desirable to enhance the informational-transfer characteristics of the visual display to improve the operator's understanding of the display, but it may also be vital to his safety to add another mode of information transfer to "make sure" he gets the information.

Although signal reinforcement is possible through all of the human sensory modalities, the most practical means are through the operator's auditory and tactile senses. Some of the considerations for combining these inputs with visual displays are discussed below.

POOR ILLUMINATION, VIBRATION — When the illumination conditions are suspected of being less than adequate to provide "good seeing" at critical periods during use of a visual display, or it is possible that undesirable vibration levels may occur to degrade legibility, it may be necessary to provide an additional information input during these critical periods to insure adequate operator performance or operational safety.

ACCELERATION STRESS — Pilots are frequently subject to high g-loads during certain periods of typical flying maneuvers. During these brief periods, the pilot's vision is considerably degraded — making it impossible for him to see his displays clearly. His auditory channel may still be available to him, however, and can be utilized to introduce critical information in spite of the acceleration stress.

SENSORY OVERLOAD — There is a tendency to overload the operator's visual-input channel. With too many things to look at, it is quite possible he may miss a most critical informational input because of inattention or because he is just not looking in the right direction.

CONFIDENCE FACTOR — Since humans are used to evaluating things with "all their senses" from the time they are born, it is natural for them to expect this. Each of the sensory inputs, in fact, raises the level of confidence of the operator in what he is receiving — thus the converse of this, i.e., lack of certain inputs, tends to reduce the operator's confidence in the information he is receiving.

CHECK LIST FOR COMBINING AUDITORY WITH VISUAL DISPLAYS

Add an auditory signal when:

THE OPERATOR'S EYES MAY BE DISTRACTED FROM AN INSTRUMENT PANEL TO VIEW THE WORLD OUTSIDE HIS VEHICLE.

THE INTERPRETATION OF THE VISUAL DISPLAY CAN BE SIMPLIFIED OR CLARIFIED BY A VERBAL MESSAGE.

VISUAL-SIGNAL-TO-NOISE RATIO IS POOR.

THE OPERATOR'S VISUAL PERFORMANCE IS DEGRADED BY THE ENVIRONMENT.

THE ENVIRONMENT, ALTHOUGH UNKNOWN, IS SUSPECTED RANDOMLY TO DEGRADE EITHER VISUAL OR AUDITORY INPUT CAPABILITIES.

CHECK LIST FOR COMBINING TACTILE WITH VISUAL DISPLAYS

Add a tactile signal when:

EXTREMELY FAST CONTROL REACTION IS REQUIRED.

CONTROL SYSTEM "FEEL" CAN CLARIFY THE VISUAL DISPLAY INTERPRETATION.

BOTH VISUAL AND AUDITORY SIGNAL-TO-NOISE RATIOS ARE BELOW ACCEPTABLE THRESHOLDS.

CHECK LIST FOR COMBINING VISUAL, AUDITORY, AND TACTILE INPUTS

Combine all three when:

A RANDOM COMBINATION OF ENVIRONMENTS MAY, AT SOME TIME, DEGRADE SIGNAL DETECTION OF ANY ONE OF THE SENSORY INPUT MODES.

SIGNAL-TO-NOISE LEVELS OF ALL THREE SENSORY INPUT MODES ARE BELOW ACCEPTABLE STANDARDS.

THE TOTAL COMBINATION IS MORE NATURAL TO THE OPERATION — OR THE ABSENCE OF ONE OF THE MODES WOULD LEAD TO DOUBT ABOUT THE OTHERS.

DESIGN REQUIREMENTS FOR COMBINING VISUAL, AUDITORY, AND TACTILE DISPLAYS

Signal strength among the several sensory modality inputs should be comparable. If one signal level is significantly greater than the others, it may mask important aspects of the other display modalities — and in extreme cases degrade the intended response by causing "alarm" or a "startle reaction."

Signal characteristics among the several modalities should be compatible in terms of expected change or rate of change. For example, if the visual display were to indicate an increase in speed, the character of the auditory display should imply "speeding up" — i.e., the rate of an intermittent sound would increase. In like fashion, the "expected" response on a control would be for system resistance to increase. Reversals of these inputs would confuse and destroy confidence rather than reinforce it.

USING SENSORY REINFORCEMENT TO CREATE SIMULATED DYNAMIC ACTIVITY BY ILLUSION

It is entirely feasible to create the illusion of vehicle movement in the trainee who is operating a training simulator (or test subject in an experimental vehicle simulator). This can be done, without actually moving the simulator, merely by proper combination and sequence of visual, auditory, and tactile display to the subject. For example, the illusion of a simulated cockpit moving to the right is created by introducing shift of a visual display to the left (in the window in front of the operator) and at the same time providing a slight vibratory disturbance in the seat — the locale of the vibration being shifted to represent physical pressures normally exerted as the subject's body is acted upon by g-forces in a typical turn.

auditory displays

WHEN TO USE AUDITORY DISPLAYS:

When the visual tasks of the operator have saturated the visual channel.

When the ambient illumination conditions make critical seeing unreliable.

When a critical seeing task requires continuous monitoring, but further information needs to be imparted at the same time.

When signal detection (at threshold visual conditions) needs to be reinforced.

WHEN NOT TO USE AUDITORY DISPLAYS:

When ambient noise levels are very near or exceed discomfort levels.

When too many other audio signals are being received.

When characteristic noise from machinery, electronic equipment, etc., is quite similar to the planned auditory display.

Audio techniques for the display of information have not been utilized to the fullest extent in equipment design. Auditory signals in conjunction with visual signals, however, in some instances have demonstrated a decided advantage over either type of signal alone. The major advantage of auditory signals is in the fact that an operator can act upon the information he receives without physically facing the source of the signal. The generalizations above are, of course, subject to considerable variation depending on the circumstances. The human auditory-perception system is a very capable discriminator of wanted versus unwanted sound and is ideal for sorting usable signals from noise. Certain cautions must be taken in the use of the auditory display, however. Too many types of sounds tend to confuse the listener, and he may orient himself to one and ignore the rest.

FIRE !

NOW HEAR THIS

WIND SOUTHWEST - TEN KNOTS

TYPICAL AUDITORY DISPLAYS
SPEECH SIGNALS:
Single-word warnings
Standard messages
Extemporaneous messages

NON-SPEECH SIGNALS:
Bell
Buzzer
Horn
Siren
Tone
Electronic (sonar echo, etc.)

COMBINED AND MIXED SIGNALS

Tone plus speech (with partial overlap)

Modulated (usually in pitch)

Interrupted (periodic, rhythmic)

Distorted (frequency-band pass limiting, clipping, etc.)

The display interface may be via direct person-to-person air conduction, loudspeaker, or earphone. It may be desirable to present the sound to one ear (monaurally) or to both ears (binaurally). If earphones are used, it is possible to present one signal to one ear and an entirely different signal to the other — or to mix them alternately.

AUDITORY WARNING SIGNALS

They should be:

Easy to hear above background noise or other auditory signals. If possible they should be at least 10 db above the ambient noise level.

Discriminable from each other and other auditory signals.

Compatible or consistent with other standard signals already in use.

Attention getting (and holding), but without traumatic distraction from other possibly sensitive or critical performance functions.

Non-masking in the sense of drowning out other auditory signals equally important to the over-all operation.

Provided with separate emergency power-source.

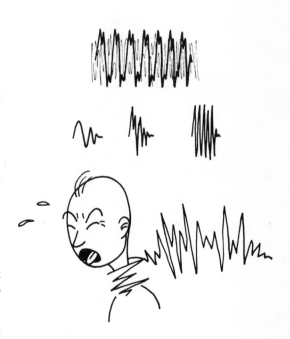

SUGGESTIONS FOR DESIGN OF AUDITORY WARNING DISPLAYS

OBJECTIVE	RECOMMENDATION
Audibility in high noise	Concentrate signal energy within narrow frequency band in which background noise or sounds are lowest. Maintain ratio of signal to noise of at least 5 to 1 if possible — audio signal power of approximately 300 milliwatts at the ear. Provide headset or helmet (or both) to exclude as much ambient noise as possible. Use repeating signal (with "shut-off" control) and provide noise-operated gain control to maintain compatible signal-to-noise ratio when background noise changes. Provide noise-canceling microphones. Consider delay of signal to one earphone by 0.01 second or by reversing the phase of one phone of the headset to improve listening effectiveness.
Quick operator-response	Make signal brief. If "canned" speech is used, provide short alerting signal (0.5 sec.) just before speech message so that listener will be prepared for first word.
Reduce operator distraction	Provide an "automatic-resetting" shutoff control for the operator. But don't provide a volume control for him!
Prevent warning signal from masking other signals	Deliver warning signal to one ear and the other audio signal (it might mask) to the other ear — alternate the signal from one ear to the other (2-3 per sec.). Avoid frequency bands normally used by common communication or navigation signals, etc.
Reduce signal confusion	Avoid selection of a warning signal whose characteristics could be confused with navigation signals, electrical interference, radio, radar, countermeasures signals, etc.
Mode of transmission	Where possible, send warning signals over system different from that of other speech communications. (See recommendations for design of receivers and headsets.)

RECEIVER AND HEADSET CHARACTERISTICS:

Sufficient electrical power should be available to drive peak sound-pressure level to 131 db when using two earphones.

A gain control with dynamic range sufficient to make the signal 15 db more intense than the ambient noise.

A reduction in frequency range below 500 cps and above 4000 cps if it results in an increase in the average power of the audio signal.

A uniform frequency response of receiver and headset between 300 and 4000 cps to avoid unpredictable distortions.

Pressure-operated gain-control switches to compensate for altitude effects in aircraft cabins.

(From Cornell Aeronautical Laboratory.[7])

AUDITORY DISPLAY EQUIPMENT PACKAGING DESIGN

HAND-HELD EQUIPMENTS

The choice of a hand-held device such as a telephone handset or a microphone should be weighed against the total operator requirements of the immediate task. It is important, for instance, to know which hand the operator will use, or whether he even has a free hand to use. Make sure that he can use the equipment before you give it to him. Once the choice is made, however, you must consider the size and shape of the package so that the operator can hold and operate the device comfortably and efficiently.

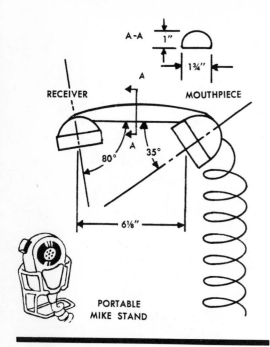

The hand-held microphone or the telephone handset must be convenient to the normal operator's hand size. Avoid the use of angular packages unless special hand grips are attached, for they are uncomfortable over long periods of use and prevent the operator from applying a secure grip to the handset.

Non-kink or self-retracting cords are another convenience which makes for higher operator efficiency. Delays caused by fouled telephone or microphone cords may mean the difference between life and death at the time of an aircraft accident.

Mouth and ear pieces should be spaced on the handset package so that the operator may seat the earpiece firmly on his ear and yet maintain a minimum and direct mouth position with respect to the mouthpiece.

Press-to-talk switches on handsets should be located so that they are convenient to either the right or left hand.

When the operator's hands must be used for other manipulatory tasks, provide him with such conveniences as boom-type microphones, foot-actuated press-to-talk switches. The boom microphone is especially good for the operator who changes head positions often, as in spotting aircraft from the air-control tower.

HEADSETS

The earpieces of a headset should be designed to exclude as much of the outside noise as possible. Ear cushions and ear tips have been designed for this purpose.

The ear cushion should fit the head as snugly as possible. Low-density materials such as sponge rubber covered with chamois are quite satisfactory.

The ear cushion should cover the outer ear without crushing it. There should be a minimum of air enclosed within the cushion socket.

Supporting structures for the ear pieces should be designed so that they do not impose discomforts of weight, concentrated pressures, or metal contact with the skin. They should be easy to remove but in turn must hold the earpiece firmly in place.

NOTE: Headsets incorporating only one earpiece are frequently illfitting. It is suggested that, in situations of this type, it is better to use two similar cushions with one of the cushions open to exterior sound, rather than to use an unbalanced headpiece.

Special packaging of aural equipment may be required when other articles of equipment or clothing interfere with the proper orientation of standard items of aural equipment.

Enclosure-mounted microphones inside an oxygen mask combine advantages of noise exclusion and free use of the hands. This arrangement, as well as other types of noise shields, accentuates the lower frequencies, causing a "booming" characteristic to the sound. Reduction of the low-frequency response of the microphone until the characteristics of the mask and the microphone are approximately uniform is an important design requirement.

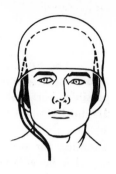

A doughnut-type cushion has been developed for use under the regulation steel helmet. The same solution applied to the telephone handset is shown.

POOR   PREFERRED

RECEIVERS AND INTERCOMS

Layout of the operating controls for a typical communications receiver should provide the "tuning or station-select" control for the right hand and the volume control for the left hand.

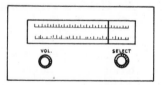

Intercom station consoles should be arranged so that there is plenty of space for the several station labels. Although this seems an obvious requirement, it is often ignored.

LOUDSPEAKERS

Loudspeakers for auditoriums should be positioned so that the sound seems to come from the speaker. In very large auditoriums the audience is usually far enough from the stage that speakers located above and to each side of the stage are satisfactory. In small auditoriums, however, a better installation is right in the speaker's stand, as illustrated.

The placement of loudspeakers should in general be such that the sound is directed *toward* the intended audience.

Speakers should normally be placed in front of and at the approximate head level of the hearer or slightly above for situations in which only one listener is involved. The basic reasoning for such a recommendation is in the fact that he will tend to face the sound source involuntarily and may find his position awkward for other tasks. This is not a hard and fast rule, however, for an operator can hear as well in any position as long as the speaker is directed toward him.

When conflicting messages arrive simultaneously, as in the radio communications of an air control tower, more than one speaker to separate the channels should be provided. Properly spaced speakers (horizontal spacing of 10 degrees or more is desirable) are more effective than vertically spaced ones, although vertical spacing may be useful in the form of pull-down speaker* arrangements where the operator has the alternative of isolating one communication channel from overhead speakers thus bringing the desired channel closer to his operating position. In multiple-channel and -speaker arrangements, it is further advantageous to provide quality differences between speakers thus enhancing the localization of the individual speakers.

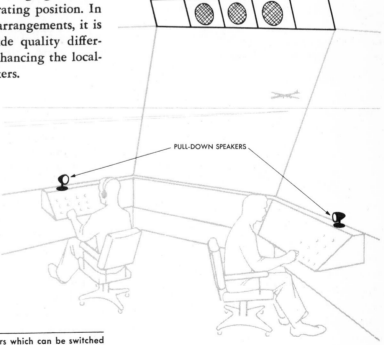

PULL-DOWN SPEAKERS

* Supplementary remote speakers which can be switched on in lieu of the normal speaker array.

Public address systems, especially those designed for auditoriums, strive for a lifelike presentation. The stereophonic sound system is most suitable for this purpose. For other, more common installations, normal speaker placement in auditoriums should be about 10 to 15 feet above stage level. In very reverberant rooms it is desirable to use several low-level speakers properly distributed (to prevent overlap) about the room; however, in a well-designed auditorium, one higher-level speaker located centrally above the stage opening is quite satisfactory. Caution: The reinforcement provided by the system should not be so great that the audience is aware of it. This reinforcement should be in speech range only (cutoff around 250 cps).

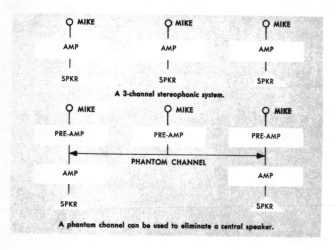

A 3-channel stereophonic system.

A phantom channel can be used to eliminate a central speaker.

STEREO COMPATIBLE SINGLE CHANNEL

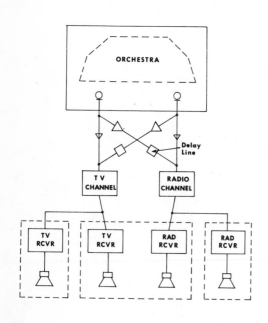

A circuit based on the psycho-acoustic phenomenon known as the "precedence effect" operates in such a manner that a single sound reproduced through two separated loudspeakers, but delayed by about 10 milliseconds in one of the speakers, will be heard as if it had come only from the speaker from which the listener heard it first. He will judge the second speaker to have been silent, since it will have been about 8 to 10 db softer than the sound from the first speaker which preceded it. Because of the cross connections (as shown in the diagram), signals from the left microphone are transmitted direct to the left loudspeaker while the same sound is slightly delayed in reaching the right speaker. The listener localizes the sound as coming direct from each speaker, and a maximized stereophonic effect is given.

Placement of loudspeakers for optimum stereophonic listening is based on the ratio of the separation distance of the speakers (S) vs the distance they are from the speakers (D). The distance of each speaker (a and b) from the listener's ears must be approximately equal, and preferably equal to S.

MONITORING

Monitoring and control of sound systems is an important but often neglected problem. The objective in monitoring a sound system, of course, is to provide the best listening conditions possible for the audience. However, in too many cases the sound-control box is either left unmonitored or is located in an off-site position where the operator has no idea of what is going on in the listening room or area. Actually the monitor should be located strategically with respect to the array of loudspeakers so that he has the best opportunity to hear what is coming from each and every speaker. In this way he can more nearly balance the effect of the total system.

Special public-address systems are utilized today for a great variety of situations where it is desirable to provide loudspeakers for individual listeners. This is primarily done because of the unusual configuration of a compartment or an abnormal amount of background noise. A typical example is the modern transport airplane. A rule of thumb is to get the speaker as close to the listener's ear as is feasible. One manufacturer provided an individual speaker for each row of seats; another put individual speakers in the back of each seat. Approaches such as these allow the intensity level of the sound to be lower and still be heard above the background noise.

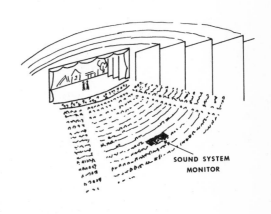

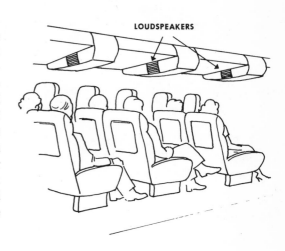

control design

A number of important factors should be considered in the design or choice of controls. These factors not only improve the general efficiency of the operator's performance, but some may perhaps affect his speed and accuracy in critical instances of operation. Typical factors to consider include:

Size

Shape

Location

Direction of motion

Extent of motion

Path of motion

Resistance

Ratio of control to display motion

Effect of temperature, vibration, etc.

Operator's position

Clothing restriction

ENVIRONMENTAL CONSIDERATIONS IN CONTROL DESIGN

Cold	Cold temperatures lead to stiffness in the operator's hands which reduces his dexterity. Wearing of gloves or mittens causes the operator difficulty in manipulating small devices and requires more space between controls.
Altitude	Heavy, cumbersome, and restrictive pressure garments must be worn, reducing both mobility and dexterity of the operator.
Vibration	Vibration and oscillation reduce manual dexterity and introduce an unsteadiness in the operation of controls that require smooth, continuous movement.
Acceleration	Acceleration and g-forces may prevent the operator from applying his full force capabilities. His limits of reach may be severely limited also.

Heat	Heat generally introduces sweating, which may limit amount of force which the operator can apply as well as hamper his finger dexterity.
Illumination	If the operator cannot see because of poor illumination, he may be subject to error and loss of time.
Retraints	Restraint imposed on movement by restrictive garments and shoulder harnesses or seat belts may make it difficult to reach and operate controls effectively.
Operator Position	The mobility of the operator (in terms of whether he is standing or sitting) affects both the choice and location of controls.
Weightlessness	In the weightless environment, the operator loses his ability to maintain his body position, and the forces he applies may upset him.
Safety, General	Dislodging a control accidentally may cause injury to the operator or to other personnel nearby. Possibility of falling against or bumping a control as the operator "passes by" should be considered in both the design and location of controls.

In many of the recommendations which follow, there are definite values which should not be compromised. In others, there is actually little effect on operator performance — however, user acceptance is more nearly assured if these preferred design limits or suggestions are followed.

All new design possibilities cannot, of course, be anticipated. If one is in doubt about a new configuration, it is suggested that a mockup be created and tested, using a representative sample of subjects and considering the appropriate factors and environmental conditions listed above. Control mock-ups should include all of the dynamic characteristics of the final operation: range of motion, location, forces, etc. If gloves or unusual operator workspace conditions are anticipated, these should be represented in the evaluation.

CHOOSING THE RIGHT CONTROL FOR THE JOB

FUNCTION	APPLICATION	TYPE OF CONTROL
Selection between two alternatives	To start or stop an equipment ON or OFF sequence To insert momentary signal	Toggle switch Bat-handle switch Push button Foot switch Thumb switch Push-pull control Trigger Pointer knob (with detents) Round knob (reostat with on-off switch combined)
Selection among three or more alternatives	To choose alternate modes of operation To select channels To select ranges	Pointer knob (with detents) Toggle switch Bat-handle switch
Precise adjustment	Continuous adjustment over a wide range For "fine" tuning or calibration	Round knob
Gross adjustment	Continuous adjustment (i.e., throttle or accelerator) Metering valve Faucet	Round knob Lever Pedal Wheel
Rapid adjustment	Slewing (such as an electronic cursor)	Hand crank Toggle or bat-handle (operating an electric drive)
Large Force application	Braking Steering	Lever Wheel Pedal Rudder bar
Multiple (continuous) positioning	Vehicle position and attitude Electronic coordinate-data pick-off	Joystick Combination wheel-joystick Pantograph Rolling ball Pressure stick

DESIGN CONSIDERATIONS	HUMAN-FACTORS CONSIDERATIONS
"Snap action" Obviously visible physical separation of alternate positions	Compatible direction of motion Equitable force requirements Proper location Adequate grip configuration
Positive detented positioning	Same as above
Smooth operation Low friction	Same as above (plus: compatible control-display movement ratio)
Smooth operation Medium friction	Same as above
Smooth operation Low to medium friction, depending on size of control in the case of a crank	Same as above (plus: optimum display-movement speed)
Optimum size	Same as above
Smooth operation Low to medium friction Optimum size Optimum displacement	Same as above (plus: compatible control-display movement ratio, self centering, and absence of cross-talk between motions)

Controls may be operated by various parts of the operator's body and limbs — in a variety of ways. Some parts of the body or limbs are more accurate, stronger, or less subject to environmental disturbances than others. In addition, some modes of operation are less subject to "human noise" being introduced into the control loop. Listed below are typical considerations:

ACCURACY — Manipulation by the fingers generally provides greater accuracy, not only because of the flexibility available, but also because of the potential independence of the fingers one from another. To obtain maximum accuracy, however, it is generally necessary to provide a considerable amount of practice and training.

STRENGTH — Maximum strength is obtained with foot-operated controls where the body can be braced against a suitable back support and from a position in which the body can be restrained from moving about. Next in order of available strength is through the arms with the torso supported against a back rest. In both cases, however, the range of movement is limited.

STEADINESS AGAINST OUTSIDE ENVIRONMENT — Steadiness against such things as vibration require provision for the operator to isolate himself or to brace himself against the interference. Generally speaking, the operator has more facility for accomplishing this while using his hands to control.

MINIMIZING HUMAN NOISE — Unsteadiness or typical oscillations introduced into the control system by the operator himself can be reduced by control operations which utilize the combined skeletal-muscle system — torso, limbs, and hands — because of the total damping effect. This requires gross human movement, however, and sometimes space will not permit the necessary range of movement. The pattern of control movement should always follow the asymmetrical pattern of the operator's natural motions.

PUSH BUTTONS

FOR OPERATION BY THE FOREFINGER

Preferred dimensions:
Diameter: 0.50 inch (minimum = 0.25 in.)
Displacement: 0.125 inch (maximum = 0.25 in.).
Force: 10-20 ounces (can be as high as 40 oz to reduce possibility of inadvertent action).
Separation from other controls should be at least 0.75 inch (1 in. if gloves are worn).

Action should be positive — i.e., elastic resistance aided by slight sliding friction, starting slow, building rapidly, with final sudden drop to indicate activation. The "snap action" should not be too heavy if button is to be operated many times in succession over an extended period.

A concave top is suggested to aid in centering the finger on the button.

Push buttons in a series may be placed fairly close together. Alternate buttons, however, must be far enough apart that the finger can select the intervening button without striking an adjoining button. Round buttons are not recommended for multi-finger operation (for this type of operation see pp. 2-96 and 2-97).

Flush buttons can be used effectively for certain operations — particularly those which have an audio feedback to confirm electrical contact. A typical example would be the common doorbell.
Diameter: 0.50 inch (0.625 in. for gloves).
Displacement: 0.03 inch (approx.).
Force: up to 10 ounces.
Separation from other controls should be at least 0.75 inch (1 in. if gloves are worn).

Buttons may be inset to prevent inadvertent action. Care should be taken to prevent too much space between the edge of the button and the edge of the inset, to prevent the finger from getting caught between the button and the edge of the hole. For example, for a 0.50-inch button the hole should be about 0.75 inch in diameter. If gloves are worn, the button should be at least 0.75 inch in diameter and the hole should be approximately 1.25 inches across.

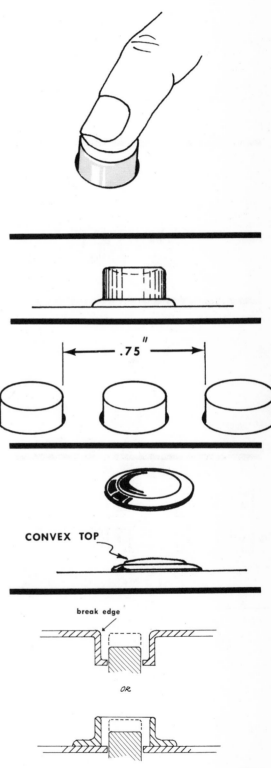

CONVEX TOP

break edge

OR

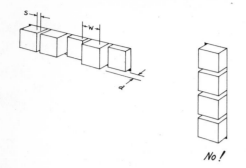

No !

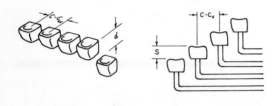

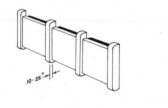

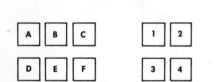

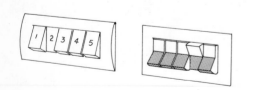

FOR OPERATION BY CONSECUTIVE FINGERS

In general, push buttons which are to be operated by alternate fingers should be approximately square rather than round to prevent the operator from slipping fingers between the buttons. One should think of such devices as though they were piano keys.

Preferred dimensions:

$$w = 0.75 \text{ inch}$$
$$s = 0.0625 \text{ inch}$$
$$d = 0.375 \text{ inch}$$
$$\text{Resistance} = 1 \text{ to } 8 \text{ ounces}$$

Alternate dimensions typical of those used for a typewriter or hand calculator keyboard:

$$C\text{–}C_w = 0.75 \text{ to } 0.875 \text{ inch}$$
$$C\text{–}C_v = 0.75 \text{ inch}$$
$$d = 0.125 \text{ to } 0.375 \text{ inch}$$
$$s = 0.25 \text{ to } 0.625 \text{ inch}$$

A concave top helps to center the finger.

Separators between switches minimize inadvertent operation of an adjacent switch. Preferred height of the barrier is approximately 0.10 inch. However, this may be as high as 0.25 inch without interfering with normal operation. If gloves are worn, the latter dimension is preferred.

Square- or rectangular-shaped push buttons are more appropriate than round ones for labeling. There is no difference so far as operability is concerned. Frequently it is possible to use differently shaped buttons for coding purposes — e.g., large round buttons may be reserved for an especially important operation while all other push-button operations utilize the square or rectangular shape.

TABS AND ROCKER KEYS

This type of push switch is particularly useful in situations where "seeing" the position is important. Such devices are pivoted in such a way that the ON position is flush with the panel surface. Such switches should not be mounted on horizontal surfaces since they are easily disturbed by accidental bumping — and it is more difficult to see what position they are in.

FUNCTIONAL ARRANGEMENTS

Push-button arrays should be arranged according to the natural sequence of operation wherever possible. Several examples follow to illustrate the proper approach to this problem.

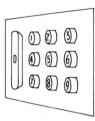

A key-set arrangement may be used for buttons numbered from one through zero. This arrangement brings all keys in close proximity so that they can all be operated with one hand.

The use of tabs for initiating action after a set of numbers poses the problem of where to put the tab. Since the tab button is the last operation in a sequence, its location should be compatible with the last step.

A tab bar used frequently and between other keying operations, such as may be found on a typewriter, should be placed so that the thumb can strike the bar without displacing the hand position. In the case of two-hand operation, as on the typewriter, the tab bar should be long enough for either thumb to reach it. Typewriter keyboards, incidentally, are fairly well laid out and can be used as a guide for similar push-button or key-set arrays.

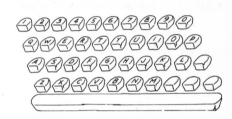

Note how each row is staggered with respect to the adjacent row or rows.

An example of push-button arrangement which is often poorly designed is the push-button gear shift on modern automobiles.

A TYPICAL ARRANGEMENT

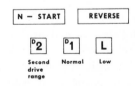

ERRORS:

- Lack of order to the gear-range progression.
- No common directional relationships.
- No order to sequence of operation.

HUMAN ENGINEERED

PRINCIPLES APPLIED:

- First operation placed in upper left since this is normally the first place the operator looks.
- Most driving is in normal-drive (1) and so it is placed according to "left to right" principle.
- Reverse is next most frequently used gear so it follows "left to right principle also.
- Drive ranges increase from slowest to fastest — i.e., bottom to top.
- Gears 2 and 3 follow a top-to-bottom pattern for lower and lower gear ranges.

ALTERNATE HUMAN-ENGINEERED POSSIBILITIES

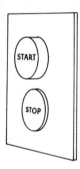

- Sequence progression is normal in both directions.
- Forward drive vs reverse is compatible.

A change in gear labels clarifies the high vs low relationship. This is similar to the preferred arrangement on the previous page. It provides better use of panel space (if this is critical), but uses vertical lettering which is not quite as desirable.

In this example the neutral-switch position assumes a "neutral" position in the array.

Push buttons for HEAVY-DUTY SWITCHES should be larger, so that the thumb or even the heel of the hand can be used to overcome necessarily heavier resistance.

Minimum diameter: 0.75 inch
Maximum resistance: 5 pounds

Minimum distance from other push buttons should be at least 0.25 inch if buttons are to be thumb operated. If it is expected that they may be operated by the heel of the hand, they should be separated from one another by at least 6 inches.

The top of the switch button may be slightly concave and also serrated, as shown, to reduce slipping. A single button should have a displacement of at least 0.125 inch. A double-button switch should have a displacement of at least 0.25 inch. Both should provide positive "snap action."

Push buttons on handles must be located experimentally since the exact position depends upon several factors, including size of the handle, shape of the handle, natural position of the hand, number of such switches on the handle, and which fingers will be used to operate the switch.

For thumb operation, place the button switch on top of the handle.

Use a tab or bar if the switch is to be operated by other fingers of the hand. The number of additional switches to be placed on a single hand-grip should be limited to no more than three. Trigger devices operated by the forefinger should be closed to prevent catching other fingers behind the trigger lever.

NOTE: In laying out special switch positions on handles as shown above, remember that positions will differ if gloves are to be worn. Use of mock-ups to locate the proper position is highly recommended!

TOGGLE SWITCHES

Preferred Dimensions:

t = 15° (30° preferred).
d = 0.25 inch (absolute minimum = 0.125 in.).
l = 0.50 inch (absolute minimum = 0.375 in. — 0.75 in. for gloved hand)

Resistance: 10 to 40 ounces. Use elastic resistance which builds up, then decreases as the desired position approaches, so that the control "snaps" into place and cannot stop between positions.

Lever shapes in order of preference are in the illustration at the right.

When more than two positions are required, be sure the extremes are at least 90° apart.

When inadvertent operation is critical, use a locking-lever design or provide a safety cover.

Spacing between multiple arrays of toggle switches should be based on clearance between the extreme-excursion case where the ends of the levers point toward each other.

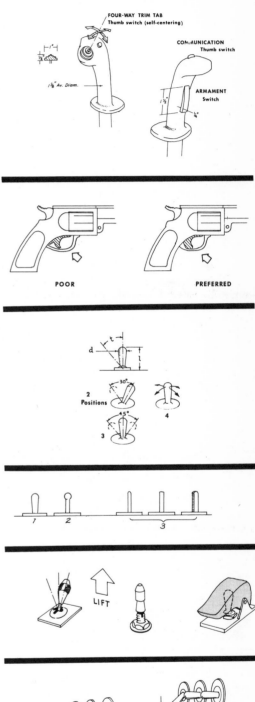

MODIFIED TOGGLE SWITCHES

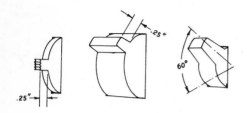

This type is for domestic use generally. "Snap action" or silent action is equally good.

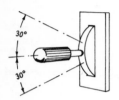

BAT-HANDLE SWITCHES

Where space is available, and the switch is used quite frequently, this type of switch is much easier to handle than an ordinary toggle switch. It should not be used if the operator has to reach over the switch for some other operation, however, because it protrudes high above the panel surface and is easy to dislodge.

SLIDE SWITCHES

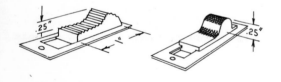

These are generally thumb operated. Provide serrations or knurling for best operation. If resistance is greater than about 10 inch ounces, serrations are preferred.

PUSH-PUSH WALL SWITCHES

The large contact surface makes this configuration easy to find in the dark. Mercury (silent) contacts make this type of switch very desirable for many operations beyond the usual light-switch application. Such a device, if properly located, can be operated with an elbow, knee, or almost any part of the body.

PUSH-PULL CONTROLS

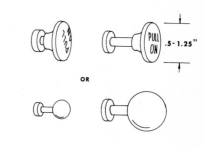

The IN position should generally represent the "non-operating" position. This type of control is usually associated with a flexible cable connection. Bearing friction should be low enough that binding does not occur when the control is pushed. If the knob is labeled, the control shaft should be keyed to the bearing so that the knob will not turn and allow the label to end "upside down."

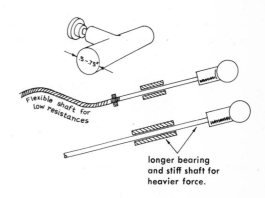

T-handle push-pull controls should be mounted on rigid shafts. This configuration allows the operator to apply more force on the control.

Modifications to the T-handle reduce the chance of catching clothing or personal gear on the handle accidentally. The orientation of such handles affects the ease with which the operator can operate them. Such handles should be keyed to prevent the handle position from changing.

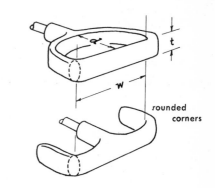

rounded corners

$w = 1.75$ inches for two-finger operation
(add 0.50 in. for gloved hand)
2.75 inches for three-finger operation
(add 0.625 in. for gloved hand)
3.50 inches for four-finger operation
(add 0.75 in. for gloved hand)
$t = 0.625$ to 0.75 inch
$d = 1$-inch minimum (1.50 in. for gloved hand)

L-handles for combination push-pull-turn operation, are typically used for brake handles where the turn is used for locking the brake in a given position.

$w = $ minimum 3.0 inches
$s = $ minimum 0.25 x 0.50 inch, maximum 0.625 x 1.0 inch

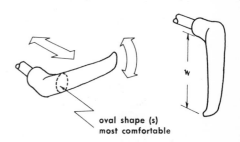

oval shape (s) most comfortable

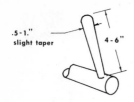

LEVERS

Typically used for such machinery operation as a forward-reverse function. Throw range should be at least 30°, but preferably no more than 60° between positions. Resistance should be 2 to 5 pounds. Slight taper improves the gripping characteristics of the handle.

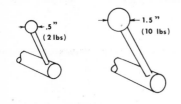

Similar to the above, but should be limited to resistances below 2 pounds if finger operated. With greater resistance (up to 10 lb), the knob diameter should be increased to 1 to 1.50 inches.

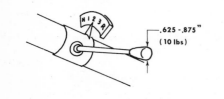

Gear-shift levers require either visual or "feel" cues to position, or preferably both. The steering-wheel-mounted type is generally operated with the fingers; therefore the required force should be limited to 10 pounds or less.

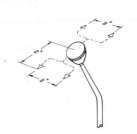

Floor-mounted gear shift is generally grasped by the fist; therefore the knob should be larger, as shown. More force can be applied from this position — up to 30 pounds.

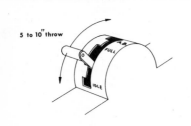

Throttle control, although generally operated as a continuous function, often requires identification of discrete positions for important settings: idle, full, afterburner, etc. Such positions should be at least 2 inches apart, with some method for temporary latching in these positions.

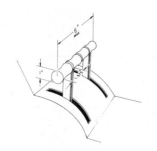

Multiple throttle-controls require operation by one hand at certain times. Therefore the over-all dimensions must be compatible with the dimensions of the operator's hand. In addition, the length of throw must be compatible with the operator's arm reach.

ROTARY KNOBS

Rotary knobs should be thought of in terms of two distinct functions: continuous multi-turn and discrete positioning. Round knobs should be used for continuous multi-turn operation, and pointer-shaped knobs should be used for discrete positioning. Pointer knobs should be applied to switches which are detented.

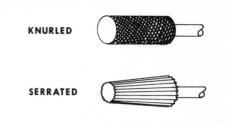

ROUND KNOBS

Round knobs of very small diameter may be used in certain limited-space situations. Even so, the depth of these small knobs should provide reasonable gripping surface. The knob surface should be knurled or serrated to improve gripping quality. Maximum resistance should be 1 pound or less.

Increasing the diameter of round knobs provides more gripping area around the edge of the knob, so the depth of the knob can actually be reduced.

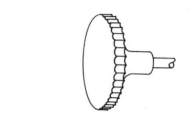

POOR   PREFERRED

Rounding off the serrations
reduces traction!

Although round knob diameters of from 0.1875 to 5.50 inches are perfectly useful, the preferred range of diameters is ½ to 2 inches. Avoid very small knobs for glove operation.

Round knobs of various shapes and sizes may be used with very little effect on operability. The following general recommendations will provide good results from the user's standpoint.

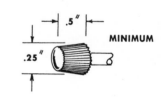

For miniature applications where space is a premium (note the depth in relation to diameter, and the use of taper and serrations):

    Diameter = 0.25 inch
    Depth = 0.50 inch
    Resistance = 4 ounces

    For normal panel layout:

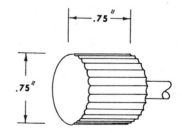

    Diameter = 0.75 inch (can vary between 0.50 and 2.0 in.)
    Depth = 0.50 to 0.75 inch.
    Resistance (maximum) = 6 ounces for 0.50-inch diameter, 3 ounces for 1-inch diameter, 10 ounces for 2-inch diameter.

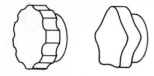

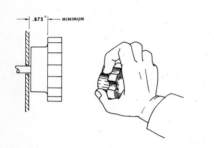

Indentations in the knob rim or special star-shaped knobs can be used. Actually, no more force can be applied with these than with plain round knobs, but they are somewhat more comfortable to operate.

> Diameter = 1 to 3 inches
> Preferred maximum-force limit = 20 ounces

It is possible to apply considerably more force to knobs of larger diameter by gripping the knob in the fist. This requires clearance between the knob and the panel. (See also p. 2-114.)

KNOB SKIRTS

Knob skirts are useful for two reasons. They provide a place for a pointer or for numbers or labels, and they prevent the fingers from scrubbing the panel surface. A properly designed skirt prevents the fingers from covering up the pointer or the numbers engraved on the skirt. A good design is shown in the illustration at the left.

NOTE: Care must be taken in the design of all knobs to make sure that both the knob and the skirt are securely fastened to the knob shaft. Military specifications require two set screws mounted 90° apart.

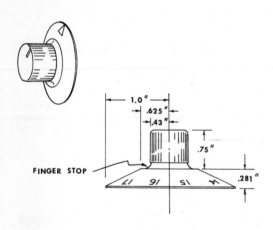

FINGER STOP

CONCENTRIC KNOBS (on same shaft)

"Stacked" knobs should be designed so as to minimize interferences as shown below. Although three stacked knobs are possible, only two are recommended.

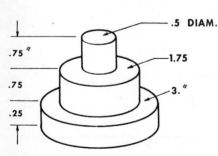

IDEAL DIMENSION FOR "GANGED" KNOBS
(after Bradley[8])

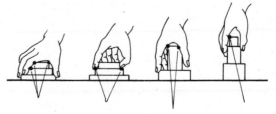

NOTE UNINTENTIONAL CONTACT POINTS

Proper association between ganged controls and the correct display or function is important.

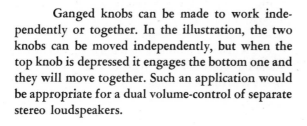

Two ganged knobs used for coarse and fine tuning

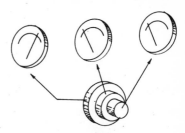

In a sequence, the smallest knob should be used last, to minimize disturbing the others

Ganged knobs can be made to work independently or together. In the illustration, the two knobs can be moved independently, but when the top knob is depressed it engages the bottom one and they will move together. Such an application would be appropriate for a dual volume-control of separate stereo loudspeakers.

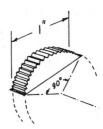

COMBINATION KNOB-CRANK

Such devices are appropriate where rapid multi-turns are required for gross setting, followed by finer tuning. Configurations in which the crank handle folds flush into the knob are recommended if there is any serious chance for bumping the control or catching clothing on the crank handle.

Minimum radius = approx. 0.625 inch
Maximum resistance = about 2 pounds

NOTE: The crank handle should be free-turning.

FREE TURNING

THUMBWHEELS

Such devices should be used sparingly, since they are neither comfortable nor easy to operate. At least 1 inch of the wheel should be exposed. Fairly deep serrations should be provided, to give efficient traction.

GOOD   POOR

POINTER KNOBS

The most important factors to consider in designing or selecting a pointer knob are that the pointer will be visible from the normal viewing position, and that the viewer can tell which end of the knob is doing the pointing! This latter principle may seem obvious, but designers quite often design knobs which look the same at either end.

Pointer knobs for miniaturized applications usually cause the greatest problem. The illustrations at the left provide reasonable solutions to this problem.

Whenever pointer knobs are used, the switch should have mechanical detents to assist in identifying the individual positions.

CODED KNOBS

SHAPE and COLOR coding is sometimes helpful in making knob controls easy to identify. The important factor to remember in coding knobs is that the codes must be selected carefully so that no two codes can be confused. Color recognition, of course, requires sufficient ambient illumination to be useful. Shape coding must be recognizable regardless of the position or size of the control. Shaped letters are not good because of the fact that they are confusing when the knob is turned over.

The group of coded shapes and colors shown at the left have been standardized by the military services for use on typical radar panels. These are available commercially.

U. S. NAVY RADAR CONTROL CODES

ORANGE Tuning   RED Gain   BLUE Intensity

WHITE Dimmer   VIOLET Focus   YELLOW Range

(MIL-STD-91528)

GREEN Marker

Note: Color coding on caps only

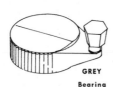

GREY Bearing

U. S. ARMY OPERATING CONTROL CODES

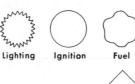

Lighting   Ignition   Fuel   Power Train   Special Purpose Equipment

Accessory Equipment

The coded knobs shown at the right have been standardized for use on military aircraft.

Whenever a new code is developed for standardization purposes, remember to consider the possibility that it will probably be required in different sizes. A shape, for instance, may be perfectly good in one size and completely indistinguishable in a miniaturized version.

SUPERCHARGER MIXTURE LANDING GEAR THROTTLE

POWER (Lift to Reverse) CARBURETOR AIR FLAPS R.P.M.

FIRE EXTINGUISHER

VEHICLE STEERING-CONTROLS

A two-dimensional joystick type of control is the most common device used for single-seat aircraft. Ordinarily such a control is mounted between the operator's knees so that he can operate it with either hand.

Handle diameter = 1.125 inches

Displacement		Resistance
Fore-aft = 14.0 inches	up to 30 pounds	
Lateral = 38.0 inches	up to 20 pounds	

Movement relationships:

Stick forward — aircraft nose down
Stick backward — aircraft nose up
Stick to left — left wing down
Stick to right — right wing down

A control wheel can be used to eliminate the lateral movement of the joystick. In this case, a counter-clockwise rotation of the wheel is used for left wing down and clockwise rotation of the wheel should provide right wing down.

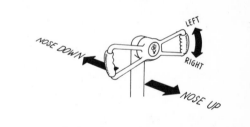

The shape of the wheel is important, as well as its position. If the wheel is placed low to provide good visibility to the instrument panel, it may be in a position to catch the pilot's leg as it is turned.

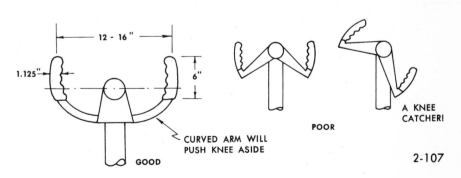

GOOD

CURVED ARM WILL PUSH KNEE ASIDE

POOR

A KNEE CATCHER!

A further design refinement is to eliminate the center post between the operator's legs, thus making egress from the seat much easier.

Console-mounted joysticks have become popular with the advent of electrically powered control-systems. They have also been used as data–pick-off devices for electronic display-readout purposes.

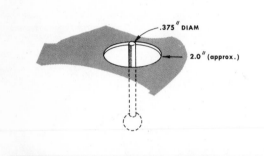

.375″ DIAM

2.0″ (approx.)

Finger-operated joysticks generally require very low friction and must have an associated arm-rest surface so that the operator can steady his hand. In the illustration at the left, the pivot point of the control is below the working surface, making the tip of the control near the working-table level. In essence this makes the control action quite similar to writing with a pen or pencil. In fact, this type of control is often referred to as the "pencil-type" joy-stick controller.

With the advent of space vehicles, and also modern submersible vehicles, it has become necessary to develop multi-dimensional controls (i.e., for pitch, roll, and yaw, and translation fore–aft, left–right, and up–down).

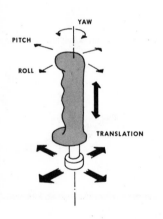

YAW

PITCH

ROLL

TRANSLATION

The most serious problem in designing a single control for all six parameters is that there is great chance for the operator to introduce motion into the control that he didn't intend; i.e., as he rolls his arm, it is difficult for him to keep from twisting his wrist at the same time. The control illustrated at the left is typical of the schemes which invariably run into difficulty because of this "cross talk."

The configurations below are presented to demonstrate the many possibilities for multi-variable control devices.

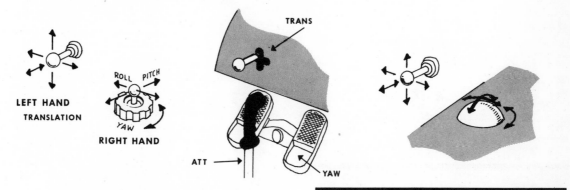

STEERING WHEELS

The most common applications, of course, are to be found on automobiles, trucks, boats, etc. They are, however, equally applicable to other control situations.

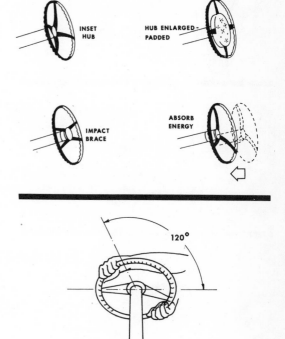

Steering wheels should be designed so that the operator cannot be impaled on the center post in the event of a head-on collision.

The preferred steering-wheel displacement should be limited to about a 120° turn, so that the operator would not have to remove his hands from the wheel in turning.

Diameter = 12 to 18 inches
Resistance = 5 to 30 pounds
Rim diameter = 0.75 to 1.50 inches
(Rim diameter for automobiles driven by women should be about 0.75 in.)

NOTE: The wheel rim should have good gripping characteristics.

FOOT-OPERATED CONTROLS

Although there is considerable latitude in the placement of foot-operated controls, the position does affect the comfort of the operator.

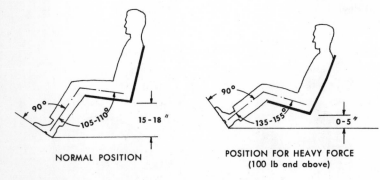

NORMAL POSITION

POSITION FOR HEAVY FORCE
(100 lb and above)

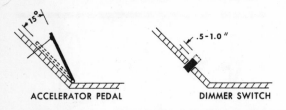

ACCELERATOR PEDAL

DIMMER SWITCH

When the operator's foot may rest on the control, resistance should be about 10 pounds to prevent activation. Normally, maximum force to operate should not exceed 20 pounds.

By pivoting the lever arm from above the pedal, the action path is made more nearly normal to the natural path of the operator's leg. The operator is able to produce his maximum leverage when following this natural path.

NATURAL PATH

When the foot pedal or footrest is more than 20° above the horizontal, it is desirable to provide a heel support.

20° OR MORE   HEEL REST

Foot pedals should be large enough to support the foot comfortably — and so that the operator has no difficulty finding the pedal without looking for it. When a foot must be shifted from one pedal to another, sufficient clearance should be provided to avoid catching the foot accidentally.

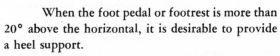

MINIMUM LATERAL CLEARANCE — 2"

3-18"
FOOT SEPARATION
(PREFERRED = 6")

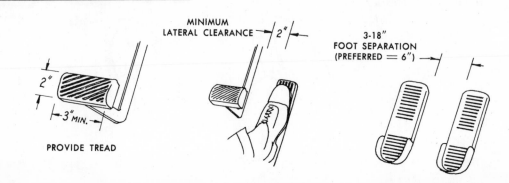

2"
3" MIN.

PROVIDE TREAD

Raising a foot pedal about 1 inch above the surrounding floor surface provides the standing operator a cue that his foot is in contact with the pedal.

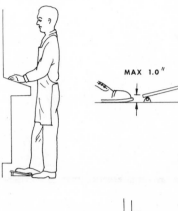

MAX 1.0"

It is sometimes difficult for the standing operator to shift his weight for operating a foot pedal — therefore the pedal must be placed so that a minimum of movement is required to reach the pedal.

Many applications require that the foot control be available to either foot. In this case the design of the pedal should be similar to that shown in the illustration at the right.

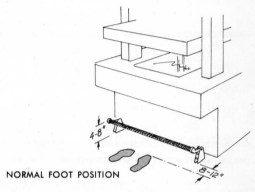

4-8"

8-12"

NORMAL FOOT POSITION

Combination rudder and toe-brake control requires special consideration of the limits of ankle flexion since the range of motion varies with the distance from the seat reference-point. When the leg is extended, not only is the range of ankle flexion reduced, but so is the amount of force which can be applied by the operator.

Recommended upper-force limits:

Ankle movement only = 20 pounds
Leg movement = 180 pounds

Rotary pedal controls should be designed to the preferred dimensions shown in the illustration at the right.

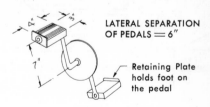

4" 3"

7"

LATERAL SEPARATION
OF PEDALS = 6"

Retaining Plate
holds foot on
the pedal

AMBIGUITY IN CONTROL OPERATION

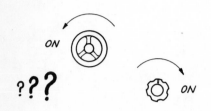

PLUMBING — A counter-clockwise motion of the control turns the water ON (actually opens the valve to let the liquid flow).

ELECTRICITY — A clockwise motion of the control turns the electrical current ON (actually allows the current to flow).

Such ambiguities are so entrenched by traditional usage that it is not advisable to change. However, with appropriate labeling, the major effect of the ambiguity can be minimized, as illustrated below:

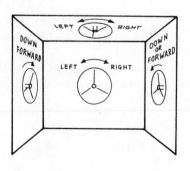

NATURAL DIRECTION-OF-MOTION RELATIONSHIPS

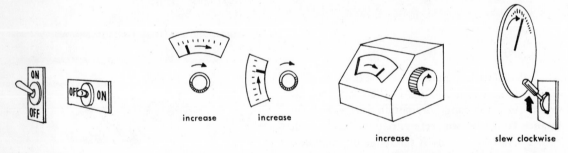

increase   increase   increase   slew clockwise

MOTION RELATIONSHIPS AFFECTED BY THE POSITION THE OPERATOR FACES

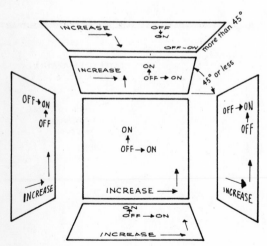

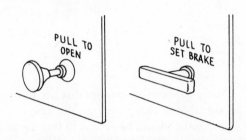

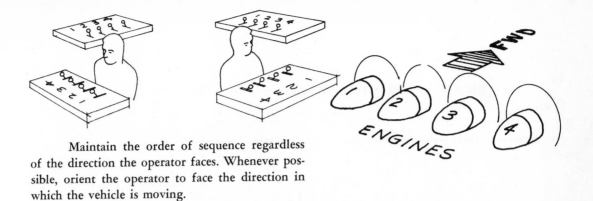

Maintain the order of sequence regardless of the direction the operator faces. Whenever possible, orient the operator to face the direction in which the vehicle is moving.

PHYSIOLOGICAL EFFICIENCY

LOCATION OF CONTROLS

Controls which must be used most often should be placed somewhere between elbow and shoulder height. Locations forward and slightly below shoulder height are found most easily when "blind" reaching is required.

Maximum forces can be applied to levers gripped at shoulder level for the standing operator, at elbow level for the seated operator.

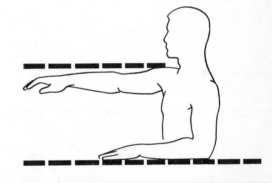

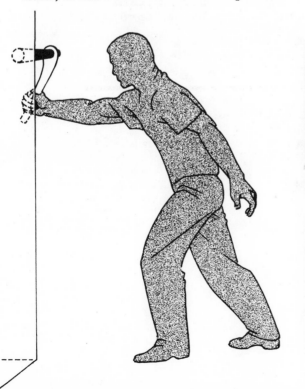

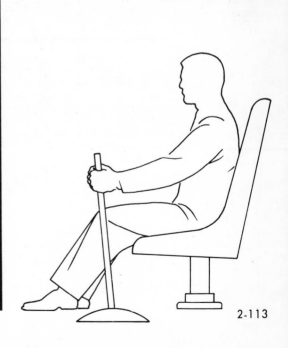

ARM STRENGTH AT SELECTED DEGREES OF ELBOW FLEXION[9]

POSITION	HAND	180°	150°	120°	90°	60°
Pull	Right	52	56	42	37	24
	Left	50	42	34	32	26
Push	Right	50	42	36	36	34
	Left	42	30	26	22	22
Up	Right	14	18	24	20	20
	Left	9	15	17	17	15
Down	Right	17	20	26	26	20
	Left	13	18	21	21	18
Outboard	Right	14	15	15	16	17
	Left	8	8	10	10	12
Inboard	Right	20	20	22	18	20
	Left	13	15	20	16	17

STRENGTH WHICH CAN BE APPLIED TO ROUND KNOBS

KNOB DIAMETER (INCHES)	KNOB DEPTH (INCHES)			
	FINGER GRIPPED		FULL-HAND GRIPPED	
	0.50	1.0	0.50	1.0
0.50	5 in. lb	6 in. lb	11 in. lb	16 in. lb
0.75	6 in. lb	8 in. lb	20 in. lb	29 in. lb
1.00	8 in. lb	10 in. lb	5 ft lb	6 ft lb
1.50	13 in. lb	15 in. lb	7 ft lb	10 ft lb
2.00	20 in. lb	24 in. lb	11 ft lb	13 ft lb
3.00	6 ft lb	6 ft lb	14 ft lb	16 ft lb

Wheel and crank diameters depend upon the mounting position and torque to be expected as well as the speed of turning required. The table below shows the optimum diameters for several mounting positions and torque conditions.

OPTIMUM CONTROL DIAMETERS

HEIGHT (in.)	POSITION (deg.)	TYPE	SIZE Handwheel (W), Diameter in Inches; Crank (C), Radius in Inches		
			AT TORQUE OF 0 in. lb	40 in. lb	90 in. lb
24	0	W	3-6	10	16
36	0	W	3-8	10-16	16
	L	W	3-6	10	10
	0	C	1½-4½	4½-7½	4½-7½
39	90	W	3-10	10-16	16
	90	C	2½-4½	4½-7½	4½-7½
40	−45	W	3-6	6-16	10-16
	−45	C	2½-7½	4½-7½	4½-7½
42	45	W	3-6	10	10-16
	45	C	2½-4½	2½-4½	4½
48	0	W	3-6	8-16	10-16
	0	C	2½-4½	4½	4½-7½

These data were based on setting the control device in only one revolution. The author infers that for less than 90-degree turn, handwheels would be more effective than cranks.

Mounting either side of center is superior to mounting in the center of the operator's position.

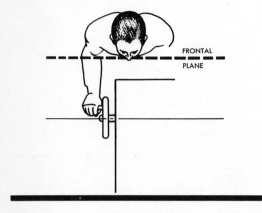

Cranks which require *extreme torque* should be mounted so that the turning axis is parallel to the frontal plane of the body.

Crank-type controls which are to be *turned rapidly* should be mounted so that the turning axis lies within a range from perpendicular to about 60 degrees off the frontal plane of the body.

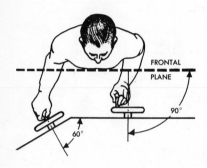

Controls which must be operated from a fixed operator's position, such as that of an aircraft pilot secured by means of shoulder harness, should be within an arc of 28 inches measured from the individual's shoulder position. (See also p. 5-33.)

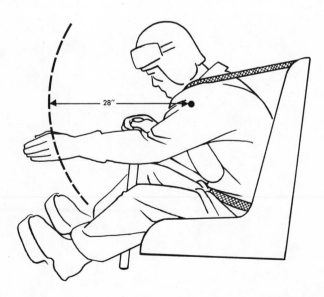

SIZE OF CONTROLS

Control dimensions should take into consideration the normal hand-grasp limitations.

Adjustment knobs for electronic-type equipments should, when possible, be limited in diameter to 2 inches or less for most convenient hand grasp.

USE ROUND KNOBS FOR CONTINUOUS TURN

BAR KNOB FOR STEPWISE TURN

Handles for cranks should be about 1½ inches in length by ½ inch in diameter for operations requiring fast wrist and finger movements, 3¾ inches in length by 1 inch in diameter for operations requiring arm movement of heavy loads.

OPTIMUM CRANK HANDLE SHAPE

For high-speed cranking, the diameter can vary from 3 to 9 inches, with 4½ inches recommended for general use.

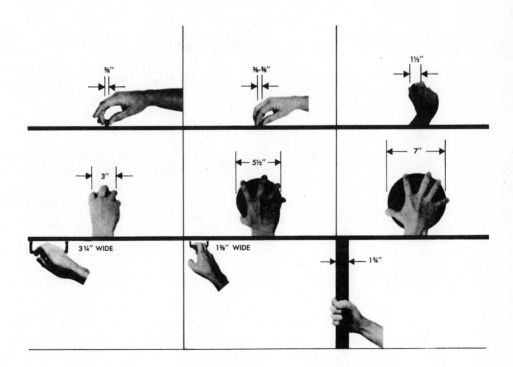

REMOTE MANIPULATORS

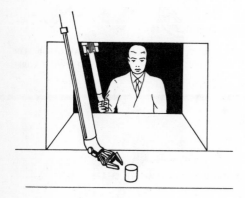

Many situations arise where it is desirable to operate devices, manipulate objects, etc., remotely. This may be necessary because of certain hazards such as radiation.

MASTER-SLAVE MANIPULATORS should capitalize on the natural characteristics of the human operator: i.e., they should utilize "slave" motions which demand the least possible reasoning on the part of the operator. Rough estimates have been made on typical manipulators, showing that it takes about 8 hours to perform a task with such a manipulator, as compared to 1 hour for doing the same task directly with the hands.

Work time increases as a function of increased distance between the operator and the task, especially as the distance approaches the range limits of the manipulator. A work range of 7 to 9 feet from the operator's eyes does not affect task performance. When the distance is increased to 11 feet and beyond, the effect becomes significant.

Closed-loop television may be used to compensate for inability to get the operator close to the work area. It is important, however, to insure that the camera viewing positions will reflect a natural view of the object and the manipulator jaws to the operator — i.e., avoid ambiguities and reversals.

Slave manipulators can be designed to provide extreme mechanical advantage. This same advantage, however, can be misused; without adequate force sensors and mechanical stops, it is possible to crush an object.

The ratio of motion between the operator's control and the manipulator jaw should always be 1:1, except for gross transport motions. Speed advantages may be desirable in getting the jaw into the general working vicinity more quickly. Transport speed should be continuously variable wherever possible.

Design of operator controls should observe the accepted direction-of-motion principles found elsewhere in this chapter. When remote-control consoles are used, it is important that the arrangement of controls is compatible with the positions and motion patterns of the slave end of the manipulator. A thorough analysis of the type of jaw and of the tools and the motion they execute is necessary to provide an optimum layout. This should be done before deciding what kinds of control knobs and switches are to be used.

Grappling jaws or special tools for the slave end of the manipulator should be designed so that they can be removed and replaced remotely. In addition, they should be designed so that they can be guided to the object to be grasped in the simplest manner from the operator's point of view — i.e., the operator should not have to exercise extremely fine adjustments to approach the object. Self-seating concepts are also worth considering in order to ease the task of the operator.

REMOTE DRONE-CONTROL

Design of controls for operation of drone vehicles from a remote positon should emphasize compatibility with other tasks of the operator. For example, a target aircraft might be controlled from a "mother" ship. The pilot of the mother ship must still control his own aircraft as well as the drone, and there must not be any conflict between the operation of his primary controls and the remote controls. It is not necessary, however, to provide reversing systems, should he need to order the drone to fly toward himself. Although this temporarily ambiguous situation may be confusing at first, an operator learns to compensate for it very rapidly.

workplace layout

The Human Operator CAN'T

**stretch his seat
to eye height!**

collapse his knees!

**stretch his
neck!**

WORKPLACE ENVELOPE

The workplace envelope must be compatible with the anthropometric dimensions of the particular population of workers who will be using the proposed equipment. Dimensions of the large worker should be used for determining clearances, while dimensions of the small worker should be used to determine limits of reach. In addition, one must consider the effects of clothing which add to the clearance requirements and also the possible restriction of movement. Human body dimensions are traditionally measured from the nude subject who is told to stand or sit erect, so that these dimensions do not reflect the dynamic characteristics of normal slumping, bending, stretching, or moving about. The designer is cautioned not to assume that quoted dimensions are to be used per se; rather, they are useful only as a guide for setting up an initial preliminary layout. It is recommended that all layouts be verified in a three-dimensional mock-up where live subjects representing the extremes of the expected population can actually try out the layout.

The series of cartoons at the left are presented to emphasize typical errors made in the layout of workplaces.

**stretch his
arm reach!**

see through people or equipment!

WORKPLACE ARRANGEMENT

In addition to the problem of providing a proper dimensional envelope based on the size and shape of the operator, it is also important to lay out the workspace according to the way it will be used. This requires consideration of psychological factors such as procedural logic, naturalness of relationships, and standardization to minimize learning time.

A good procedure to utilize in planning an effective workplace layout is as follows (from Thomson *et al.*[10]):

● PLAN THE WHOLE, THEN THE DETAILS.

● PLAN THE IDEAL, AND THEN THE PRACTICAL.

● FOLLOW THE CYCLES OF LAYOUT DEVELOPMENT AND MAKE THE PHASES OVERLAP.

● PLAN THE PROCESS AND EQUIPMENT AROUND THE SYSTEM REQUIRE-MENTS.

● PLAN THE LAYOUT AROUND THE PROCESS AND EQUIPMENT.

● PLAN THE FINAL ENCLOSURE AROUND THE LAYOUTS.

EFFECTS OF HUMAN BODY SIZE AND DYNAMICS

In the drawings below, the circled numbers indicate the maximum reach, the others indicate minimum clearance or recommended design values. (See also Chap. 5, Body Measurement.)

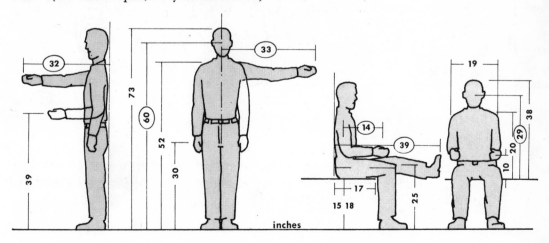

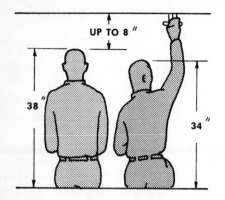

In the seated position, the difference in seated height between the 95th percentile and 5th percentile operator is only 4.2 inches. The operator can operate controls comfortably at a height of 10 to 12 inches above his head momentarily, and at 6 inches above his head for longer periods. This leaves a vertical area of about 6 to 8 inches in which equipment can be located.

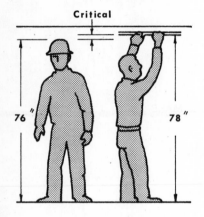

If equipment is located above an aisle, it is restricted to a fairly limited range since the vertical clearance for a tall man (plus shoes and possibly a helmet) is about 76 to 77 inches. Since the height which can be comfortably reached by a short man is only about 76 to 78 inches, depending on the grasp and strength required, the vertical clearance range can be only about 1 to 2 inches.

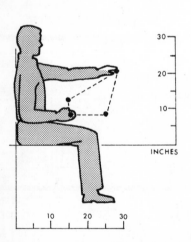

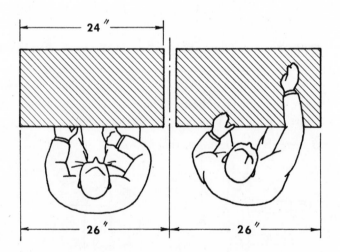

Optimum operating-area dimensions are derived from the body measurements of the small operator. Additional space should be provided for side-by-side operators.

The short operator must be used as the standard where it is necessary for the operator to see over an equipment rack.

For seated operation, the height of the upper console should not be more than 25 inches above the seat reference-point.

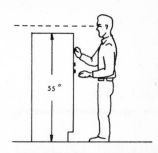

Controls on vertical racks should not be placed more than 74 inches above the floor, and about 30 inches should be allowed behind the operator to give him adequate working clearance.

If it is necessary for the operator to stoop to operate a control or see a display, be sure to allow sufficient space behind the operator.

For maintenance performed from a seated position, allow sufficient clearance for the technician to move about in manipulating his tools.

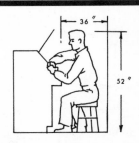

The squatting position is often necessary for maintenance of equipment in the lower part of the equipment rack.

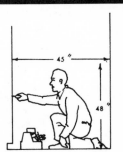

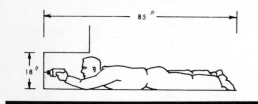

Although the position shown in the illustration at the left is not recommended, it is sometimes necessary to perform maintenance in this position as a compromise. Minimum dimensions are shown.

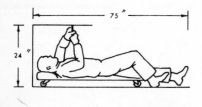

Whenever a technician must perform a task as illustrated, remember to design the task so that he does not have to remain in this position very long. Consider the hazard of dirt or grease falling in the technician's face or eyes and provide some means for preventing this.

Clearances for performing various maintenance tasks are shown at the left and below. They are only approximate.

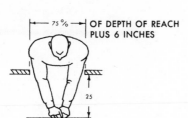

OF DEPTH OF REACH PLUS 6 INCHES

BOX WIDTH PLUS 4 INCHES

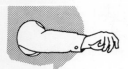

ARM TO ELBOW
4.5" DIAM.

ARM TO SHOULDER
5" DIAM.

ADD 3" FOR WINTER CLOTHING

EMPTY (FLAT)

EMPTY (CLINCHED)

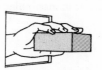

1.75" CLEARANCE
AROUND OBJECT

ADD 0.75" FOR
GLOVES

PUSH BUTTON ACCESS
1.5" DIAM.

TWO-FINGER TWIST
2.5" DIAM.

VACUUM TUBE INSERT
MINIATURE = 2 x 2"
LARGE = 4 x 4"

console design
and panel layout

The layout and design of instrument panels with suitable packaging into a well human-engineered unit are, at best, a compromise. It is important to approach each design in such a manner that the best compromises are made. As in the design of any piece of hardware, it is of utmost importance to have answers to certain technical aspects of the problem in hand before starting to work on the actual layout. The engineer must know the answers to the following questions if he wishes to incorporate good human-engineering principles into his finished panel or console.

Armed with answers to these questions, the engineer is ready to acquaint himself with the human-engineering rules for panels and consoles.

CHECK LIST FOR CONSOLE DESIGN AND PANEL LAYOUT

● WHAT LIMITATIONS ARE FIXED BY SPECIFICATION OR BY ULTIMATE SPACE FACTORS IN THE INSTALLATION AREA?

● WHAT VISUAL DISPLAYS ARE NECESSARY? WHAT SIZE MUST THEY BE? WHICH OF THESE MUST BE ACCESSIBLE TO THE OPERATOR DURING OPERATION AND WHICH ACCESSIBLE ONLY TO A MAINTENANCE MAN?

● WHAT CONTROLS ARE NECESSARY? WHAT SIZE? WHICH MUST BE ACCESSIBLE TO THE OPERATOR; TO THE MAINTENANCE MAN?

● WHAT AUDITORY DISPLAYS AND WHAT MEANS OF COMMUNICATION BETWEEN OPERATORS ARE NECESSARY?

● WHAT OPERATING CONDITIONS ARE EXPECTED — ILLUMINATION, NOISE ENVIRONMENT, TEMPERATURE, VIBRATION, PITCH AND ROLL?

● WHAT OPERATOR CONDITIONS ARE EXPECTED — ONE OR MORE OPERATORS, CONTINUOUS OR INTERMITTENT OPERATION, OPERATOR'S POSITION (STATIC OR DYNAMIC)?

● WHAT MAINTENANCE FACILITIES ARE REQUIRED DURING OR BETWEEN OPERATIONS?

HUMAN-ENGINEERING RULES FOR CONSOLE DESIGN

Controls and displays which are to be used most often, most effectively, or most rapidly should be given first priority as to location on the panel or console. The choice will depend upon the functional requirements — reading distance, angle of view, illumination, presence of other instruments, location and method of actuation of related controls.

Controls should be mounted for efficient selection and manipulation, and in proper relation to the display they affect. Positioning leading to accidental displacement of the control or injury to operating personnel should be avoided. Controls to be used simultaneously require special consideration with respect to operational convenience.

Visual displays should be oriented so that parallax and glare are minimum and viewing distance and illumination are optimum.

Loudspeakers should be placed to enhance intelligibility, directivity, or localization. Consoles should be designed to package the above hardware with the least crowding and with optimum functional arrangements — with due consideration for the ease of access for maintenance, relationship to other associated equipments, displays, and passageways.

NOTE: See rules on motion economy, p. 6-42.

At this point it is suggested that a mock-up be constructed. The mock-up need not be elaborate, but it should be accurately scaled. The miniature mock-up is recommended at this point because it is easier to handle and may be all that is required to solve the problem, thus saving the expense and time consumed in the construction of a full-scale mock-up. A $\frac{1}{8}$ scale is suggested since it is easy to locate a common rule for checking measurements later. The scale model may be made from materials such as cardboard, solid wood pieces, or erector-type building blocks.

To assist the designer in the construction of his mock-up, certain dimensional information about the human body and orientations of panel position which are adequate for all but the extreme cases are provided. Forms for constructing a 1/16-scale, two-dimensional manikin are given below. This model will be found to be quite helpful even when used in connection with engineering drawings. (Consult also pages 2-141 through 2-175 on Furniture and Workspace.) It is suggested that this manikin be reproduced in 1/16-inch clear plastic and that the joints be flush riveted. Stiff cardboard may be used in lieu of plastic.

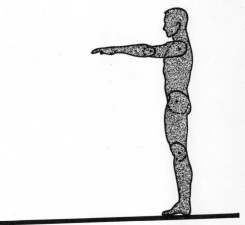

ASSEMBLED

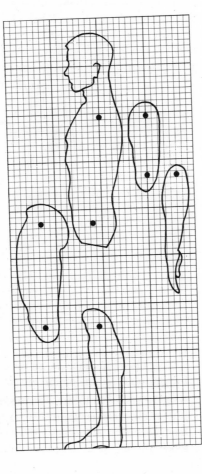

UNASSEMBLED

1/16 INCH = 1 INCH

2-127

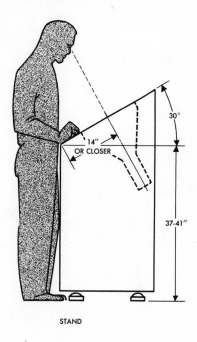

STAND

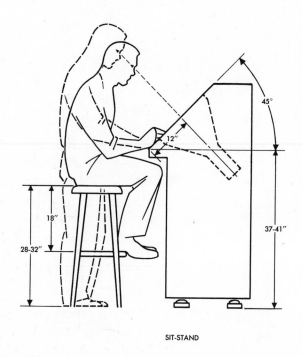

SIT-STAND

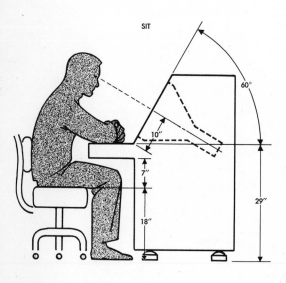

SIT

The illustrations show recommendations for angular mounting of visual displays such as PPI-type CRT's. These dimensions are only approximate. They do, however, represent usable standards for about 90 per cent of the male population.

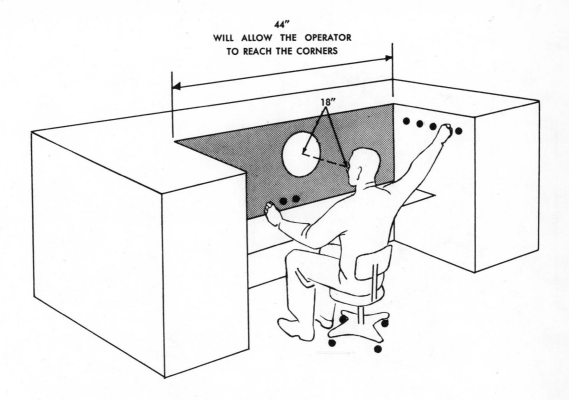

44″
WILL ALLOW THE OPERATOR
TO REACH THE CORNERS

18″

The *size* of an instrument panel depends primarily upon the normal arm reach of the human operator. In general, convenient arm reach is about 28 inches from the respective shoulder pivot point. This rule cannot be hard and fast for the obvious reason that in most situations the operator has freedom to bend his body and thus extend the useful reaching distance. A word of caution, however, is that we cannot expect him to bend two directions at once, so don't take advantage of his flexibility unless it is clearly necessary.

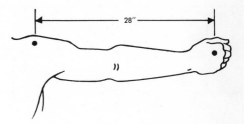

28″

Convenience limits for placement of controls on horizontal, 60-degree, and 30-degree console panels are shown in the illustrations on the facing page. A visual display may limit the flexibility of the operator's position, or special apparatus may restrict his flexibility for reasons of safety. Convenience limits may be established to restrict necessary arm reach when the operator is restricted to a more-or-less static position.

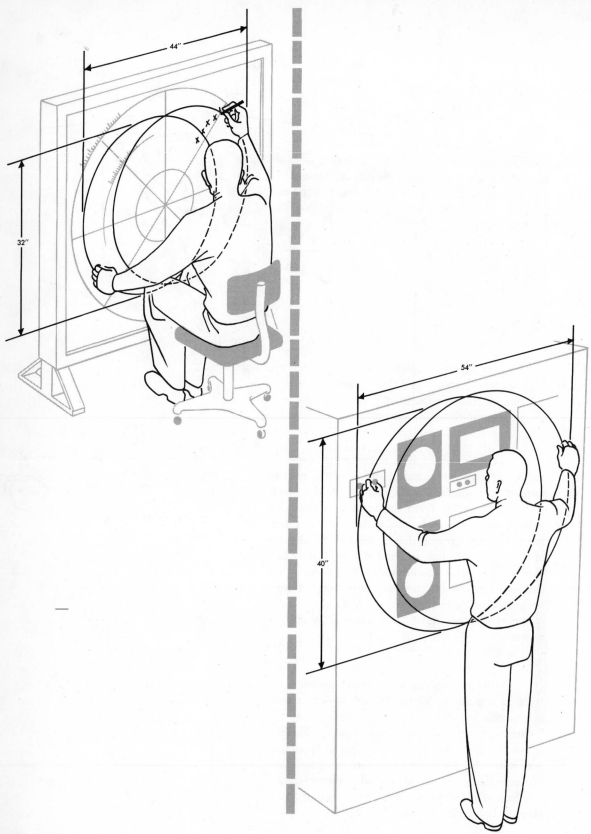

Arm reach from static sitting and standing positions are shown, when the operator is at a normal viewing distance (28 inches) from the control panel. These are not maximum reaches, but do take into consideration some normal bending of the operator's body.

It is important that we evaluate the use of human-body dimensions from the standpoint of maxima vs minima since we cannot always rely on the average man for optimum measurements. The illustration demonstrates an example of the need for other than average measurements.

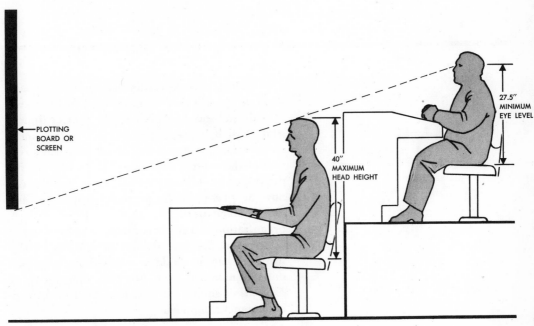

PLOTTING BOARD OR SCREEN

40" MAXIMUM HEAD HEIGHT

27.5" MINIMUM EYE LEVEL

Once a rough idea of the form and size factors of the panel or console have been decided upon, it is then necessary to organize the components that are to be placed on the panels. The components will undoubtedly vie for optimum positions and compromises will have to be made. A suggested method for arriving at the best compromise and organization is, first, itemize all components by related groups.

A	B	C

PPI scope
PPI controls
  Focus & intensity
  Range cursor
  Video gain
	Speaker
	Controls
	  Audio gain control
	  Output meter
	  Frequency selector
		Intercom controls
		Phone jacks

D	**E**	**F**

Navigation inst.
  Compass
  Course indicators
  Controls for these
	Check-reading inst.
	  Manifold pressure
	  Engine temp.
	  Oil pressure
	  Fuel gauges
		General flight inst.
		  Turn & bank ind.
		  Gyro horizon
		  Tachometer
		  Altimeter

Next, prepare cardboard "cutouts" of each separate item. These "cutouts" should be drawn to scale and should represent the exterior dimension of such items as dial face or control knob, and the interior dimension of the physical structure of the control mechanism that will limit the proximity of adjacent items. These cutouts can now be placed in the proposed panel area and moved about until you have arrived at the best organization and fit. It is much more economical to find out that you do not have room in this manner than to build a finished package that must be modified later. The following *grouping procedures* should be used as a guide in organizing panel components.

GROUPING PROCEDURES FOR PANEL LAYOUT

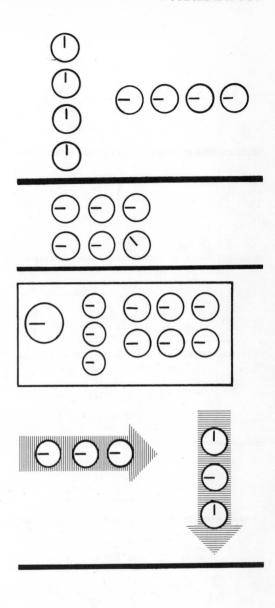

CHECK-READING DIALS—For a single group of five or fewer check-reading dials in a horizontal row, normal operating position of the pointers should be located at the 9-o'clock position; for the vertical groups, orient the pointers at the 12-o'clock position.

For groups of six or more use rows or columns rather than extend a single row; long rows or columns impose undesirable scanning movements upon the operator.

For several groups on the same panel, use a consistent pointer position regardless of the above recommendations.

Linear gauges or meters should follow the same general rules as specified for dials.

The positions of specific dials which are grouped together should be determined by the sequence in which they are to be read, that is, the operator should be able to read in order of sequence from left to right or from the top of the panel to the bottom.

CONTROLS should be placed:

Close to the display which they affect when possible.

Below or to the left for left-hand operation; below or to the right for right-hand operation.

Sequentially with respect to the expected order of operation.

At the optimum position of manipulatability for the control which is to be used most frequently.

So that there is an equitable distribution of work load between right and left hands; right hand operation should be reserved for operations requiring the finest adjustment.

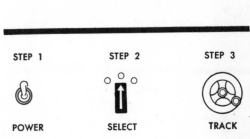

STEP 1   STEP 2   STEP 3

POWER   SELECT   TRACK

2-133

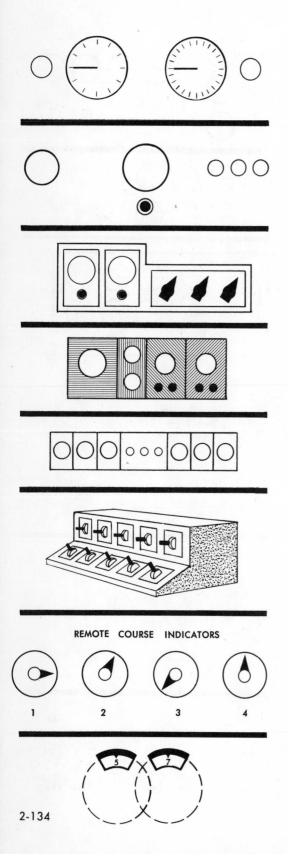

CONTROL-DISPLAY organization should be such that visual displays occupy central areas and controls occupy peripheral areas so that hand movements do not obstruct the view of visual indicators.

Area or group identification is quite important in complex layouts. It may be accomplished satisfactorily in several ways.

Adequate spacing of display or control groups; horizontal separations are preferred to vertical separations.

Marked outlines around each group.

Area color patterning.

Symmetry.

Differential plane of mounting.

Label consistently either above or below for a specific category, that is, group title above, as shown, individual labels below or centered. Label in terms of what is measured (RPM), not by the name of the instrument (tachometer). Company trade names should not appear on the face of a dial.

Space saving may be accomplished by overlapping partially hidden dials.

REMOTE COURSE INDICATORS

1   2   3   4

Instruments are normally protected by a glass cover. This glass cover often becomes a source of glare — making it practically impossible to see the markings on the instrument face. The worst situation occurs on panels which are used in high ambient-light conditions, such as in the cockpit of an airplane. Here the sunlight illuminates the pilot's shirt front to the point that if it is reflected in the glass cover of the instruments in front of the pilot, he cannot read the indications at all. Although it is recommended as a general rule that instruments should be normal to the line of sight, this actually creates the worst situation for self reflection. Therefore it is desirable to slope the instrument faces slightly off the normal line of sight, as shown in the graphic illustration below.

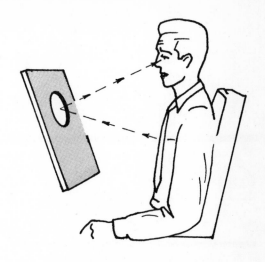

TO PREVENT "SELF" REFLECTION

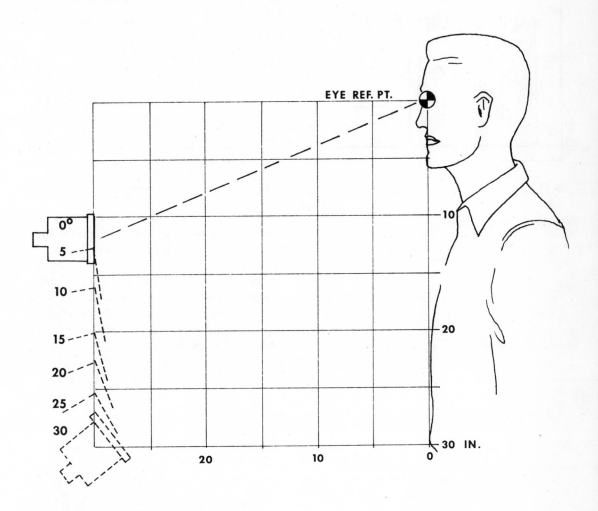

Some manufacturers develop a standard panel design in order to make their equipment appear distinctive. This also has the advantage of making it simple to group several equipments together and yet make them look as though they were designed as a complete unit. Modular panel-design techniques increase the discriminability of functional groups of displays and controls. For example, a dark-colored module contrasted against a light-colored background produces an association among the components within the module.

A typical modularized panel specification is shown below.

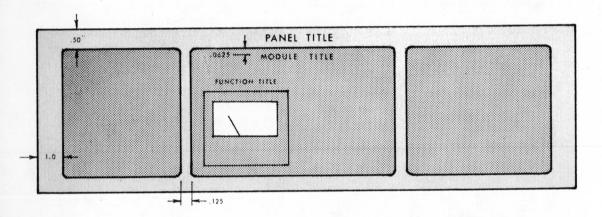

The panel titles are centered at the top of each panel. The panel modules are located in an area $\frac{1}{2}$ inch from the top of the panel, 1 inch from the sides, and $\frac{3}{16}$ inch from the bottom of the panel. The module title is also centered within the module, as shown. Naturally, space limitations may sometimes require modifications, but the manufacturer attempts to maintain the specifications as nearly as possible in each new layout.

In addition to the general layout, color specifications are usually provided in order that all equipments may maintain a uniform color scheme — even
when newer equipments are added at a later date.

TYPICAL MODULAR-PANEL COLOR SPECIFICATION

UNIT	COLOR	FEDERAL STANDARDS 595
Basic panel	Light gull gray	36492
Non-critical module	Dark gull gray	36231
Emergency or Critical-operation modules	Red	31136
Lettering on modules	White	37875
Lettering on panel outside Modules	Dark gull gray	36231

Lettering styles and sizes are also specified
and usually a style-guide of type fonts is made a
part of the specification.

Finally, control types are specified, generally
related to a given manufacturer's line of knobs.
Colors, sizes, methods of mounting, etc., are all included in the specification.

CAUTION: Although the basic objective of
standardization is commendable, the designer is re-
minded not to be led astray by aesthetic or "arty"
concepts which destroy good human-engineering
practices. Remember that a bad standard is worse
than no standard at all! First analyze your present
and future needs, then apply good human-engineering principles in developing a standard. The end
result *can* be beneficial both to the operator and the
reputation of the company.

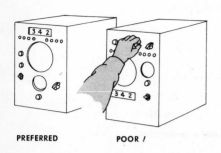

PREFERRED   POOR !

Visual displays and controls should be arranged in such a way that it is not possible for the operator to obstruct his view of any of the displays. In general, arrange the principal visual displays in the center of the panel near the level of the operator's eyes, with the controls arranged appropriately around the periphery of the panel.

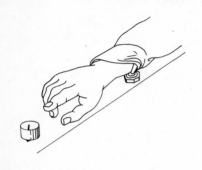

Check the layout to make sure that the operator cannot inadvertently catch his clothing on one control while he is reaching for another.

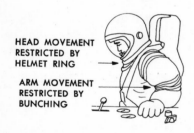

HEAD MOVEMENT RESTRICTED BY HELMET RING

ARM MOVEMENT RESTRICTED BY BUNCHING

Special clothing such as the personal protective suit worn by pilots is very restrictive. Controls and displays must be arranged so that the operator can reach the controls or see the displays without undue strain. If there is any doubt as to the availability of a control or display, test the layout with an operator in the typical garment which eventually will be worn.

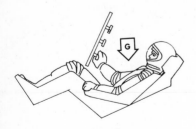

When an operator is subjected to severe g-force, it is often impossible for him to move his arms or legs more than a very few inches. Plan the layout so that he doesn't have to reach, or make sure that the operation of a given control doesn't coincide with the time in which severe g-forces will be present. (See also p. 5-33.)

CALCULATING MINIMUM VISUAL DOWN-ANGLE

One of the major visual cues used by pilots in maintaining precision ground reference during low-level flight is that of object blur. We are acquainted with the object-blur phenomena experienced when driving an automobile. Objects in the foreground appear to be rushing toward us while objects in the background appear to recede slightly. There is a point in the observer's line of sight, however, at which objects appear to stand still for a moment, before once again rushing toward him with increasing angular velocity. The distance from the observer to this point where objects appear stationary is sometimes referred to as the "blur threshold" range.

For this presentation it will be assumed that this blur-threshold range is the critical minimum distance in the forward direction which must be seen by the pilot for efficient control of his aircraft. The range from 3 degrees per second to about 10 degrees per second represents the upper limits of blur threshold for human vision. At a relative angular velocity of 3 degrees per second an object out front will appear to be almost stationary and at 10 degrees per second it will begin to blur almost beyond recognition.

The charts on the next page have been prepared to aid in developing the minimum visual down-angle for seeing over the "nose" of an aircraft. This is, of course, not intended to imply that more down vision should not be provided if this does not degrade some other factor in the design, such as a structural requirement. Rather, this will indicate the absolute minimum which should be provided if the pilot is to utilize direct vision over the nose to accomplish a particular flying task, such as landing or close terrain following.

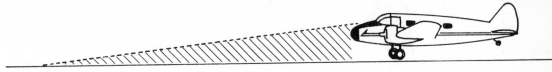

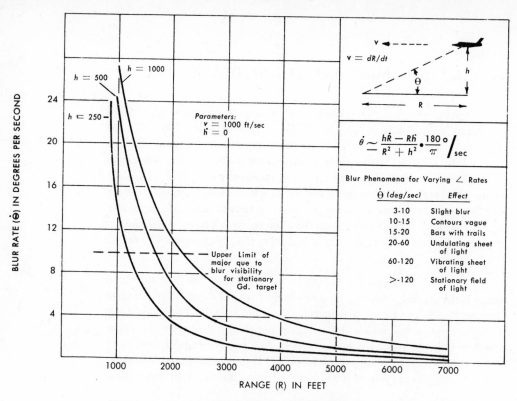

**BLUR RATE AS FUNCTION OF GROUND RANGE FOR
LOW FLYING AIRCRAFT**

**SLANT RANGE FROM PILOT'S POSITION TO BLUR POINT
ON GROUND AS FUNCTION OF VELOCITY**

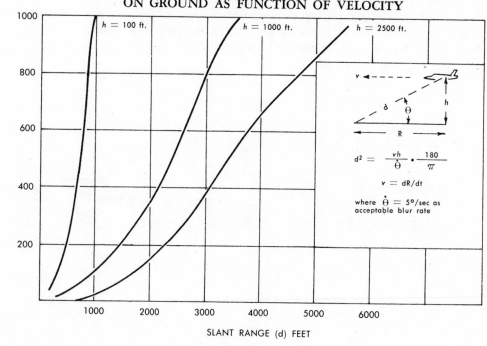

2-140

furniture and work space

WORK SEATING

Design of work seating covers a wide scope, from the simplest bench or stool to the most elaborate adjustable seat. Proper seat design can reduce fatigue and promote increased production by its occupant; it can save time and energy. Poor seating may be the cause of poor morale and may actually interfere with optimum operation of equipment and cut down the efficiency of an operator.

Much has been done recently on the design of work seats. Evidences in point are improved secretary's chairs, drafting stools, and aircraft-pilot seating. The recommendations that follow are not to be construed as the ultimate, but are rather to provide definite points to consider in planning for good work seating.

DESIGN PRINCIPLES

Effective work-seat design should provide a supporting framework for the body relative to the activity in which it is engaged.

The seat should be convenient to the task of the worker. The seat should be of proper size and should be adjustable not only in height but position when the application demands mobility.

The seat should support the body properly to avoid poor posture. Cushioning should be used to distribute body weight evenly over the surface of the seat.

Arm rests should be provided when they do not interfere with the individual task at hand. Foot rests should be provided to maintain optimum seat-to-foot-rest distance.

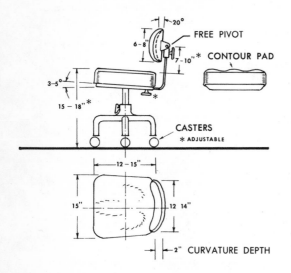

SECRETARIAL CHAIR

The basic consideration for this type of chair is the providing of good posture control. Proper support to the small of the back is very important to prevent fatigue over extended lengths of time spent in the chair during a normal workday. The chair should be adjustable and mobile, provide swivel motion in the seat pan, and have sufficient padding in the seat and back rest. The upholstery should provide ventilation to prevent sweating during hot, humid weather.

Adjustment knobs or handles should be designed so that they are easy to manipulate. Remember that the chair is used most often by women who do not have as much strength in their hands as men.

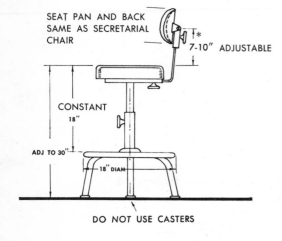

DRAFTING CHAIR

The upper part of the drafting chair should have approximately the same dimensions and features shown above for the secretarial chair.

In addition, however, this type of chair will be used normally at a drafting table whose working height requires a higher seat-hight. With dimensions shown at the left, the chair can be used equally well for "sit" and "stand" operating heights with minimum fatigue to the draftsman as he alternates positions. Note that caster wheels are not recommended.

SPECIAL OPERATOR CHAIR

The chair illustrated at the right is recommended for such activities as sonar, radar, air traffic control, etc. Although the base shown would be fastened permanently to the floor or deck (as in the case of a sonar aboard a tossing vessel), it could very easily be replaced with a mobile base found typically in office furniture. In the latter case, caster wheels would allow further mobility in moving the chair about on the floor.

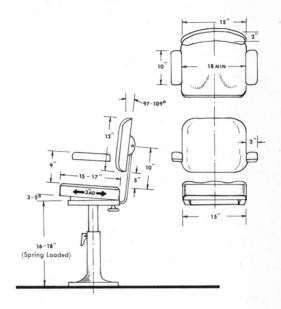

For added comfort and security of the occupant, the features shown in the illustration at the right are suggested. Note that the back rest provides not only more surface area, but adds an additional curved section about the operator's lower-rib section. This design, created specifically to aid sonar operators, helped to stabilize the man's body as the ship pitched and rolled in medium to heavy seas. The armrests also pivot inward to act as a "thigh clamp," thus providing a seat that holds the operator in!

The final added feature shown is the fully retracting armrest, making it simple for the operator to slide out of the seat.

It should be noted that the swivel capability of these seats should have means for stopping and securing at least every 45 degrees.

The fore-aft adjustment of the seat pan should also have fixed stopping positions.

All adjustment handles should be placed where the operator can operate them while seated in the optimum position he has selected.

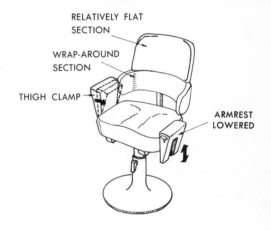

RELATIVELY FLAT SECTION

WRAP-AROUND SECTION

THIGH CLAMP

ARMREST LOWERED

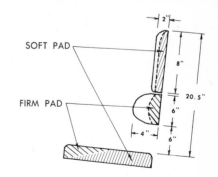

SOFT PAD

FIRM PAD

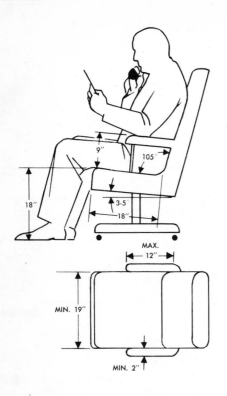

EXECUTIVE CHAIR

The executive chair must support its occupant both while he is working at a desk and during casual lounging for relaxed conversational periods. The general dimensions must be greater than those of the secretarial chair, and the addition of arm rests and tilt adjustment is suggested. Posture control is not as important as even distribution of weight over a larger area. Mobility and swivel motion are again desirable.

HUMAN DIMENSIONAL REQUIREMENTS IN AIRCRAFT COCKPITS

WHEEL TYPE CONTROL
(ALL VALUES IN INCHES UNLESS OTHERWISE NOTED)

A	B	C	D	E	F	G	H	I	J	K	L	M	N	O	P	Q	R
37	30¼	5	21°	101°	29¾	10	16⅝	19	6	9	10	36	5	9¼	15	7	25
39	30¾	5	19°	101°	30¼	9¾	15¾	19	6	9	10½	35	5	9¼	15	7	25
41	31½	5	16°	101°	31	9¾	15⅛	19	6	9	10¾	34½	5	9¼	15	7	25
43	31¾	5	16°	101°	31¼	10	15⅛	19	6	9	11	34½	5	9¼	15	7	25

STICK TYPE CONTROL
(ALL VALUES IN INCHES UNLESS OTHERWISE NOTED)

A	B	C	D	E	F	G	H	I	J	K	L	M	N	O	P	Q	R
37	30¼	5	21°	101°	29¾	10	14½	19	6	9	11½	36	5	9¼	15	7	25
39	30¾	5	19°	101°	30¼	9¾	13¾	19	6	9	13¾	35	5	9¼	15	7	25
41	31½	5	16°	101°	31	9¾	13½	19	6	9	15½	34½	5	9¼	15	7	25
43	31¾	5	16°	101°	31¼	10	13	19	6	9	17½	34½	5	9¼	15	7	25

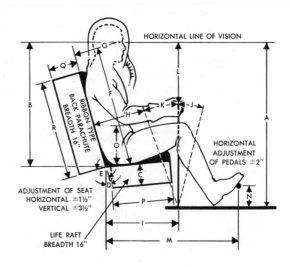

FIGHTER PILOT'S SEAT

Special considerations in this type of seat are convenience to controls, seat-to-eye height, and accommodations for parachute, life raft, and other essential gear.

PILOT'S EJECTION SEAT

Military aircraft normally are equipped with pilot's (and sometimes other crew member's) seats which can be ejected from the fuselage in the event an emergency occurs. As the speeds of such aircraft have increased, the problems of ejection-seat design have become more and more complex. For example, in supersonic aircraft, it is frequently impossible for the pilot to crawl over the side and jump, either because of the extremely high altitude or because of the excessive speed. Some of the problems which must be recognized in the design of ejection seats for such applications are listed below.

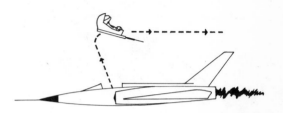

- The seat (and pilot) must be ejected far enough from the aircraft to clear the rudder — which is frequently quite high in supersonic aircraft.

- The rate of ejection must be extremely rapid (also to clear the rudder).

- The pilot must be protected from excessive wind-blast which may occur because of the speed of the aircraft.

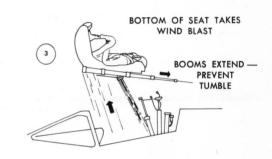

BOTTOM OF SEAT TAKES WIND BLAST

BOOMS EXTEND — PREVENT TUMBLE

- Because of the rapid seat-operation required, some means must be provided to protect the pilot from adverse accelerations. In most cases the seat will be ejected by means of rockets which create high g-loads on the pilot.

- Also because of the rapid operation, some means must be provided to pull the pilot's extremities into the confines of the minimum escape-envelope; i.e., all parts of his body must clear the cockpit and attendant controls, windscreen, etc.

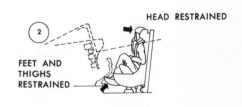

HEAD RESTRAINED

FEET AND THIGHS RESTRAINED

- Special precautions are required with tandem cockpit arrangements to "sequence" the ejections of both seats so that one will not strike the other during the ejection process.

- Special provisions must be made to provide automatic chute-opening in the event the pilot is unconscious or otherwise unable to operate chute-release systems.

- Special provisions must be made for survival and rescue gear as part of the ejection-seat system — in the event landing is made on the water or in remote areas.

TYPICAL EJECTION SEQUENCE

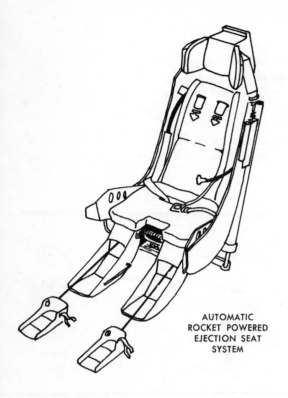

AUTOMATIC
ROCKET POWERED
EJECTION SEAT
SYSTEM

● Special provisions must be made for stabilizing the seat as it is projected into the windstream — otherwise the seat may go into an uncontrolled tumbling motion, causing additional hazard to the pilot.

● The seat should be designed to absorb severe shock upon landing — in case the pilot has chosen to remain with the seat, or in the event he remains with the seat owing to being unconscious.

● Special precautions must be taken in the design of release and propellant systems to safeguard against inadvertent firing of the ejection mechanism by ground servicing crews.

● Zero-launch capability should be designed into ejection seats so that it is possible for the pilot to escape at low altitude or on the ground.

MANNED SPACE VEHICLE LAUNCH ABORT

Many of the same considerations discussed above apply to escape systems for space crews on the launch pad. In most cases it is desirable to eject the entire manned space-capsule from the launching booster-rocket. Such ejection places extreme g-forces on the crew for a brief period, however, and they will not be able to operate controls — other than switches which may be placed directly under their hands.

NOTE: Manned space-capsules are normally sealed on the launch pad by ground crews, so it is necessary to provide means for the space crew to open hatches after landing, following an abort.

PRONE PILOT'S POSITION

This type of seating is designed to offset G-force limitations of the human body. Proper angles are necessary to allow the pilot to manipulate controls, see where he is going, and provide maximum comfort over extended periods of operation. Special supports for the head and neck are required to relieve the strain on neck muscles.

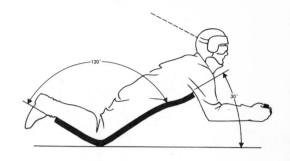

SPACE COUCH

With the advent of space vehicles, new seating requirements are imposed. It has been found that man can tolerate higher g-force accelerations in a transverse direction. Therefore the seat is positioned so that the feet and head are generally placed along a horizontal base-line as shown in the illustration. In addition, the couch is designed to provide maximum distribution of the body weight by form-fitting contours. Actually, these contours are tailor-made to each astronaut and placed in a standard frame or seat shell. The contours also provide lateral support to prevent soft body members from spreading out and being distorted.

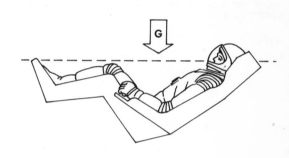

LOW-PROFILE SEATING

Certain applications (such as in Armored vehicles) require that the seat allow the operator's body to be lowered as much as possible to maintain a low ceiling-height, as shown in the illustration.

The position shown also provides for maximum force application on pedals and other foot controls. Note that the operator should be anchored by a seat belt, since the overhead clearance will probably be minimum and the operator cannot afford to be bounced vertically. Special mock-ups should always be constructed for testing this type of close-tolerance seating.

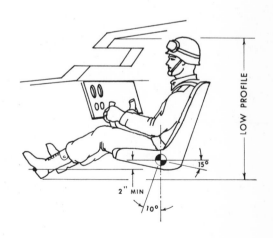

The driver's seat should be designed separately from the passenger's seat. Unfortunately, this is seldom the case in actual practice. It is practically impossible to provide proper support for the driver in his "working position" while also providing the relaxed position enjoyed by the passenger.

The dimensions shown at the left will provide a near optimum seat for the driver who must remain alert, and also give him sufficient comfort over long periods of time on the road.

In recent years, the "bucket seat" concept has been reintroduced to the motoring public. This concept attempts to provide some lateral support so that the driver is not affected by side-sway.

SEAT WIDTH FOR 3 PERSONS SIDE-BY-SIDE = 58″

AIRCRAFT PASSENGER SEATS

Semi-reclining seats for aircraft and bus passengers present unique problems in adjustment and spacing. For the full-recline position, the maximum angle is 45 degrees from the vertical. Adequate dimensions for getting in and out of such seats is an all-important item with respect to passenger popularity.

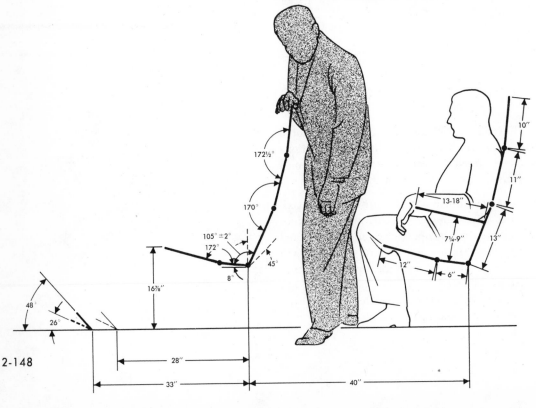

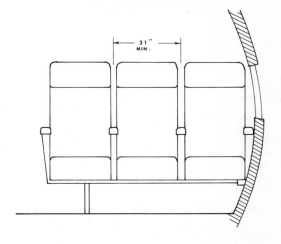

Much controversy exists over how closely passengers may be packed together laterally. The airline companies naturally wish to put as many seats in the aircraft as possible for the sake of economy. The dimensions at the right should be considered minimum for any trip which exceeds an hour's duration. It is possible to reduce this minimum for short haul to 19 inches across.

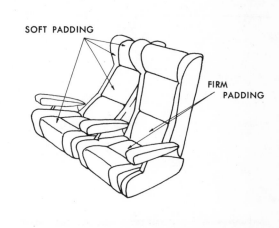

In the seats illustrated at the right, padded contours have been provided for the passenger's head.

Note that the density of the padding varies. Firm padding is desirable for support of the load-carrying parts of the body; softer padding is desirable in other areas.

Care must be exercised to design the contours of such seats so that they fit the passenger both in the erect and the reclining position. Since the passenger's body is pliable and flexible, it is important to avoid contours which may support in one position while "poking" the passenger in another position.

HIGH-DENSITY SEATING

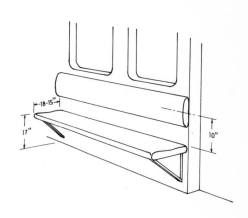

High-density seating is made simpler by creating a continuous seat. In this way a small passenger takes up less room while a larger passenger is allowed more room as the need arises. Unfortunately, such seating does not provide much postural support, and so should be used only for short-haul transportation. Padding for this type of seat should be fairly firm to reduce the tendency for the passenger to roll in the seat.

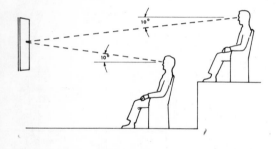

Seating of individual viewers should be arranged so that each person can see the object of viewing without undue strain. As a rule of thumb, none of the people should have to lower or raise his head more than about 10 degrees from the horizontal line of sight.

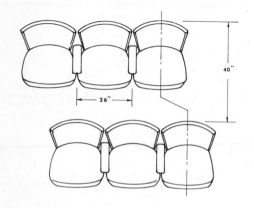

Since it is possible that a short person may be seated behind a tall person in the auditorium, special care should be taken to make sure that the short man can see over the head of the person in front of him, or the seats should be staggered, allowing each person to have a view between the heads in front of him.

The illustration at the left shows recommended spacing for seats. Although seats can be spaced closer, the result is less comfort, especially when it is expected that the audience will remain in the auditorium for extended periods.

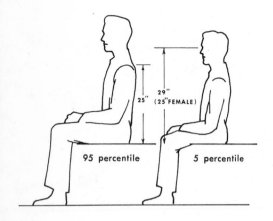

The dimensions at the left are indicative of requirements for a short person to see over the shoulder of a tall person seated in front of him (assuming a staggered seating arrangement).

AUDIENCE SEATING

The modern trend for auditorium design is toward special treatment for each type of presentation, ranging from small lecture rooms to the huge sports arena. We are here limiting our recommendations to the lecture room and theater situations.

Inasmuch as slide and movie projectors are important elements of class or lecture rooms and theaters, the criteria for optimum viewing of the projection screen should govern the planning of seating arrangements.

DISTANCE from the screen — maximum and minimum.

ANGLE at which the screen can be viewed — maximum.

STAGGERING or stepping (or both) of seats so that each person has as nearly unobstructed view of the screen as possible.

TELEVISION

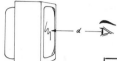

TV Screen	Viewing Distance
9 in.	18–30 in.
15–17 in.	30 in.–6 ft.
17–19 in.	6–10 ft.
19–23 in.	10–20 ft.
21–30 in.	20–30 ft.

MOVIES

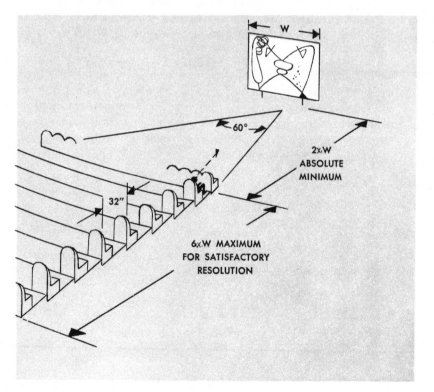

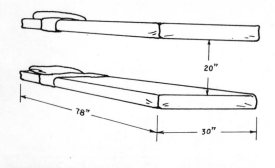

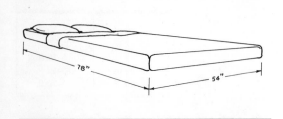

BEDS AND BUNKS FOR SLEEPING

The dimensions shown at the right are minimum for bunks which are stacked one above the other. The 20 inches is the minimum to allow the person on the lower bunk to turn over without bumping the upper bunk. This minimum must be maintained, considering the sag of the springs in the upper bunk with a heavy occupant!

The bed for two occupants does not necessarily require doubling of the lateral dimension of the single bed. The length, however, should consider the problem of bedclothes being tucked tightly at the bottom. Any less length than shown will restrict the occupant's feet, owing to the tucking of the bedclothes, and will annoy the occupant considerably.

GENERAL FURNITURE DIMENSIONS

Although furniture dimensions are not so critical as devices which are designed to improve working conditions, it behooves the furniture designer to remember that the human body is still the basic consideration for determining the size and shape of furniture.

The dimensions shown below will provide furniture which is compatible with the over-all population of users — including both men and women. Padding should be packaged in such a way as to prevent bunching and sagging. Special care should be taken in this respect for multi-person units, recognizing that one or more heavy persons sitting in the center of a couch or davenport can cause it to sag sufficiently to roll the persons at each end toward the sagging center.

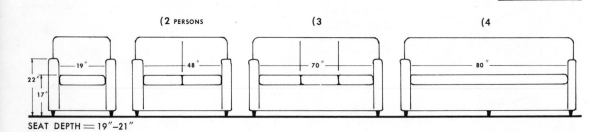

SEAT DEPTH = 19″–21″
BACK HEIGHT = 19″–34″

DESKS — TABLES — COUNTERS — WORKBENCHES

In general, all such work areas should be at elbow-level height with reference to the working position of the user, whether he is sitting or standing. Abnormal table heights reduce efficiency and hasten fatigue. Insufficient leg and foot room causes poor posture and constant irritation.

MINIMUM USEFUL
WRITING AREA

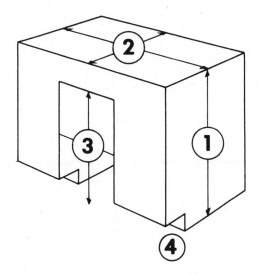

Important dimensions to remember in the design of any desk or table are:

① Working height.

② Working width and depth.

③ Knee room height and depth.

④ Kick room.

The dimensions shown are the *minimum* allowable.

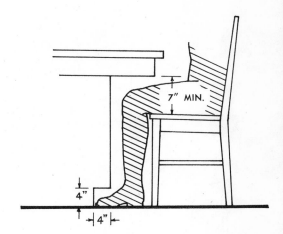

For special applications of custom builtins, etc., consult the tables on body dimensions (pp. 5-16 through 5-19) for maximum and minimum requirements.

TABLES

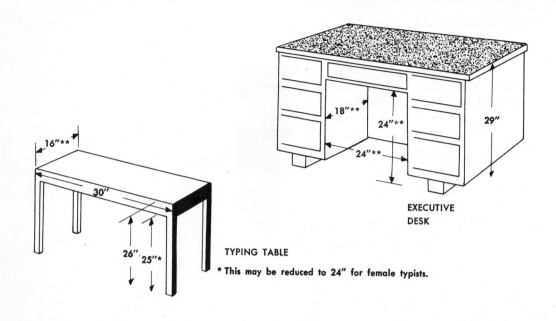

16"**

30"

26" 25"*

TYPING TABLE

* This may be reduced to 24" for female typists.

18"** 24"** 29"

24"**

EXECUTIVE
DESK

TABLE FOR
MULTIPLE SEATING

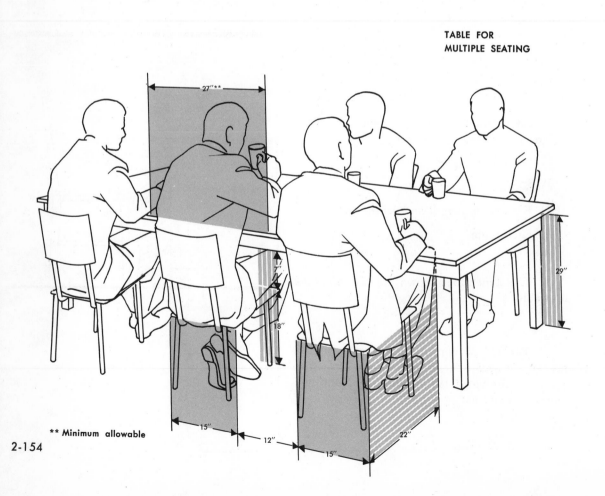

27"**

7"

18"

29"

** Minimum allowable

15"   12"   22"

15"

2-154

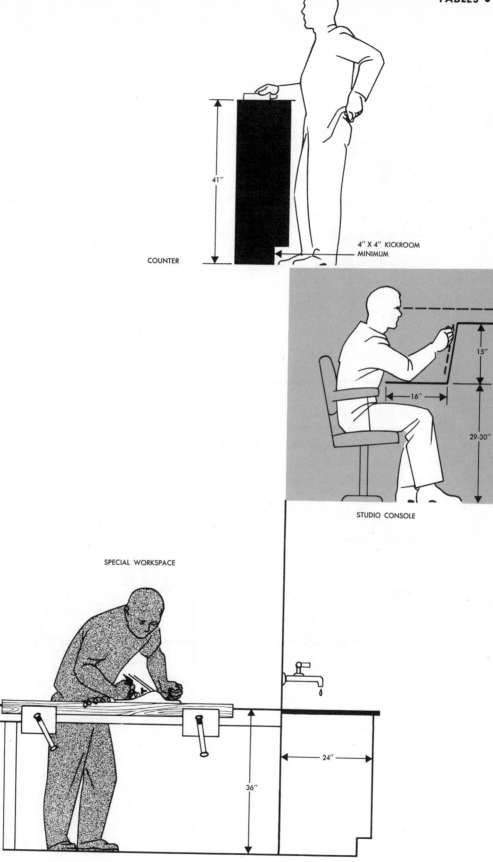

COUNTER

4" X 4" KICKROOM
MINIMUM

41"

STUDIO CONSOLE

15"

16"

29-30"

SPECIAL WORKSPACE

36"

24"

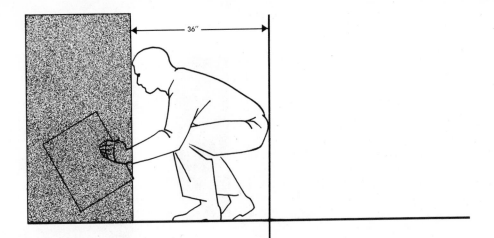

Shelves are most useful when their contents can be both seen and reached. The top shelf should be no higher than 76 inches and the depth should be determined by considering the unit size of its contents — for example, bolts of cloth require deep shelves, canned goods relatively shallow shelves.

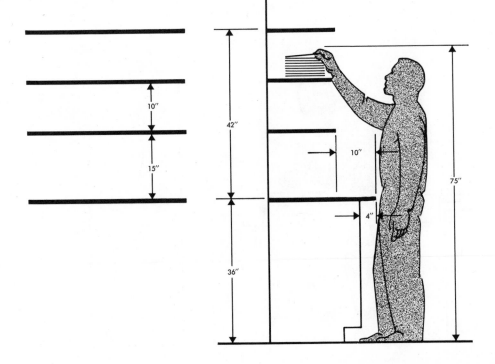

The sewing machine should be mounted at a working height which fits the woman of the house, hence the 28-inch table height. The other dimensions shown will make the workplace a very compatible size for handling the materials as well as preventing cracked knees.

Obviously, the larger the work area, the better — up to a certain point. In the illustration, a typical machine has been inset into the table, and sufficient table-top area allowed around the machine for materials to be spread out.

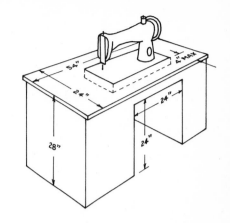

Many women have found that they can reduce ironing fatigue by changing alternately from a sitting to standing position — or using a high stool for the ironing task.

An adjustable board is recommended to accommodate a continuous range of positions from 26 to 36 inches high. Such boards should be designed such that the legs adequately support the raising of the center of gravity — considering the added weight of the iron and other materials on the board.

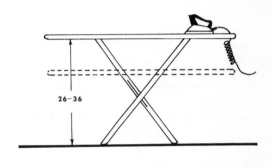

The convenience of a record player is frequently forgotten. There is no reason why the user should have to stoop to put records on the machine. The dimension recommended at the right will make the operation convenient (and incidentally will save a few records from damage) and still allow the stylists to maintain a low silhouette.

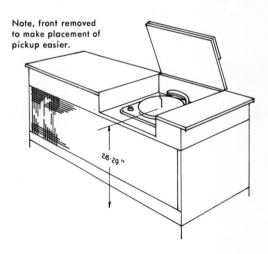

Note, front removed to make placement of pickup easier.

EQUIPMENT ARRANGEMENT

The arrangement of equipments and the people who must operate those equipments can mean the difference between accomplishing and not accomplishing the original mission. Proper arrangement of the components (man and machine) should be based upon the visual, auditory, and control links between them and an analysis of the task to be accomplished.

A suggested procedure for analysis of control links follows.

List the major components of the system, including the equipments and the necessary operator, and assign consistent symbols to each.

Determine the type of link between each of the equipments and operators; equipments and equipments; and operators and operators.

Determine the value of each link, that is, the frequency with which it will be used, and its *importance* when it is used.

A three-point scale should be adequate for rating the link values.

Prepare an analysis chart of the link values of the components of the system. From this chart you can determine the relative importance and priority for placement of each component.

Prepare a drawing of the area you have at your disposal (to scale, preferably) and make a scaled three-dimensional cutout of each component. Place the component with highest link value first, adjusting the lesser values next. If compromises are necessary it would be well to assess further the original link values in terms of the physical environment, sit or stand operation, or other applicable factors.

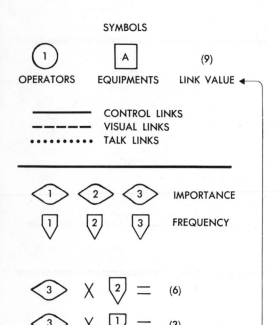

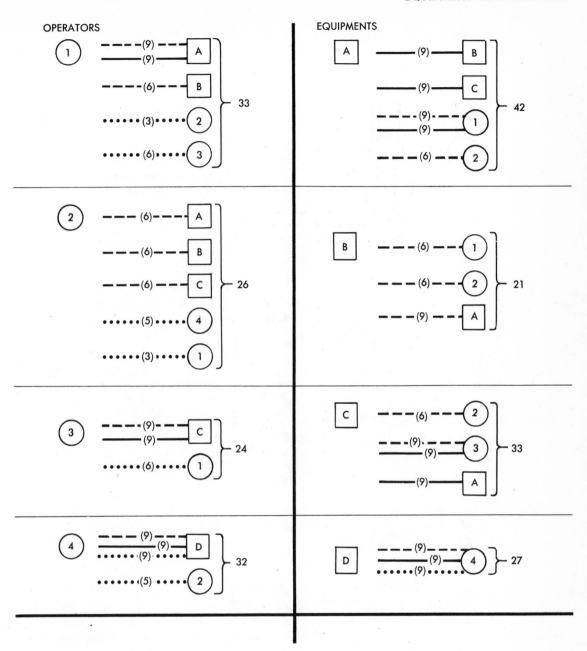

OPERATORS

EQUIPMENTS

FINAL ANALYSIS CHART

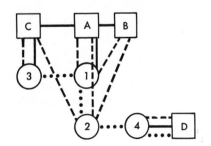

FINAL ANALYSIS CHART

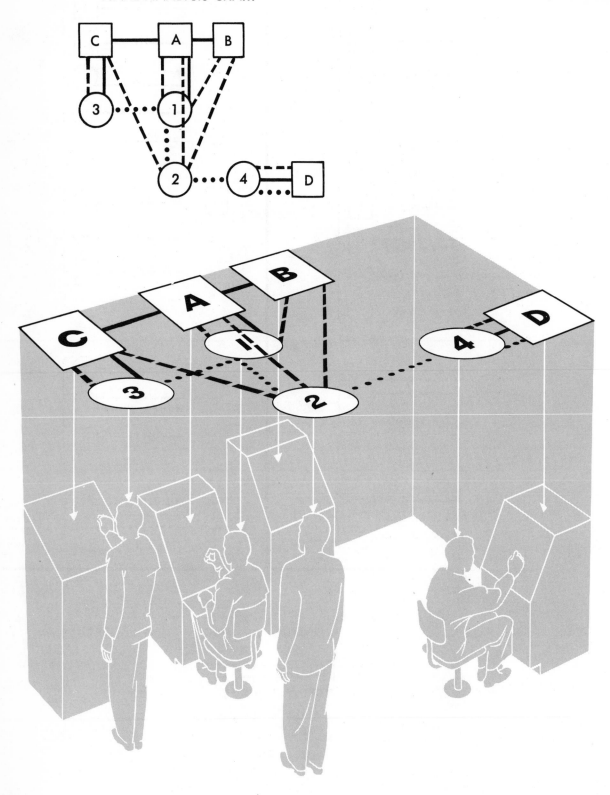

Check the final arrangement for:

VISUAL LINKS — Be sure that viewing distance is not too great, that viewing is not obstructed by other equipments or people, and that illumination of the visual object is adequate.

TALKING LINKS — Be sure that the distance between two talkers is not so great that shouting becomes necessary.

WALKING LINKS — Be sure that walking time is not excessive and that interference is minimized.

WORKING SPACE — Be sure that operators have room enough to manipulate controls. When crowding becomes critical, prepare mock-ups for study and evaluation of the particular components or areas involved.

Once you feel that your arrangement has taken care of the general operating requirements of the man-machine system, review the environmental conditions for safety and efficiency. Proper ventilation, convenient storage and maintenance facilities, safety in the form of protective devices, and conveniences such as ash trays will provide for smoother operation and less physical and mental fatigue among operating personnel.

AISLES AND PASSAGEWAYS

Proper design of passageways is necessary to insure the expeditious flow of human traffic. If due consideration is not given to over-all dimensions, directions of traffic flow, or the illumination of such areas, serious bottlenecks and even accidents may occur. It is recommended that the following factors be considered in the design of all aisles, corridors, and special passageways.

- Approximate traffic load at any one time.

- Number and size of entrances and exits.

- Number and location of doors opening into the passageway.

- Illumination of the passageway and the intelligible identification of exits.

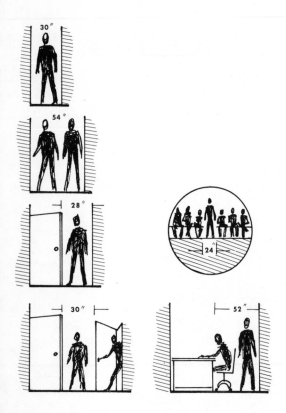

Normal aisle and corridor dimensional requirements are shown in the illustrations to the left and below. Special attention is called to the aircraft illustration. In this case, one must consider the fact that the motion of the vehicle creates an additional hazard for the person trying to navigate the narrow aisle. Care should be taken to avoid protrusion which may be part of seats, particularly at the lower extremities. The person who is walking down the aisle will probably be too preoccupied to notice these.

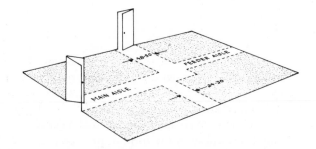

CATWALKS

In large military aircraft, catwalks permit movement of personnel through the plane. Such a passageway should, of course, be designed so that it is structurally sound and offers the least possible restriction to movement of personnel, particularly those wearing bulky suits and other essential gear. A trapezoidal structure gives maximum structural strength, and tests have determined minimum dimensions to be as shown.[11]

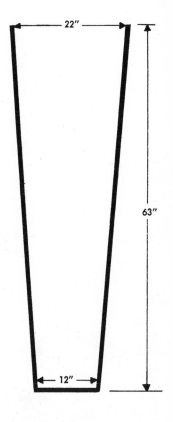

INTERCOMMUNICATION TUNNELS

Intercommunication tunnels are now used on large aircraft to connect pressurized sections forward and aft. Crew members pull themselves through the tunnel by means of a four-wheel "creeper" and an overhead cable.

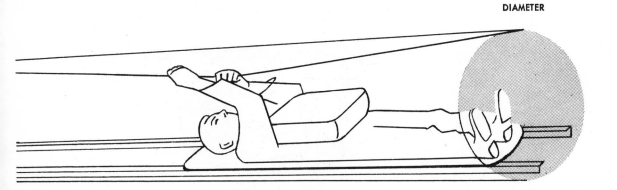

30"
DIAMETER

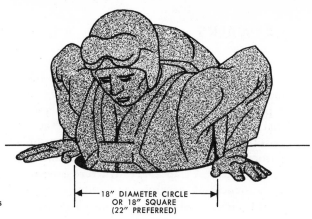

18" DIAMETER CIRCLE
OR 18" SQUARE
(22" PREFERRED)

* The illustrations on this page represent minimum sizes and optimum shapes for escape hatches.

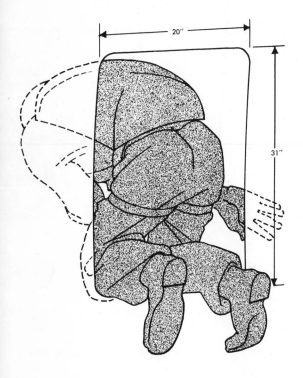

SIDE HATCH

BELLY HATCH

ESCAPE HATCHES

Emergency exits are most important to the airman who must ditch his aircraft, for he is usually hampered by clothing or equipment or the position of the airplane at the moment. His situation is further aggravated by the speed with which he must escape.

Full equipment for personnel who would use TOP-DITCHING HATCHES includes flying clothes, emergency vest, life vest, and dinghy. Full equipment for personnel who would use SIDE or BELLY HATCHES includes flying clothes, emergency vest, life vest, and parachute.

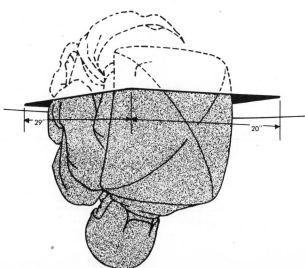

Space-vehicle hatches must of necessity be as small as possible owing to the over-all limits on vehicle size and the critical requirements for pressure integrity. The dimension shown at the right is minimum for the typical space suit which may have to be inflated. Extra equipment, such as a portable bio-pack, must be taken into consideration in determining the size of such hatches. Designers should use full-scale mock-ups to confirm all dimensions.

Walk-through pressure hatches or water-tight hatches also require consideration of the minimum opening size because of the problems of weight and sealing. The dimensions on the drawing at the right should be adhered to if at all possible if the human user is to function effectively. If the user frequently carries certain types of portable equipment through such openings, the size and shape of this equipment must be considered relative to the over-all envelope of the man plus the equipment.

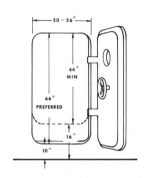

Crawl-ways which are provided for servicing purposes must be large enough to allow the man to maneuver swiftly and surely. If the crawl-way does not have smooth sides — i.e., has equipment projecting randomly along the way — extra space should be provided or special covers should be placed over the projections to prevent the man's clothing from catching on them. In such limited confines he will find it almost impossible to turn and free himself, once caught!

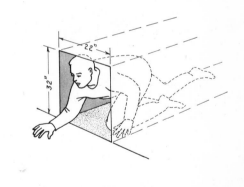

Emergency escape hatches for aircraft passengers who may have to ditch the vehicle should be large enough for them to get out quickly and easily. It is particularly important not to have the sill of the opening so high that smaller passengers have difficulty stepping over and out onto a wing surface.

INCLINES

The choice of ramp, stair, or ladder is dependent upon the type of traffic, distance between the two levels to be joined, the space available, and the safety of the user.

If we limit our traffic to the human being and do not include movement of equipments, the most important factor becomes one of safety, which dictates the design considerations as well as the choice of device.[12]

RAMPS are satisfactory for inclines of 20 degrees or less, the ideal being about 15 degrees. The walking surface should present good traction in either a wet or dry condition. Hand rails are recommended, especially when the ramp is open on either side.

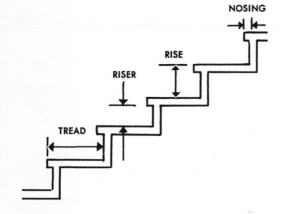

STAIRS are satisfactory for inclines between 20 and 50 degrees, the preferred range being 30 to 45 degrees. Stair treads should be at least as deep as the stair riser is high, and in no case should the rise be more than 8 inches. The ideal stair would consist of a rise of 7 to 7½ inches, tread depth of 9½ to 11 inches, and a nosing of ¾ to 1½ inches. Hand rails are recommended for either enclosed or exposed stairs and should be 34 inches above the treads.

Stairs which are exposed, that is, have no enclosing walls on the sides or risers between treads, as in the outdoor fire escape, should be designed with special safety precautions.

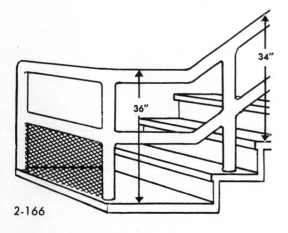

Guard rails halfway between the regular hand rail and step should be provided. Rails at landings should have special guard screen from the platform up to the guard rail (railings should be at least 42 inches high if they are to be used on platforms 4 feet or more above the ground).

Special guard screen should be provided beneath open steps to prevent the foot from sliding through.

Non-slip treads should be provided on *all* stairs and should be kept in optimum state of repair at all times.

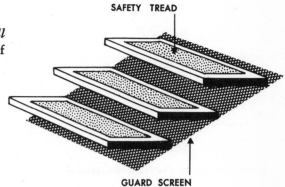

LADDERS are suggested for inclines which are between 50 and 90 degrees. Those ladders which range from 50 to 75 degrees should have flat treads; rungs may be used from 75 to 90 degrees. The distance between treads or rungs may vary from 7 to 16 inches, 12 inches being the most desirable.

Safety devices similar to those suggested for stairs should be used, especially in the case of very tall ladders, 20 feet and taller. *Vertical ladders more than 8 feet tall should be avoided.*

Hand grips should be provided on all ladders. The main ladder supports may act as the hand grips for ladder with rungs, but special hand rails should be designed for ladders which are at the shallower angles.

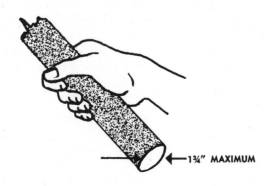

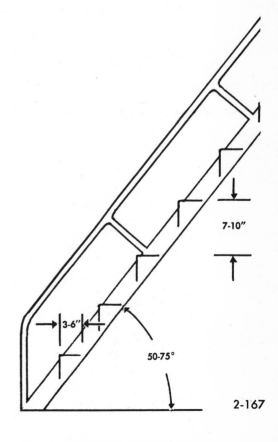

2-167

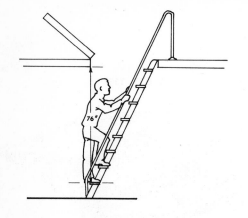

Stairs or ladders which proceed through openings such as shown in illustration to the left create a hazard to the man's head. Design of the stair and opening must be considered jointly to avoid possibility of severe accidents.

When a man climbs a vertical ladder through a hatch, it is necessary for him to have clearance between his body and the ladder in order to manipulate his feet and knees. This extra space is often forgotten in providing sufficient hatch size.

If the climber is expected to have extra equipment on his back, this must also be accounted for in the design. The illustration at the left shows a good clearance dimension for the average situation.

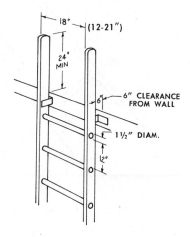

Several small design factors which improve the utility of vertical ladders are shown in the illustration at the left. The extension of the ladder above the opening is not only a convenience, but will forestall accidents. The clearance between the ladder and the wall is necessary for the man's feet, and the size of the rung is the best over-all diameter to insure that the user can get a firm grasp on the ladder.

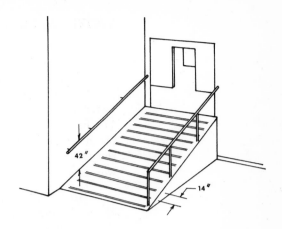

Handrails and floor cleats are recommended safety measures to be included in the layout of ramps.

If the ramp is used for movement of wheeled vehicles as well as pedestrian traffic, the center of the ramp can be left clear with walking cleats only at the sides near the hand rails. In this case, the cleats should be at least 18 inches long.

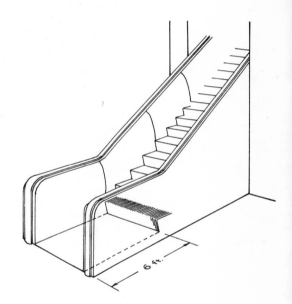

Escalators are particularly useful in situations where the user may be burdened with packages or heavy luggage. They have been utilized in many different situations — most often in the department store. The recommended rate of travel should be 120 to about 140 feet per minute. The slower speeds are preferred for mixed domestic use where older people and children may use the devices. The preferred angle of ascent of an escalator should not be more than 30 degrees.

The entryway to the escalator should be long enough for the user to take hold of the traveling handrail and begin to adjust his own sense of the speed before stepping onto the first step.

WORK AREA LAYOUT

The layout of work area — i.e., office space, engineering drafting, assembly, machine shop, etc. — is subject to many interpretations by many people. Unfortunately, very little scientific work has been done to establish factual data or to provide principles which have been tested experimentally. The better solutions to these problems have resulted from sound logical planning, however, and if certain considerations are kept in mind, the end result will be increased efficiency and satisfaction on the part of the worker.

In the sketch below, an imaginary layout is shown for the purpose of expounding on some of the important factors to consider in arriving at a good layout. A general rule of thumb for area requirements is the following: (*a*) provide 65 to 100 square feet per worker — depending on accessory equipment needed for each individual; (*b*) provide full floor-to-ceiling offices for scientific or highly technical workers — maximum of two per office 10 by 12 feet, or 9 by 10 feet for a single worker; (*c*) provide semi-private 7-foot partitioned spaces for supervisors; (*d*) provide 4-foot partitioned spaces for assistant supervisors. Drafting tables may be placed end to end but with sufficient space between pairs for passage of personnel as shown in the sketch below. Full ceiling-height partitions should separate the drafting-engineering area from the regular office area and also from the assembly and shop areas. Locate noisy machine areas as far from the principal office area as possible, and also separate it by a full wall from any adjacent area such as the drafting and electronic assembly areas shown in the sketch below.

Note the single secretarial office located centrally to serve two Chief Supervisor offices — saving not only space, but personnel.

The Reception area should be considered as the first point of entry to the visitor — with the Manager's office adjacent to it as the second step in the visitor's progress into the organization. Note that the series of offices from then on proceeds according to rank.

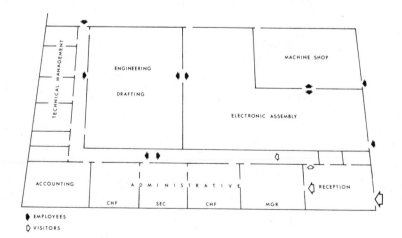

Plans for the physical location and arrangement of groups of people can be evaluated in terms of how well they meet the following recommended conditions:

Locate closely related groups in the same building.

Locate closely related groups on the same floor of the building.

Juxtapose groups according to the normal plan of work flow.

Integrate related activities (such as mechanical and non-mechanical, professional and non-professional, etc.) in accordance with the actual requirements for contact (i.e., do not separate simply because their work is different).

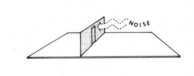

Although related activities should be close together, avoid disturbances such as noise by use of walls or partitions. Provide privacy for supervisors.

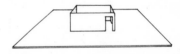

Locate supervisors so that they can readily contact their subordinates and yet maintain contact with each other for management coordination.

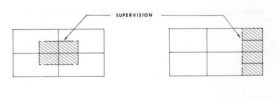

Provide "face to face" access for related groups.

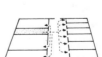 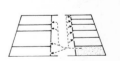

Locate centrally a group which has many repeated contacts with other groups.

Shield quiet areas from noise of main traffic artery.

2-171

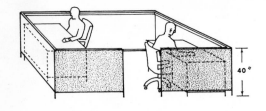

Many people cannot work effectively when crowded together. Even a minimum separation by means of partial partitions will improve worker morale and work output.

A partition 40 inches high provides a reasonable amount of privacy and yet allows the worker to see over the partition.

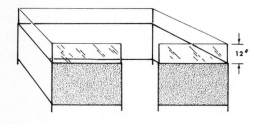

Addition of a 12-inch transparent extension on top of the partition will reduce the interference of adjacent conversation to a considerable extent and yet still allow adjacent employees to see each other.

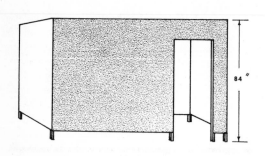

In cases where it is desirable for more privacy — i.e., you do not want to be annoyed by passers-by looking in on the work area — the partition should be at least 7 feet high.

Note that in each of the above cases there is a space between the partition and the floor to improve ventilation.

Since space is nearly always at a premium, planners are prone to arrange desks in less than the optimum manner for worker efficiency. Desks should be placed end to end or back to back rather than as shown in the illustration at the left — i.e., occupants back to back. This arrangement is to be avoided since each occupant is subject to being backed into by the person behind him.

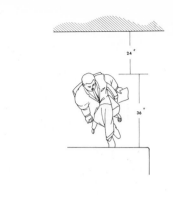

In a CONFERENCE ROOM, aisle space is usually no problem because the general layout assures easy access to the seats and other points in the room. A minimum clearance of 4 feet between the table edge and the nearest wall will provide a 2-foot aisle along the wall when people are seated at the table. An additional clearance of 1 foot will retain 2 feet of aisle space and allow freedom of movement for the seated persons.

With 6 feet or more clearance between table and wall, this wall can be used for displays which can be seen by all persons at the table.

The executive will find his conference table especially convenient if it is arranged as shown in the picture. This arrangement makes it a simple matter for him to turn directly about from his desk and work at the conference table.

Arrangement of tables in the conference room should be such that all conferees can adjust their seats so that they can face the speaker or the central display. In the small conference, a single table arranged as shown in the illustration at the right is normally quite adequate.

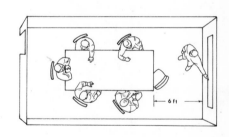

In the case of a large conference, however, it may be desirable to arrange the tables in a "U" shape and possible to modify this into a semi-V configuration as shown in the illustration at the lower right.

drawer length
+
14″

drawer length
+
24″

36″

CLEARANCE around the workplace, or the cabinet, or machine being worked on is very important to the efficiency of the worker. In laying out the office, shop, or general work area, make sure you have considered the various positions the worker may assume, and then provide enough room so that he will not bump into or be bumped into.

In the upper illustration, the worker has small, short file drawers, and will not be required to stoop over. As shown in the next illustration, however, he does have to stoop and, in so doing, requires considerably more space behind him.

Although the space for working at filing cabinets is usually the one which is forgotten, there are others which are equally as critical — and in some cases more so. Take, for example, the drafting table. In this case we often forget to leave enough space not only for the draftsman (who becomes very perturbed when someone bumps his elbow and spoils a drawing), but for his drafting machine, which also requires extra room.

In some situations, the operation is sufficiently critical that it is advisable to provide a protective railing around the worker. This type of device will reduce the chance of a passer-by bumping the worker and causing interference with his work or causing him to injure himself.

Railings are also useful to direct personnel traffic in many other situations, such as lining them up at a ticket counter, or at a lunch counter. Such railings used for organizing people must be made very secure, however, for they are excellent leaning-posts and can be easily displaced if not fastened down.

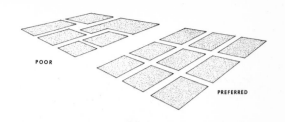

In planning for economic and efficient layout of large groups of personnel, it is important to organize the layout so that it is easy to recognize and understand. In the illustration at the right, one layout has irregular paths which confuse the people who are trying to find their way around the plant. The second layout, on the other hand, is very regular and the employee can quickly learn the layout and thus save time finding his way around. The same holds true for laying out buildings.

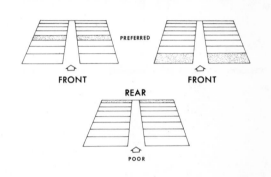

Many facilities which are used frequently, such as rest rooms or tool cribs, should be located at the front of an area as you enter, or at least midway, rather than at the rear — as is so often done. Contrary to the beliefs of some planners, the rest room isn't something to hide from the employee!

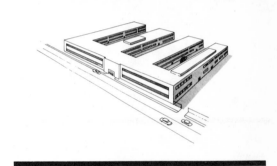

Many new laboratories in recent years have found that windows and sunshine are just as important for the workers as they are for the executives. In the illustration at the right, a typical "headhouse" with shop or laboratory wings is shown, where a courtyard between wings provides window area for all of the shop areas. This arrangement also provides more convenient access to the shop areas from the outside.

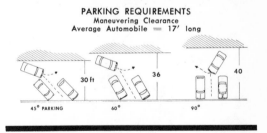

PARKING has become a serious problem in the modern plant or laboratory plan. A typical error is often made, in that a single large parking area is generally provided at one side of a building. This makes some workers have to walk considerable distances to get to their office or shop. In the illustration at the right, a perimeter parking arrangement is suggested, allowing workers to get to their particular part of the plant from the side nearest to their work area. Parking should be planned along with building planning from the very beginning to create the greatest convenience.

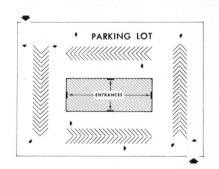

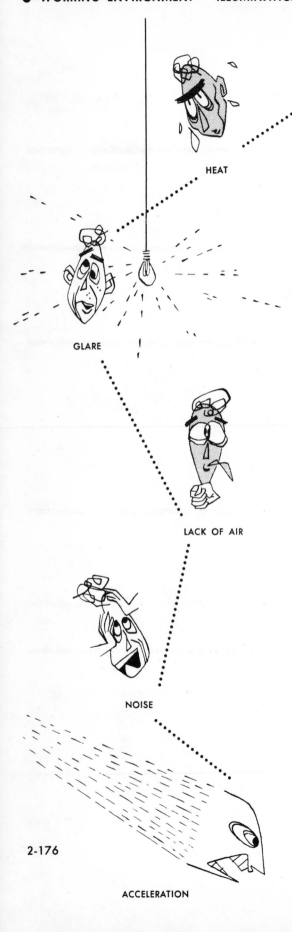

HEAT

GLARE

LACK OF AIR

NOISE

ACCELERATION

THE WORKING ENVIRONMENT

The problems of illumination, temperature, humidity, and ventilation; the effects of noise and vibration; the maintenance of body equilibrium; resistance to g-forces; and fatigue —each is of such importance as to demand separate lengthy dissertation. However, for the present, we will merely touch upon each area as it affects general operator performance.

illumination

Good illumination is necessary for most human operator tasks. It is not attained, however, merely by adding light in large quantities. The type of task that is to be illuminated, the speed and accuracy with which it must be performed, the length of time it is to be performed, and variations in operating conditions must be known before a suitable lighting system can be designed. There are several important factors that should be considered in the design of any lighting system.

Suitable brightness for the task at hand.

Uniform lighting on the task at hand.

Suitable brightness contrast between task and background.

Lack of glare from either the light source or the work surface.

Suitable quality and color of illuminants and surfaces.

It is difficult to specify exact levels and limitations for all the problems that may arise in designing an efficient lighting system, but analysis of the following recommendations will undoubtedly serve as a safe guide to better seeing for most applications. Design and placement of all lighting elements should facilitate maintenance and cleaning in order to retain optimum illumination characteristics.

Variations in the time of day or night, bright or cloudy days, or complexity of the seeing task such as looking out of an airplane cockpit alternating with observation of instruments within the cockpit, make illumination solutions extremely difficult. Don't assume that good lighting for a daytime operation is equally good for night operation — and vice versa.

The human eye adapts to general illumination levels, thus making it necessary to provide different lighting solutions — for example, daytime vs nighttime viewing. To emphasize this point, try looking out of a window at night with a lighted bulb behind you. You will probably see nothing outside the window, and instead see only the light bulb reflecting brightly on the window surface. However, if you repeat this observation in the daytime, the brightness of the outside scene is raised to such a high level because of the sunlight that you are hardly aware of the light bulb reflecting on the window surface at all. It is practically impossible to compete with the brightness of the sun reflecting on a surface — even if the surface is painted a dull black color.

A common error to avoid is direction of a light source at the observer instead of at the object to be illuminated. Even a small amount of light so directed in the observer's eyes will change his adaptation level to the point that he will be unable to see the object you have tried to illuminate as well as you had planned.

Another illumination error to avoid is to plan a general lighting system for an interior area without regard to what will be built into the area after it is occupied. Partitions, large cabinets, and even people may absorb, obstruct, or shut off natural paths of light from the fixtures you have provided.

Some special activities are not at all appropriate to the general lighting approach. For example, a room where some of the occupants have to monitor displays which have low contrast characteristics, such as on cathode-ray presentations, must be reasonably darkened. In the meantime, other occupants in the same room may have to work on charts or colored maps and therefore require fairly high illumination levels.

Adequate solutions to lighting problems such as the one just mentioned cannot always be worked out by the use of charts and illumination-level tables. Such problems call for an experimental approach. Use of portable luminaries with variable-intensity controls is suggested. Such experimental lights are easy to move about and will allow measurements to be taken — as well as give a chance to observe side effects, such as reflection and glare problems.

Good lighting solutions cannot be obtained by concerning ourselves with the source only. We must also consider the interaction of surface texture, color, and the characteristics of objects which may be introduced into the "seeing task." For example, a glossy white sheet of paper viewed on a dark desk-top in a dimly lit room becomes a disturbing glare source to the observer.

GLOSSY   MATTE

Lighting is also a psychological tool. Mood lighting can create feelings ranging all the way from rest to excitement. Creating an "atmosphere" by means of lighting should, however, not be allowed to interfere with adequate "seeing" requirements.

USE AND CONTROL OF NATURAL DAYLIGHT

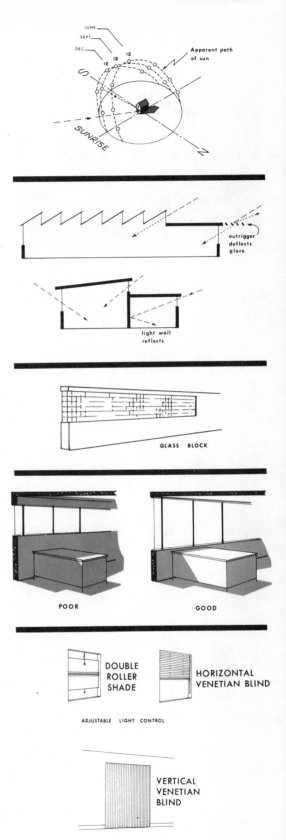

Proper use and control of natural daylight is desirable not only from the standpoint of economy, but also for the sake of the general efficiency of people. Some people become irritable when they are shut off from the outside sunlight for very long.

It is desirable to consider the position of the sun in orienting a new building. Take advantage of the natural light. This means that one must consider the path of the sun for the particular latitude and even altitude of the building site.

The construction of buildings should be considered in terms of how best to introduce natural light into the work area. In the illustrations at the right, several suggested configurations are shown which provide a method for introducing natural light and controlling its distribution.

In addition, consideration should be given to transparent and or translucent materials in terms of filtering and equalizing the distribution of natural light.

Certain design configurations may create shadow difficulties — e.g., excessively deep window headers or sills. These should be avoided whenever possible.

Temporary light-control devices can also be added, as shown at the right. These devices may create maintenance problems if they are not designed carefully to simplify the job of adjustment and cleaning.

The reflectance characteristics of internal walls, floors, and ceilings should be considered along with the design of the window openings. For example, a dark wall around a bright window will cause glare because of the extreme contrast between the wall and the window area. In general, light-reflecting colors are recommended for most applications. Shiny surfaces, however, should be avoided.

One exception that must be considered, in terms of light interiors, is that case where a night operation requires the worker to see out the window. In this case, a light interior is a potential source of reflectance on the window glass and is quite difficult to control.

DIRECT

INDIRECT

DIFFUSED

SYSTEMS OF ARTIFICIAL LIGHTING

Direct lighting offers maximum utilization of light at the working plane with from 90 to 100 per cent of the luminaire* output directed usually downward, toward the work area. Undesirable brightness ratios, shadows, and glare are the most prominent faults of direct lighting.

Indirect lighting offers general, even lighting without shadows or glare, by shielding the source so that between 90 and 100 per cent of the light is directed toward the ceiling and upper walls, from which it is reflected more or less evenly about the room.

Diffuse lighting is undirected light scattered evenly in all directions. It requires less wattage than either of the above systems but does cause some glare and shadows. Fluorescent units with baffles solve most of the glare problems of the diffusing enclosure.

Either direct or indirect light may be combined with diffuse lighting to provide modifications as needed. For example, a fluorescent desk lamp combines the downward-directed characteristics of direct lighting with the diffusing characteristics of fluorescent tubes.

Ocular efficiency is, of course, lessened over prolonged periods of continuous reading. However, tests have shown that, over a three-hour period, indirect lighting causes only 10 per cent loss while direct lighting (because of glare) causes 80 per cent loss of reading efficiency.

---

* Luminaire: the entire lighting unit — socket, bulb, and directing or diffusing element.

GENERAL ILLUMINATION LEVELS

TASK CONDITION	LEVEL (foot candles)	TYPE OF ILLUMINATION
Small detail, low contrast, prolonged periods, high speed, extreme accuracy	100	Supplementary type of lighting. Special fixture such as desk lamp.
Small detail, fair contrast, close work, speed not essential	50-100	Supplementary type of lighting.
Normal desk and office-type work	20-50	Local lighting. Ceiling fixture directly overhead.
Recreational tasks that are not prolonged	10-20	General lighting. Random room light, either natural or artificial.
Seeing not confined, contrast good, object fairly large	5-10	General lighting.
Visibility for moving about, handling large objects	2-5	General or supplementary lighting.

SPECIFIC RECOMMENDATIONS, ILLUMINATION LEVELS

LOCATION	LEVEL (foot candles)	LOCATION	LEVEL (foot candles)
Home:		*School:*	
Reading	40	On chalkboards	50
Writing	40	Desks	30
Sewing	75–100	Drawing (art)	50
Kitchen	50	Gyms	20
Mirror (shaving)	50	Auditorium	10
Laundry	40		
Games	40	*Theatre:*	
Workbench	50	Lobby	20
General	10 or more	During intermission	5
		During movie	0.1
Office:			
Bookkeeping	50	*Passenger Train:*	
Typing	50	Reading, writing	20–40
Transcribing	40	Dining	15
General correspondence	30	Steps, vestibules	10
Filing	30		
Reception	20	*Doctor's Office:*	
		Examination room	100
		Dental-surgical	200
		Operating table	1800

RECOMMENDED ILLUMINATION LEVELS, INDUSTRIAL AND MANUFACTURING

TYPE OF WORK	LEVEL (foot candles)	TYPE OF WORK	LEVEL (foot candles)
Drilling, riveting	30	Drafting	100
Layout and template	50	Lofting	150
Welding	30	Machining:	
At work point	1000	Rough	20
Assembly	30	Extra fine	200
Extra-fine assembly	300	Sheet metal:	
Finishing, inspection	200	Punch, stamp	30
Paint booth	30	Scribing	100
Glass — grind, polish	50	Receiving, shipping	10

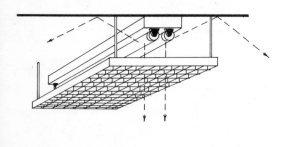

Regardless of the level of illumination provided, it is possible to create difficult seeing conditions by improper positioning of the lighting fixtures. A common error in installing fluorescent fixtures is one illustrated at the left. In this case, the fixture has been mounted flush with the ceiling, thus causing the ceiling to appear considerably darker than the luminaire. This extreme contrast is annoying and causes eye fatigue.

Fluorescent fixtures should not be used in the above manner. The luminaire should be mounted in such a way that light is reflected from the ceiling as well as directed down on the work area. In the illustration at the left, "egg crate" barriers have also been used to prevent the light from being seen directly by the worker below.

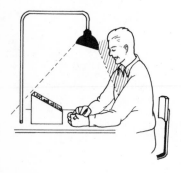

In addition to the general illumination, it is wise to consider a special supplementary light near the immediate work area. Care must be taken to make sure it is positioned so that it is not directed into the operator's eyes — or is not positioned so that the light reflects from the bench into his eyes. Watch for shadows which may be created by position of piecework or operator's hands.

PROBLEMS OF GLARE

Glare is the most harmful effect of illumination. There is a direct glare zone which can be eliminated, or at least mitigated, by proper placement of luminaires and shielding, or, if luminaires are fixed, by rearrangement of desks, tables, and chairs. Overhead illumination should be shielded to about 45 degrees to prevent direct glare. Reflected glare from the work surface interferes with most efficient vision at a desk or table and requires special placement of luminaires.

Eyeglasses cause disturbing reflections unless the light source is 30 degrees or more above the line of sight, 40 degrees or more below, or outside the two 15-degree zones as shown.

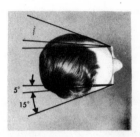

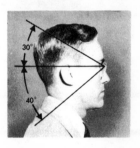

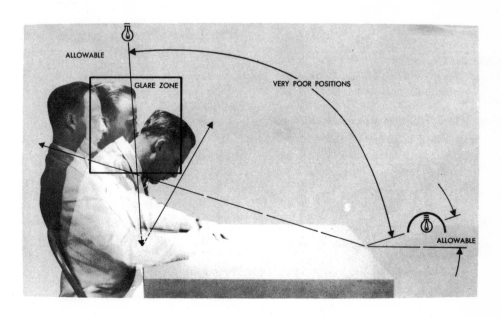

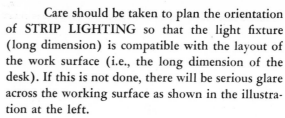

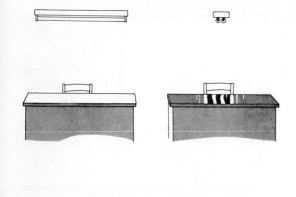

Care should be taken to plan the orientation of STRIP LIGHTING so that the light fixture (long dimension) is compatible with the layout of the work surface (i.e., the long dimension of the desk). If this is not done, there will be serious glare across the working surface as shown in the illustration at the left.

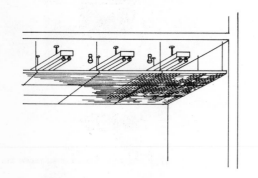

An ideal illumination procedure is to provide an apparent LUMINOUS CEILING as shown in the accompanying illustration. In this case, a translucent egg-crate barrier has been placed between the fixture and the work area. Since the barrier is open, it cannot catch dirt and thus reduce illumination. The barrier should be designed and mounted so that it is easily removed for replacement of light bulbs.

It is recommended that incandescent bulbs be interspersed with fluorescent fixtures for best results, since many people find that all-fluorescent lighting is very fatiguing. The incandescents add a certain amount of yellow to the over-all effect, helping to reduce the "blueness" of the fluorescents.

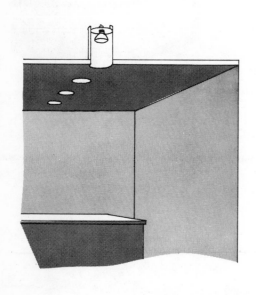

In rare cases it may be desirable to use RECESSED LIGHTS to create special effects or to maintain a fairly dark ambient environment while flooding specific areas. Care must be taken to keep the actual source (bulb) deep inside the recess so that it cannot shine directly into the eyes of the observer.

This type of lighting controls the placement of the illumination, and if used properly, reduces the probability of glare. Care must be taken in using this type of lighting, however, in that it can produce extreme shadows. This effect is most apparent at the floor level, and it is sometimes desirable to provide additional low-level illumination of the walking area so that people do not have difficulty moving about the room. Paint the inside of the recess a dull black.

LOUVERED LIGHTS provide one of the best methods for combining optimum diffusion and reduction of glare for general illumination. The inside of the louver and immediate wall area should be painted matte white in order to maximize reflection of the light on the ceiling area. The ceiling should be painted a light color although most situations do not necessarily require that it be pure white.

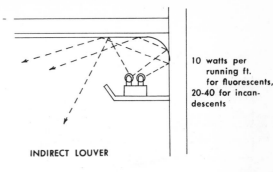

10 watts per running ft. for fluorescents, 20-40 for incandescents

INDIRECT LOUVER

Adequate illumination for MAINTEN-ANCE TASKS is frequently overlooked. Equipment racks can very easily produce shadows which make it difficult to see adequately for servicing. If the lighting fixtures are already installed, it is necessary to arrange the racks accordingly. Be sure to examine the illumination level at the bottom of the racks. Fluorescent fixtures should be arranged parallel to the rack rows as shown in the accompanying illustration for best results.

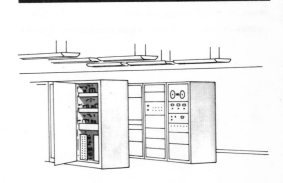

Interiors of EQUIPMENT CABINETS AND BOXES should be painted white to take advantage of all light that is available. Labeling strips will be more legible if black lettering is used on a white background, since this also reflects more of the preciously small amount of ambient illumination that gets into the box. Chassis painted white are superior to plain aluminum as background for black printing.

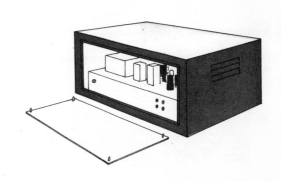

An AUDITORIUM should be provided with controlled illumination. Primarily, the light should be on the stage and not on the audience. In addition, however, there must be light enough for the audience to get around and to read programs. Dimmer controls are recommended for all such lights.

Aisle lights are suggested to prevent people stumbling around in a dark theater.

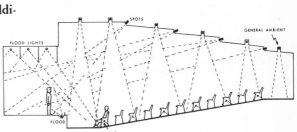

A typical error in KITCHEN LIGHTING occurs when no light is provided under wall-hung cabinets. This not only creates a shadow from the cabinet, but is in addition to the shadow of the worker, making it difficult to see anything on the shelf below the cabinets. Luminaires placed under the cabinets as shown are recommended. Forty-watt fluorescent fixtures placed as shown will provide excellent working conditions for the housewife.

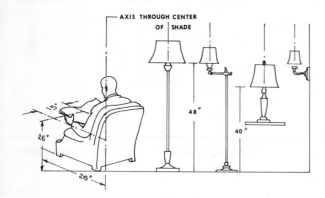

LAMPS for the home are frequently designed, or at least placed, improperly for optimum seeing conditions. General principles and dimensions for placement of lamps for reading are shown in the accompanying illustration.

Opaque lamp shades are not reccommended, because they cause too much of the light to be lost and in addition create extreme light-dark contrasts which are fatiguing.

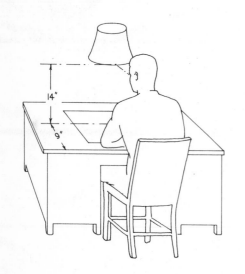

Location of lamps above desks used for reading, writing, or drawing should be as shown in the illustration to the left. For a 30-inch desk height, the plane of the eyes should be considered to be 14 inches above the desk. The axis of the lamp should be forward of the viewer about 9 inches. This, of course, is an approximate point which can vary as long as the light does not create glare on the reading material. The lower edge of the lamp shade should not be higher than 15 inches above the desk top, to keep the viewer from seeing the extremely bright interior of the lamp shade. Two lamps set about 30 inches apart can be about 17 inches forward of the edge of the desk.

For the seated position in front of a DRESS-ING TABLE, the planes to be illuminated are selected to represent the two sides and the front of the face. They are at right angles to each other and meet at a line directly in front of the face. This line of convergence is 16 inches out from the mirror. For table-based or wall-hung lamps, the vertical axis through the centers of the light sources should be placed 36 inches apart and about 6 inches out from the wall.

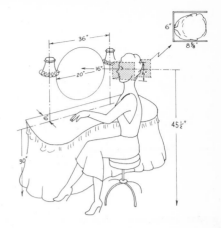

Illumination for a standing position should be laid out similarly, except that the eye height is now changed to 58½ inches above the floor.

Fluorescent luminaires are not recommended for applications such as these, since the blueness of the fluorescent lamp is very unflattering to the complexion. Light sources of 40 to 60 watts are quite adequate for such applications. Lamp shades should not be opaque, but translucent, to allow the illumination to fall on the viewer's face without glare.

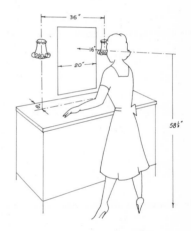

Illumination for a BATHROOM MIRROR arrangement is shown in the illustration at the right. The planes to be illuminated include not only the front and sides of the face, but also the top of the head. The plane representing the top of the head is an area about 16 inches square which is tilted up about 25 degrees above the horizontal, and its center is 61 inches above the floor. The vertical axes through the centers of the light sources on each side of the mirror are 30 inches apart.*

---

*Recommendations on this page through the courtesy of the Illuminating Engineering Society, Committee on Residence Lighting.[13]

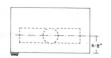

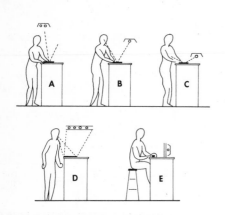

Many factors should be considered in locating the luminaire for a WORKBENCH. Since the workman may be required to lean forward in performing his task, it is necessary to place the luminaire high enough that he will not strike his head on it.

Generally, the luminaire should be placed closer to the leading edge of the bench, as shown in the illustration at the left. In the lower drawing, the rectangular dotted pattern illustrates location of a fluorescent fixture, while the round one denotes an incandescent luminaire. A double 40-watt fluorescent source or a 150-watt incandescent is recommended.

Other examples of placement of supplementary luminaires:[14]

A. Luminaire located to prevent reflected glare.

B. Reflected light coincides with angle of view where high contrast on work is desirable, as in examining engravings.

C. Low-angle lighting to emphasize surface irregularities.

D. Large-area surface source and pattern are reflected toward the eye.

E. Transillumination from diffuse source for examining film.

Many special applications, such as the AIR TRAFFIC CONTROL TOWER, require rigid control of all stray light and reflections. Hooded, low-level console luminaires are recommended to keep any more light than is necessary from reflecting off the clothing of the controller or in turn reflecting on glass windows. In this way the controller maintains an acceptable level of dark-adaptation for outside viewing.

In addition to the illumination of the console, it is also important to consider other auxiliary lighting requirements, such as the floor area. One must remember that in blacking out the general area, shadows on the floor are increased, making it difficult to find one's way around. Small hooded luminaires of very low intensity should be provided, as shown in the illustration. A small 15-watt night light is sufficient. A final illumination requirement is for maintenance purposes. Since the tower will ordinarily be in operation 24 hours a day, it may be necessary to trouble-shoot equipment during night operation. Small portable luminaires are useful for this purpose; however, it is best if equipment is designed with special interior lighting so that there is no chance for the maintenance technician inadvertently to shine his trouble light toward windows, or into the eyes of the operator on duty.

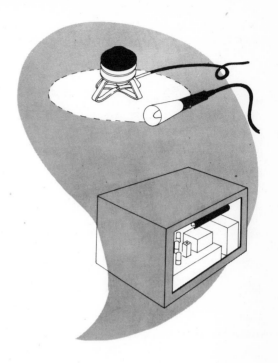

General ceiling luminaires are also required for regular house-cleaning purposes, since they may be needed even during the daytime.

Similar illumination considerations are necessary for other types of operations where the operator must see both outside and inside detail. Examples of these are automobiles, buses, locomotives, ships, and aircraft. The same general principles hold for all such lighting arrangement; i.e., "direct the light where it is needed, and keep it from those areas which degrade the operator's dark-adaptation level."

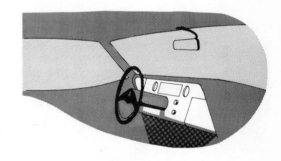

In general, the levels of illumination required when the operator is dark adapted are much less than for normal daylight-adaptation levels. However, because of possible extreme variations in the ambient conditions (i.e., city lights, flashes of lightning, etc.), it is advisable to provide a sufficient range of intensity for these unusual conditions — but with provisions for dimming the illumination to fit the conditions.

For situations where extreme dark adaptation must be maintained, red illumination is desirable (see table, p. 2-199).

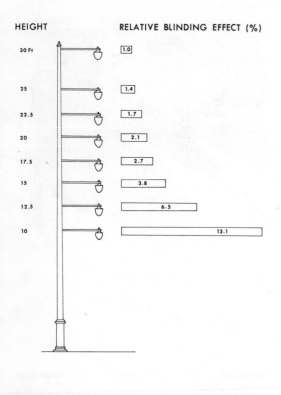

HEIGHT | RELATIVE BLINDING EFFECT (%)

HEIGHT	
30 Ft	1.0
25	1.4
22.5	1.7
20	2.1
17.5	2.7
15	3.8
12.5	6.5
10	13.1

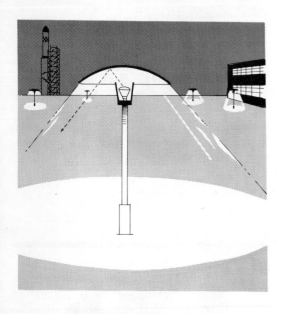

Visibility is basic to TRAFFIC SAFETY. Fundamental factors which influence visibility are:

Brightness of objects on or near the roadway.

Size of the object and its identifying detail.

Brightness contrast between the object and its surroundings.

Time available for seeing.

Extent of interference from glare.

Evaluation of the degree of visibility produced by a lighting installation involves consideration of three principal factors:

Brightness of the pavement at various points.

Brightness of objects on or near the roadway.

Glare attributable to the lighting installation and to the headlights of opposing traffic.

Illumination levels for concrete surfaces with 20 per cent reflectance:

Highways: 0.3 lumen per square foot

Intersections: 0.4 lumen per square foot

Indirect reflectors are recommended for use in outdoor illumination where minimum visibility of the light from above (i.e., aircraft) is required.

General illumination of the outside of buildings should be planned so that the light source does not shine directly into the eyes of viewers.

Illumination of airport ramps should be arranged so that both sides of an aircraft are illuminated. Modern airports are usually arranged so that servicing of the aircraft can be accomplished while passengers are being loaded and unloaded (ie., servicing and baggage loading on one side while passengers are loaded and unloaded on the other). Too frequently illumination is provided on the passengers side while the technicians are forced to work in the dark.

All outdoor illumination should be diffused.

COMMERCIAL AIR TRANSPORT LIGHTING

The modern airliner has one of the most extensive sets of lighting requirements of any system today. The following list of lighting requirements is typical:

Cockpit lighting
Buffet area lighting
Lavatory lighting
Entryway lighting
Storage area lighting
Aisle lighting
General cabin lighting
Passenger seat (reading) lighting
Baggage area lighting
Emergency cabin lighting
Special maintenance lighting (wheel wells, etc.)
Exterior inspection lighting
Navigation lights
Anti-collision lights
Landing lights
Taxi lights

It is not appropriate to cover all possible details of each of the lighting problem areas, but rather to present some of the more important considerations for each as it affects the efficiency of working personnel and passengers.

THE COCKPIT

The cockpit is, of course, the most critical area. The flight crew has a complex task to perform which affects the safety of the entire operation. The range of ambient lighting environment varies from the nighttime condition when the pilot must be able to see dim outlines of objects outside the cockpit as well as read instruments on the inside, to the daytime condition at very high altitudes when glare from the outside can make the interior of the cockpit appear as a "black well." Since the pilot's reaction to what he sees must often be very rapid, it is important that his "seeing environment" is optimized for all conditions.

One of the most difficult problems occurs in providing "even" illumination of all instruments. There should never be more than a 7:1 difference in brightness between point or area brightness intensities. No light source should ever be visible to the pilot. Controls must also be visible — or at least the pointer markings on the controls. The pilot should have both white and red lighting available, with capability for dimming both.

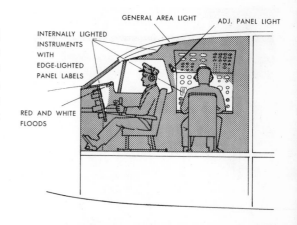

GENERAL AREA LIGHT
ADJ. PANEL LIGHT
INTERNALLY LIGHTED INSTRUMENTS WITH EDGE-LIGHTED PANEL LABELS
RED AND WHITE FLOODS

APPARENT BRIGHTNESS MUST BE SIMILAR

Since some areas of the instrument panel will have more instruments than others, these areas will give the appearance of being brighter. Therefore it is necessary to provide more than one dimming circuit, so that the pilot can balance out the over-all illumination effect. Special thunderstorm lighting should be provided to take care of the sudden changes in his adaptation level caused by flashes of lightning. General cockpit illumination must be arranged to provide reasonable capability for moving about in the cockpit, but without affecting the general adaptation requirements of the pilot.

BUFFET LIGHTING

Quite frequently the lighting for buffets is inadequate because the designer has attempted to create an aesthetic atmosphere. Remember, the stewardess has a difficult job to perform in a very limited time. Do not use spot lights, since these create annoying shadows. Most buffet equipment will include bare stainless steel or polished aluminum surfaces for the sake of cleanliness. Diffused illumination will reduce the spectral glare from such surfaces. The illumination level in the immediate work area should not be less than about 40 foot candles.

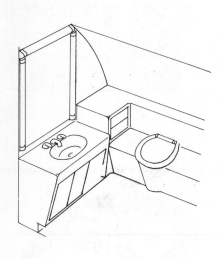

LAVATORY

Although the lavatory area is not critical in terms of general efficiency or safety, it is important to make the illumination compatible with passenger requirements. The illumination level should be at least 25 foot candles, with diffused sources. The color of the illuminant should not be too "blue" (typical of fluorescents), since this is not very flattering to the female passenger who wants to apply fresh make-up. The lighting should be arranged so that opening of the door doesn't allow a bright glare of light to enter general passenger cabin areas. One approach has been to provide a very low-level illumination as the door is opened, with a higher level after the passenger is inside the lavatory.

Some type of illuminated sign indicating that the lavatory is occupied should be provided on or adjacent to the lavatory door. Remember that some passengers will be embarrassed by the situation anyway, and fumbling with a locked door only adds to their embarrassment.

THE ENTRYWAY

Probably the most important factor to consider in lighting the entryway is to insure that the passenger can see where he is walking! Some of the most frequent errors are (a) decorative spot lighting of the floor, (b) lights directed at the incoming passenger, or (c) illumination levels which are so bright that the passenger stepping out of the aircraft can't see the stairway which is less well illuminated.

Particular attention should be taken to illuminate unusual projections which may be a part of the doorway configuration, such as low overheads, sills which are higher than the floor, or door hinges.

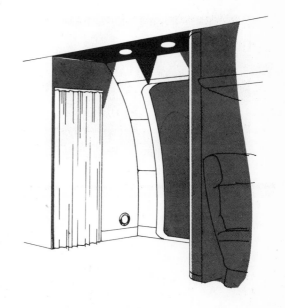

STORAGE AREAS

Although illumination levels of storage areas (hatracks, cloak racks, etc.) do not have to be high, it is important to arrange the lighting so that materials inserted into the area do not block off the illumination.

AISLE LIGHTING

It is easy to forget aisle illumination, assuming that general cabin lighting will somehow get to the floor. This is not always true, and the designer is cautioned to consider the floor problem on its own merits. Of particular importance is the necessity to provide emergency aisle lighting which is independent of the normal lighting circuits. In the event of an abnormal landing when the aircraft may not be straight and level, the passengers must be able to evacuate the aircraft quickly. Since they may already be in a state of emotional disorientation, not being able to see the floor (aisle) leading to an escape exit can lead to general panic and possible inability to get out of the aircraft safely. Obviously, the illumination must be arranged properly, and be maintained at a level so that it does not annoy passengers who may be sleeping on night flights.

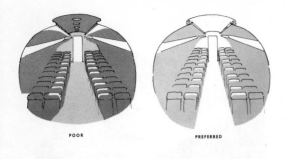

POOR   PREFERRED

GENERAL CABIN LIGHTING

A primary objective should be to provide a diffused, shadowless condition in the cabin. Seats and hatracks can easily create shadows if point-source fixtures are used. Fluorescent luminaires placed behind louvers and reflecting on smooth surfaces create the best diffusion. The illumination should be designed so that the level can be adjusted for the ambient conditions by the stewardess. Levels should range from about 3 to 40 foot candles. Interior surfaces in the cabin should be relatively light in color (reflectance about 70 per cent). The color of the illuminant should not be too "blue."

PASSENGER READING-LIGHTS

Arrangement of individual reading-lights for each passenger should be such that the light illuminates an area of 18 by 12 inches directly in front of the passenger at lap height above the seat. The intensity level should be between 25 and 40 foot candles. The brightest point should be at the center of the area, diminishing gradually toward the edges. Do not try to create a sharp cutoff at the edges!

The light source should never be visible to any of the passengers or their neighbors. Although some fixtures have been made which are adjustable in terms of direction, this makes it difficult to keep one passenger from placing the rays of his light where he thinks he wants it without disturbing his neighbor, who may want to sleep.

CAUTION: Since reading lights create a great deal of heat within the limited area of the fixture housing, the fixture must be designed to dissipate the heat — to keep the passenger from burning his fingers when trying to adjust the light.

LIGHTING FOR BAGGAGE COMPARTMENTS

The principal caution in lighting baggage compartments is to remember that the baggage obstructs the path of light. If diffused sources are provided, there is less chance for shadows. Suitable protection must be provided to keep boxes and suitcases from damaging the light fixtures. The intensity level need be not more than about 5 foot candles.

EMERGENCY LIGHTS

The need for emergency lighting under abnormal conditions is recognized by the Federal Aviation Agency — which has made this a mandatory requirement. The placement of these lights should consider the exit routes and openings. The emergency lighting system must be independent of the regular circuitry. The emergency system should come on automatically, since it is quite possible that no crew member will be in a position to turn it on. Care should be taken once again to see that the illumination is on the floor area, the exits, and any special escape and rescue devices — not glaring into the eyes of the passengers!

All exits should be located and marked clearly. They should be internally lit — preferably.

SPECIAL MAINTENANCE LIGHTING

Although normal maintenance may be performed in well-lighted hangers, it may be necessary to provide auxiliary illumination fixtures in critical places such as wheel wells, etc. The important factor to consider in deciding whether an auxiliary maintenance light is needed is the criticality of the task: i.e., if a particular inspection must be made frequently, and the item affects the safety of the flight, then "put a light on the subject"!

In many instances, color coding has been provided to prevent inadvertent misconnections, etc. Remember that color coding is useless if not properly illuminated.

EXTERIOR IN-FLIGHT INSPECTION LIGHTS

Special luminaires are frequently required which allow the pilot to inspect engine mounts and wing areas at night while in flight. Such lamps must be housed under transparent covers within the fuselage — to maintain the aerodynamic characteristics of the aircraft. Location of these lights must be such that no stray light or reflection from shiny surfaces gets back to the cockpit and into the pilot's eyes.

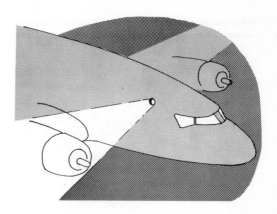

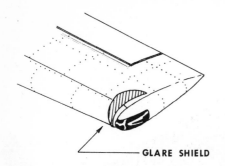

GLARE SHIELD

NAVIGATION LIGHTS

These lights are considered more fully under Signal Lights in another section of the Guide. The principal point here is to suggest to the designer that such lights can cause glare and poor seeing conditions for the pilot if not mounted or shielded properly. It is suggested that such installations should be tested under several flight conditions, including fog, before the final installation is fixed. (These tests are performed on the ground — of course.)

ANTI-COLLISION LIGHTS

The same conditions hold here as for the navigation lights above. Flashing or rotating systems may be somewhat worse in a cloud or fog environment. There has been some discussion of the possible introduction of vertigo in pilots flying in fog — seeing the flashing reflection of an anti-collision light on clouds at night. There has been no experimental verification of such a phenomenon, however.

LANDING LIGHTS

Landing-light placement and intensity depend on configuration and hardware state-of-the-art. Obviously, it is desirable to provide the most powerful luminaire possible with well-controlled beam pattern compatible with runway width and aircraft landing speed. Unfortunately, there are no specific data to define these parameters completely. Next in importance to providing as much intensity as possible is to provide good control over the direction of the beams. Beams should overlap to provide a broad and constant illumination of the area directly in front of the aircraft with manual control of beam depression and elevation. (See also page 2-139.)

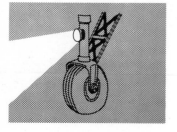

TAXI LIGHTS

Taxi lights are normally used when the aircraft is moving much slower than for landing. Therefore, the intensity level does not have to be as high. However, it must be sufficiently bright to illuminate poor reflecting surfaces such as macadam, etc. The light fixture should either be steerable, or move with the nose wheel. Location of such lights with respect to inadvertent damage is important also. Flying rocks and other runway debris may damage the light if it is mounted low on the nose-wheel structure.

VISIBILITY RANGE OF LIGHTS FOR VARIOUS ATMOSPHERIC CONDITIONS

The relationship between threshold illumination, source intensity, atmospheric transmissivity, and the range of visibility is expressed as follows:

$$I = \frac{E_0 R^2}{T^R} \quad \text{candles (Allard's Law)}$$

Where $E_0 =$ threshold illumination (mile candles) for specified conditions

$R =$ range of visibility (miles)

$T =$ transmissivity of atmosphere, expressed as a fraction per mile

$I =$ source intensity in candles

Transmissivity of the atmosphere is related to daytime object visibility (subjective) by the formula, $T^d = 0.02$, where $d =$ daytime object visibility in miles and T is defined as above. Using this relation, Allard's law becomes:

$$I = \frac{E_0 D^2}{(0.02)^{D/d}} \quad \text{candles}$$

A plot of the intensity required for threshold illumination as a function of range, with atmospheric conditions as a parameter is shown on page 2-198. Approximate values for d under varying conditions are:

exceptionally clear	more than 32 miles
very clear	12 to 32 miles
clear	6 to 12 miles
light haze	2.5 to 6 miles
haze	1.3 to 2.5 miles
thin fog	0.6 to 1.3 miles
light fog	0.3 to 0.6 mile
moderate fog	0.1 to 0.3 mile
thick fog	Less than 0.1 mile

Calculations for the curves are based on $E_0 = 0.5$ mile candle, a generally accepted practical value for threshold illumination for the dark-adapted eye, observing lights against a moonless sky. (NOTE: The observer is assumed to be concentrating his attention on the general direction of the light.)

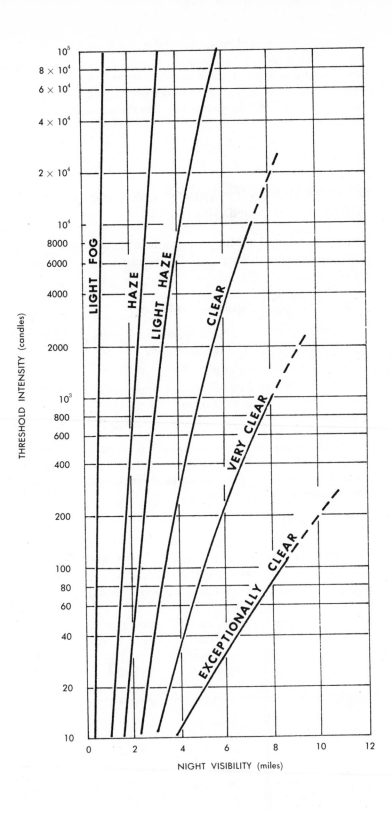

Multiple environments create a problem of competing contrasts. Recommended brightness ratios are shown in the table at the right:

MAXIMUM BRIGHTNESS RATIOS

5:1	Between task and immediate surround
20:1	Between task and remote surround
7:1	Between instruments on same panel
40:1	Between luminaires or sky and surfaces adjacent to them
80:1	Maximum between immediate work area and remainder of environment

SPECIAL LIGHTING TECHNIQUES

Certain human-operator tasks involve the need for maintaining the eye at optimum dark-adaptation level and yet allowing for adequate visibility of instrument markings on a panel or console. The pilot, for instance, must read his flight instruments in the cockpit and also scan the night sky for dimly lighted objects such as other aircraft or landmarks. Unfortunately, the optimum level of dark adaptation is seldom achieved even with a minimum amount of instrument illumination, but it is possible to reach a satisfactory compromise with a minimum amount of "red light" of the proper wave lengths.

Other special tasks require reduced ambient illumination for optimum visibility, but the required level of dark adaptation is not so stringent. The sonar or radar operator, for instance, needs a rather low level of ambient illumination in order to see his scope satisfactorily, while other operators in the same area may need to write, move about, or maintain equipment. This condition we have chosen to call "dimout" since actual blackout is not absolutely necessary or even desirable for the scope operator.

For BLACKOUT CONDITIONS (aircraft cockpits, night lookouts, ship's bridge, etc.) use illumination (RED) at wave lengths above 600 millimicrons. Incandescent light passing through filters conforming to Federal Standard No. 3, Identification Red, meets this requirement.

RED-LIGHTING LEVELS FOR DARK ADAPTATION[15]

AREA	LIGHT	LEVEL (foot candle)
Control Rooms	Illumination on working areas	0.01-0.4
	Illumination on black and white dials, figures, name plates	0.03-0.10
	Brightness of instrument faces (white portion)	0.02-0.08
	Brightness of indicator lights (not to exceed 1 square inch area)	0.10-1.00
Ready Areas; crew's mess, wardrooms	Illumination at table-top height	0.50-2.00
	Brightness of any area in the visual field not to exceed	2.00

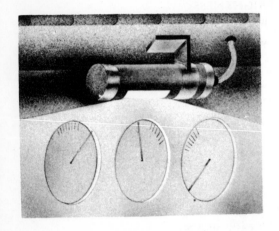

For DIMOUT CONDITIONS (communications rooms employing radar, sonar, or other scope-reading tasks; aircraft control towers) use red illumination and/or very low-level white illumination. The upper limit for reflected ambient light should be no more than 2.00 foot candles.

The use of optimum materials and techniques has progressed quite rapidly in recent years and is, of course, still under development. The following suggestions are, therefore, not to be construed as the ultimate, but rather the best we can recommend to date.

FLOODLIGHTING

Red or white light for floodlighting may be furnished by small fixtures on approximately 8-inch centers above the panel to throw an even illumination over the whole area. The operator can change the light from white to filtered red as needed, by rotating the sleeve of the lamp housing. Experiments have shown that such floodlighting in aircraft cockpits in conjunction with individual instrument lighting is superior to either type of lighting alone.

Individual ring lighting may be provided satisfactorily by housing two miniature lamps under a hinged shield which protects the operator from direct glare.

A stand-out fixture provides maximum compactness for individual instrument illumination.

CAUTION: Floodlighting casts shadows. Keep instrument faces flush with the panel; orient sources so that shadows do not interfere with other instruments; diffuse the light by use of translucent or sand-blast filter materials.

TRANSILLUMINATION

Transillumination is an indirect type of illumination utilizing edge- and back-lighting techniques on clear, fluorescent, or sandwich-type plastic materials.

Clear plastics such as Plexiglas or Lucite possess excellent light-transmitting characteristics which can be used to advantage in instrument-lighting problems.

Figures may be engraved on the reverse side of clear plastic and EDGE LIGHTED for dials, pointers, and name plates. Maximum contrast for reading may be achieved by backing up the display with a black panel. Illumination may be in any desired color by dyeing the edges of the plastic.

Excellent blackout displays may be made with a sandwiched fabrication of clear plastic plus a white layer of translucent paint or vinyl topped with an opaque black paint or vinyl. Illuminated with red light, this type of display, when engraved properly, will serve for daytime use (the figure will appear white on a black background) as well as for nighttime use (the figures will appear red on a black background). Similar results may be accomplished with a silk-screen process.

Light piping may be accomplished by bending clear plastic. Such devices may serve to pipe light to hard-to-reach pilot indicators or may be used to illuminate a lubber line or index in front of a moving scale dial. In the latter use, a single light illuminates the translucent dial as well as the inscribed index.

Counter illumination is possible with clear-plastic edgelighting techniques. The plastic panel edges should be roughened to diffuse the light.

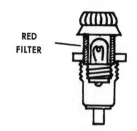

RED FILTER

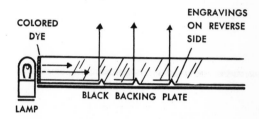

COLORED DYE

ENGRAVINGS ON REVERSE SIDE

BLACK BACKING PLATE

LAMP

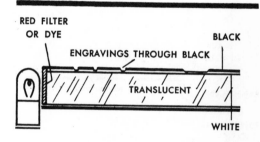

RED FILTER OR DYE

BLACK

ENGRAVINGS THROUGH BLACK

TRANSLUCENT

WHITE

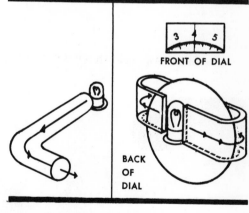

FRONT OF DIAL

BACK OF DIAL

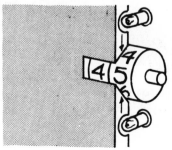

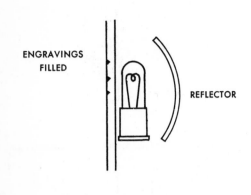

ENGRAVINGS FILLED

REFLECTOR

Translucent plastics in various colors may be used for BACK LIGHTING purposes. Figures should be engraved on the front surfaces and filled with an opaque paint, preferably black, for best results. Even illumination requires that the lamp be placed very close to the surface of the plastic for best results; a reflector behind the lamp helps. The brightness drops off rapidly within a very short distance from the light source. This type of material is not recommended for large displays but rather for individual nameplates with a minimum number of figures.

Lamicoid sandwich-type plastics combine translucent with opaque characteristics and are treated somewhat the same as the clear sandwich. The major difference is that back lighting rather than edge lighting is necessary. The same problems of even illumination are found here as were mentioned in the foregoing paragraph. These displays are more satisfactory for small nameplates than for large area displays. Engravings appear white in daylight and red at night.

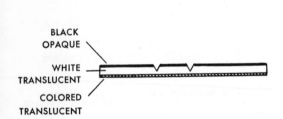

BLACK OPAQUE

WHITE TRANSLUCENT

COLORED TRANSLUCENT

SPECIAL TECHNIQUES FOR ILLUMINATION OF PANEL CONTROLS

FLOODLIGHT FOR MOVING SCALE CONTROL

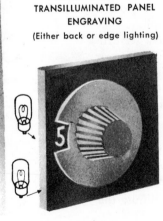

CUT-OUT SKIRT WITH TRANSILLUMINATED PANEL ENGRAVING
(Either back or edge lighting)

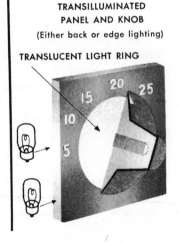

TRANSILLUMINATED PANEL AND KNOB
(Either back or edge lighting)

TRANSLUCENT LIGHT RING

Holes, cutouts, and counterbores should be kept to a minimum and placed so that nomenclature is not in the shadow of the hole.

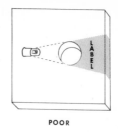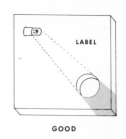

POOR   GOOD

Where thin sections are necessary, the light source should be placed as close as possible to the nomenclature, or the nomenclature as close as possible to the thicker section. Brightness of individual letters varies inversely as distance from the source. Extremes in location of individual letters relative to the source should be avoided.

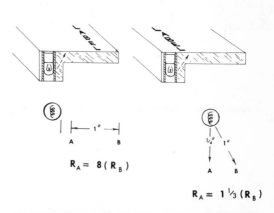

$$R_A = 8 (R_B)$$

$$R_A = 1\tfrac{1}{3} (R_B)$$

In the illustration to the right are capabilities of several basic lamps—used with red filters.

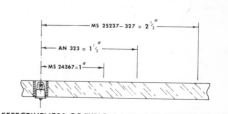

EFFECTIVENESS OF TYPICAL LAMPS (MODIFIED TO 28 V.)

Self-contained panels are now manufactured with both printed and embedded circuitry. Embedded circuitry has greater reliability and is essential on large panels with large numbers of lamps and large power requirements. Embedded lamps are also available which provide lamp life in excess of 60,000 hours.

WEDGE LIGHTING can be used for front-lighting dial and pointer. The sides of the transparent wedge are at 2 degrees' angle to each other. Complementary angles gradually diminish until the light ray strikes the surface at less than a critical angle and refracts out of the wedge. A reverse wedge-cover glass reduces stray light refraction approximately 50 per cent.

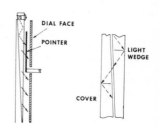

FRONT-LIGHTED INSTRUMENT

AREA-SOURCE ILLUMINATION, a new innovation, offers to provide even illumination. The electroluminescent lamp, as it is called, resembles a basic capacitor. A major advantage in addition to the evenness of illumination is that the lamp will not burn out all at once. It is a form of cold light resulting from excitation of a phosphor.

There are three major types of electroluminescent lamp:

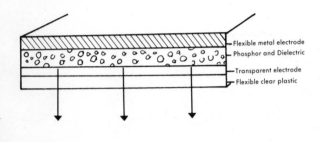

FLEXIBLE LAMP — The phosphor and organic dielectric layer is applied to a flexible plastic substrate which has been coated with a transparent conductor. The back electrode is an opaque metal layer. Owing to the flexibility and thinness, this type of electroluminescent lamp adapts well to applications with curved surfaces.

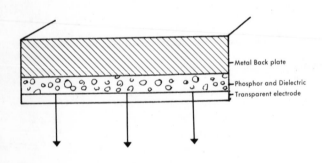

METAL SUBSTRATE LAMP — Construction employs a glass frit dielectric and phosphor mix which is "fired" onto a heavy metal plate. A tin oxide transparent conductor is applied to the front surface to complete the assembly. The metal plate provides an extremely sturdy assembly which withstands most normal-use environments well.

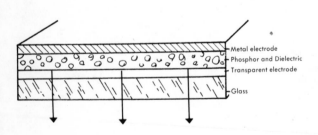

GLASS SUBSTRATE LAMP—Glass, coated with tin oxide, serves as a substrate and a transparent front electrode. The phosphor dielectric layer is applied to the conductive surface, and an opaque metal electrode is deposited on the opposite surface. Generally, this type is the most efficient, and brightest, and is easily adapted to instrument displays. However, each of the above techniques has its peculiar advantages, and all can be combined in a single instrument.*

---

*Information on this page is furnished through the couresty of Lear-Sigler Inc., Instrument Division, Grand Rapids, Michigan.

GENERAL RECOMMENDATIONS

GENERAL RECOMMENDATIONS FOR INSTRUMENT, COCKPIT, AND CONSOLE LIGHTING[16]

CONDITION OF USE	RECOMMENDED SYSTEM	BRIGHTNESS OF MARKINGS (foot Lamberts)	BRIGHTNESS ADJUSTMENT
Instrument lighting, dark adaptation critical	Red flood, indirect, or both, with operator choice	0.02 to 0.1	Continuous through range
Instrument lighting, dark adaptation not critical	Red or low-color-temperature white; flood, indirect, or both, with operator choice	0.02 to 1.0	Continuous through range
Instrument lighting, no dark adaptation required	White flood	1 to 20	May be fixed
Control console lighting, dark adaptation required	Red edgelighting, additional optional red or white flood desirable, with operator choice	0.02 to 1.0	Continuous through range
Control console lighting, dark adaptation not required	White flood	1 to 20	May be fixed
Possible exposure to bright flashes	White flood	10 to 20	Fixed
Very high altitude, daylight restricted by cockpit design	White flood	10 to 20	Fixed
Chart reading, dark adaptation required	Flood, operator's choice of red or white	0.1 to 1.0 on white portions of chart	Continuous through range
Chart reading, dark adaptation not required	White flood	5 or above	May be fixed

DESIGN OF NUMERALS
AND LETTERS

Transilluminated types of displays require special height-width and stroke-width specifications not covered in numeral and letter recommendations found elsewhere in this book. Special care must also be taken in engraving the sandwich materials, for the slightest variation in the engraving depth makes a great difference in the brightness of the emitted light. Designers are warned that the thickness of commercially available plastic sheets varies considerably and the engraving techniques ordinarily used will not give satisfactory results. *Engraving depth must be measured from the opaque top surface.*

Letters should be all capitals, similar to Futura Demi-Bold type or Groton Extended engraving. Numerals should be similar to Futura Medium or Tempo Bold type or Groton Condensed engraving. For stroke width and height-width ratios, see the letter and numeral samples following.

Letters may be reduced in size to a height-width ratio of 5:3 when there is not sufficient space for the 1:1 ratio shown.

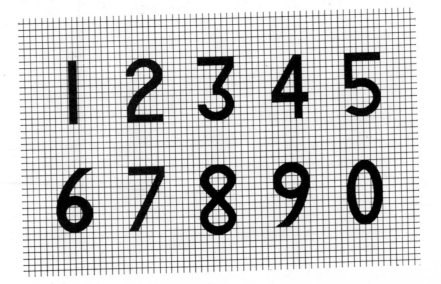

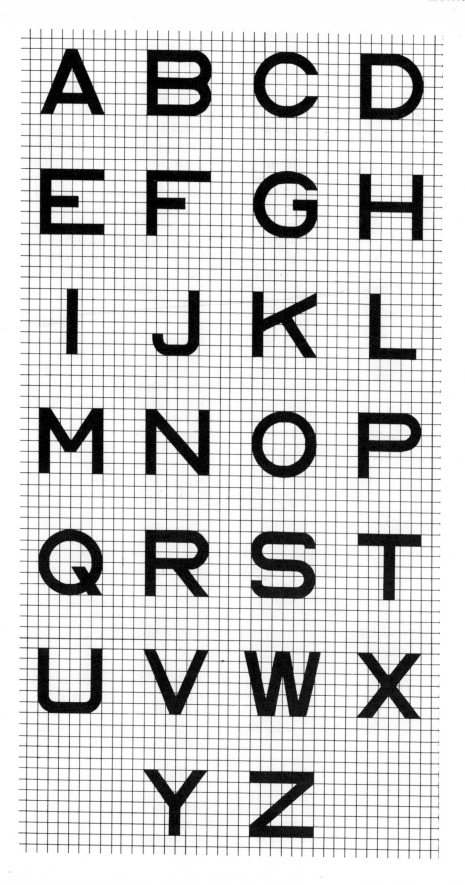

use of color

Color, as an aid to man and his daily functions, has received considerable attention recently. Color for safety, color for see-ability, color for cleanliness, and color for morale — all are covered in the general field of thought and research in the study of color and its relation to human engineering. The Faber Birren Company has compiled one of the most comprehensive reports[17] to date on the use of color in shore establishments for the U. S. Navy Bureau of Yards and Docks. It is recommended that a copy of this report serve as a guide in all industrial establishments. (See also Department of the Navy, Bureau of Yards and Docks, Design Manual,[18] Chap. 11.)

Principles of color scheme in painting buildings and equipment should, in general, follow utilitarian rather than aesthetic standards. In planning the color scheme of any area or job, however, you should consider both the physical and psychological factors.

EXTERIORS

The reflection and absorption characteristics of colors are the most important factors to consider in choosing exterior paint colors. In warm climates it is important to select light colors to reflect the heat of the sun. Dark colors have the reverse effect for colder climates.

Another factor in the selection of colors for the exterior walls of buildings is the reflected glare. This problem is particularly pertinent when opposite building wings reflect blinding light into facing windows. Dark colors will reduce this hazard.

From an aesthetic viewpoint it is recommended that all buildings in an industrial or military area have a consistent color scheme.

USE OF COLOR FOR INTERIORS

Selection of interior color-schemes should be based on both physical and psychological considerations. The principal physical consideration involves creating good reflection of ambient light so that "seeing" efficiency is maintained. Light shades of any color are necessary to prevent absorption. In general, maximum reflection values should be used on the ceilings, with slightly less for walls and floors. Personal preference for different hues makes it difficult to specify so-called best colors. However, there will be less objection if all hues are of a "pale" or pastel shade.

Compatible families of colors are recommended to prevent a particular color appearing to be out of place, or to "stick out"!

COMPATIBLE COLOR FAMILIES

CEILING	UPPER WALLS	DADO	FLOORS	DRAPERIES	FURNITURE
Off-white	Pale green	Medium green	Medium green	Medium green	Greenish gray or light tan
Pale yellow	Pale yellow	Tan	Medium brown	Medium brown	Light brown
Off-white	Pale pink	Medium rose	Medium tan	Medium tan	Medium tan or light brown
Off-white	Pale blue	Medium blue-gray	Gray	Medium blue	Gray with bluish tint

NOTE: Certain family colors can be intermixed. However, it is suggested that the following mixtures be avoided: blues and greens, blues and yellows, reds and greens. Light shades of any family color can be the same for ceiling and walls (including woodwork). Painting ceilings, walls, and woodwork the same color tends to make a small room look larger. Natural wood finishes are applicable in any of the above combinations, but should be light in color. Subtle variations of many shades and hues can be used together, but should be tested by trying them out on miniature scale-models of the room and equipments. (Test under both natural and selected artificial illumination.)

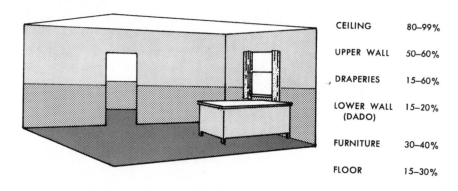

CEILING	80–99%
UPPER WALL	50–60%
DRAPERIES	15–60%
LOWER WALL (DADO)	15–20%
FURNITURE	30–40%
FLOOR	15–30%

GENERAL REFLECTANCE FACTORS OF
PAINT, PAPER, AND WOOD

COLOR	PER CENT OF REFLECTED LIGHT	COLOR	PER CENT OF REFLECTED LIGHT
White	85		
Light		Dark	
cream	75	gray	30
gray	75	red	13
yellow	75	brown	10
buff	70	blue	8
green	65	green	7
blue	55		
Medium		Wood finish	
yellow	65	maple	42
buff	63	satinwood	34
gray	55	English oak	17
green	52	walnut	16
blue	35	mahogany	12

The above table gives reflectance factors of typical paint, paper, and wood finishes.

The choice of colors to suit the purpose of a room brings in the psychological factor. Restful colors such as greens and blues and certain shades of browns should be used for places of relaxation. More saturated hues which tend to stimulate are recommended for work areas. Certain colors lend "warmth" to a room, whereas others create a feeling of "coolness." Reds, yellows, and browns are considered warm colors; blues and greens give the impression of coolness.

Dark colors or saturated hues "protrude," and pale or de-saturated colors "recede." This principle should be applied in areas where pipes and other devices or equipments project into a room and tend to make it appear smaller than it really is. Paint these projections the same color as the ceiling or wall — preferably a very light shade to make them appear to recede into the ceiling or wall.

FEDERAL COLOR STANDARDS (No. 595)[19]

In the table of FEDERAL COLOR STAND-ARDS at the right, the first digit of the Federal color number indicates the gloss range of the color (1, gloss; 2, semi-gloss; 3, lusterless). Where a color appears in more than one gloss range, the last four digits are the same. The Federal color numbers listed are gloss colors. Federal Standard: Colors, No. 595, includes these colors in semi-gloss and lusterless when required for Shore Establishment use.

COLOR	FEDERAL COLOR NUMBER	REFLECTANCE PER CENT
Light green	14516	55
Medium green	14277	25
Deep green	14158	14
Soft yellow	13695	75
Medium tan	10219	21
Light ivory	13711	75
Peach	12648	64
Terra cotta	10233	20
Pearl gray	16492	46
Light blue	15526	50
Sun tan	13613	60
Spruce green	14159	15
Fire red	11105	7
Brilliant yellow	13538	58
Vivid orange	12246	23
Bright green	14260	26
Clear blue	15177	19
International orange	12197	15
Light Navy gray	16251	28
Medium Navy gray	16187	14
Deep Navy gray	16081	7
Highlight buff	13578	55
Marine Corps green	14052	4
Passive green	14077	7
Passive maroon	10075	7
Radiation purple	17142	15

An understanding of color characteristics will aid in the proper selection of color treatments:

HUE — This is the property that distinguishes one color from another, e.g., red from yellow.

CHROMA — This is that quality which indicates the degree of color strength of the hue. It is sometimes referred to as intensity or saturation.

VALUE — This is the degree of lightness or darkness of the color relative to a white to black scale.

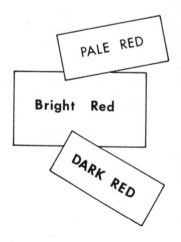

COLOR AND ILLUMINATION

Satisfactory color selection can be made only if it is done under the proper illumination conditions. Colors selected under an incandescent light will not appear the same if they are inspected under a fluorescent luminaire.

APPEARANCE RATINGS OF COLORS UNDER ARTIFICIAL LIGHT SOURCES[18]

COLOR	FLUORESCENT LAMPS					INCAN-DESCENT LAMPS
	DAYLIGHT	STANDARD COOL WHITE	DELUXE COOL WHITE	STANDARD WARM WHITE	DELUXE WARM WHITE	
Maroon	Dull	Dull	Dull	Dull	Fair	Good
Red	Fair	Dull	Dull	Fair	Good	Good
Pink	Fair	Fair	Fair	Fair	Good	Good
Rust	Dull	Fair	Fair	Fair	Fair	Good
Orange	Dull	Dull	Fair	Fair	Fair	Good
Brown	Dull	Fair	Good	Good	Fair	Good
Tan	Dull	Fair	Good	Good	Fair	Good
Golden yellow	Dull	Fair	Fair	Good	Dull	Fair
Yellow	Dull	Fair	Good	Good	Brown	Brown
Olive	Good	Fair	Fair	Fair	Brown	Brown
Chartreuse	Good	Good	Good	Good	Yellowed	Yellowed
Dark green	Good	Good	Good	Fair	Dull	Dull
Light green	Good	Good	Good	Fair	Dull	Dull
Peacock blue	Good	Good	Dull	Dull	Dull	Dull
Turquoise	Good	Fair	Dull	Dull	Dull	Dull
Royal blue	Good	Fair	Dull	Dull	Dull	Dull
Light blue	Good	Fair	Dull	Dull	Dull	Dull
Purple	Good	Fair	Dull	Dull	Good	Dull
Lavender	Good	Good	Dull	Dull	Good	Dull
Magenta	Good	Good	Fair	Dull	Good	Dull
Gray	Good	Good	Fair	Soft	Soft	Dull

Appearance Rating Key:

Good — Color appears most nearly as it would under an ideal white-light source, such as north skylight.

Fair — Color appears about as it would under an ideal white-light source, but is less vivid.

Dull — Color appears less vivid.

Brown — Color appears to be brown because of small amount of blue light emitted by lamp.

Yellowed — Color appears yellowed because of small amount of blue light emitted by lamp.

Soft — Surface takes on a pinkish cast because of red light emitted by lamp.

(See also p. 2-215).

LIGHT BUFF
WORKING AREA

MEDIUM GRAY

ELECTRICAL
OUTLET BOX
BLUE

DANGER
HIGH VOLTAGE
ORANGE

EQUIPMENT

Large expanses of fixed mechanical equipment body should be painted neutral, eye-resting
colors, such as gray, with the immediate working
area a light buff for good seeing. Stand pipes,
hose connection, fire mains, etc., should be painted
red. Fresh-water hydrants should be yellow with
red tops.

Mobile shop machinery, such as loaders
and scooters, should be bright yellow, with the
larger machines slightly darker and having black
and yellow bumpers. Yellow has also been
adopted for certain maintenance equipment, and
a similar but slightly more orange shade has been
accepted as the national standard for school-bus
bodies.

Electric controls and outlet-box exteriors
should be painted blue with the inside of the box
door orange to indicate danger. High-voltage
locations should be indicated by orange paint.

The indication for First Aid equipment
has been standardized as a green cross on a white
background.

2-213

COLOR STANDARDS FOR CODING PURPOSES

The railroad systems of the United States have standardized their traffic signal light system as follows:

RED: danger, stop.

PURPLE: stop.

YELLOW: proceed with caution.

BLUE: caution, men working.

GREEN: all clear, proceed.

The National Safety Council has recommended the following color coding:

RED: fire-protection equipment.

GREEN: safe materials, such as water and brine. Gray, white, or black is also acceptable for these.

BLUE: protective materials, such as antidotes for poison fumes.

PURPLE: valuable materials, caution against waste.

Dangerous products being shipped are to be labeled in the following manner, as required by the Interstate Commerce Commission:

RED letters on WHITE background: poisons, explosives, poisonous gases, and tear gas.

BLACK letters on GREEN background: compressed gases.

BLACK letters on RED background: inflammable liquids and fireworks.

BLACK letters on YELLOW background: inflammable solids and oxidizing materials.

BLACK letters on WHITE background: acids.

Color code standards for marking FLUID LINES and VALVES for military equipment are identified as follows, (after Air Force, Ballistic Missile Division[20]):

FUEL: red

ROCKET OXIDIZER: green, gray

ROCKET FUEL: red, gray

WATER INJECTION: red, gray-red

INERTING: orange, green

LUBRICATION: yellow

HYDRAULIC: blue, yellow

PNEUMATIC: orange, blue

INSTRUMENT AIR: orange, gray

COOLANT: blue

BREATHING OXYGEN: green

AIR CONDITIONING: brown, gray

MONOPROPELLANT: yellow, orange

FIRE PROTECTION: brown

DE-ICING: gray

ROCKET CATALYST: yellow, green

COMPRESSED GAS: orange

ELECTRICAL CONDUIT: brown, orange

ALL OTHER: white

APPEARANCE OF COLORS UNDER COLORED LIGHT SOURCES

COLOR OF LIGHT	COLOR OF PIGMENT	RESULTANT HUE	VALUE	CHROMA
Red	Red	Unchanged	Raised	Unchanged
	Yellow	Yellow-red	Raised	Unchanged
	Green	Brownish gray	Raised	Unchanged
	Blue	Reddish gray	Lowered	Unchanged
	Purple	Imparts yellow-red	Raised	Strengthened
Yellow	Red	Yellow-red	Raised	Unchanged
	Yellow	Yellow	Unchanged	Unchanged
	Green	Yellow-green-yellow	Raised	Weakened
	Blue	Grayish yellow	Lowered	Strengthened
	Purple	Brownish	Lowered	Weakened
	Purple-red	Burnt orange	Raised	Weakened
Green	Red	Brownish gray	Lowered	Weakened
	Yellow	Lemonish yellow	Raised	Weakened
	Green	Neutral green	Unchanged	Unchanged
	Blue	Bluish green	Unchanged	Weakened
	Purple	Grayish brown	Unchanged	Weakened
Blue	Red	Reddish purple	Unchanged	Weakened
	Yellow	Neutralized	Unchanged	Weakened
	Green	Blue-green	Unchanged	Weakened
	Blue	Unchanged	Unchanged	Strengthened
	Purple	Grayed	Lowered	Weakened

RESISTOR

CONTROL KNOBS

PILOT LIGHTS

CHOICE OF COLORS FOR CODING PURPOSES

The principal objective in selecting colors for coding purposes should be to make sure that each color is recognized as different from any other color. Although we have presented several standard sets of colors on the previous pages, new color codes will undoubtedly be required from time to time. In selecting new codes, it is important to recognize that there are only about seven colors which can be identified consistently. Even these colors may be confused if they are not selected with extreme care. Generally, such colors should be saturated hues rather than mixtures. As we have shown on the previous page, color of lighting also affects our choice.

Recommended color list:

SURFACE COLORS*   red 11105
                 orange 12246
                 yellow 13655
                 blue 10B 7/6
                 green 5G 6.1/11
                 brown 1YR 4.1/4
                 purple 2715

COLORED LIGHTS   red
                 amber
                 green
                 blue

CAUTION: The color of adjacent areas also influences the apparent color of the coded element. For this reason, it is suggested that black, white, or gray be used for the immediate surround in order to make the code stand out.

Use of bright colors for such things as rescue rafts, clothing for traffic officers, aircraft-carrier deck officers, etc., are recommended because of their inherent conspicuousness. "International orange" (fluoresces in sunlight) is seen best at great distances.

*Surface colors refer to Federal Standards[19] except for blue, green, and brown, which are Munsell notations.

For other standards see American Standards Association, Safety Color Code, ASA Report No. Z53.1.

Color-coded SIGNAL LIGHTS which are used in critical situations may not be discriminable by some observers who are color deficient. Three specific colors are recommended to make sure that even the color-deficient observer can recognize the differences. These are;

Aviation red

Aviation blue

Aviation green

as defined by MIL-C-25050 (ASG), "Colors, Aeronautical Lights and Lighting Equipment." No attempt should be made to use yellow or white in conjunction with these three, since color-deficient persons will confuse red with yellow, green with white, etc.

LIFE RAFT — VIVID ORANGE (FEDERAL STANDARD No. 59S, #22246)[19]

When choosing colors to be used against various backgrounds, consider the following (after Baker[2]):

Choose color which contrasts most with all colors in the background.

Choose brightness which differs maximally from background (bright against dark, etc.).

Use fluorescent color, particularly against dark background.

Use solid color — not patterns.

MAPS AND CHARTS which will be used under monochromatic colored light, such as in the aircraft cockpit at night or aboard a ship during blackout conditions, must be designed to accommodate for the effect of the colored illumination. Under blackout conditions where red light is used, it is suggested that the basic background of the chart or map should be black, with lines and printed matter white or other light color. Color coding is very limited for such applications, and it is suggested that shape coding is much more appropriate.

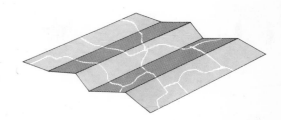

WALL CHARTS

The use of colored tabs or targets for large opaque wall charts has been the subject of concern, especially in military command posts, executive offices, and the like. The major requirement of these charts is to provide a good display of discrete conditions or positional information to numerous observers at various viewing distances. The movable tabs or targets used for this purpose present a visibility problem, since they tend to become indistinguishable from the background color of the chart. Such loss occurs when visual angle decreases (viewing distance increases, and/or the actual size of targets is diminished). The following recommendations serve to reduce these undesirable tendencies.

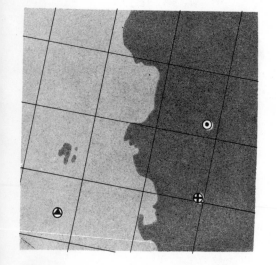

Colored targets are more effective if the chart background is of a neutral shade of gray. When two backgrounds are needed, as in the case of a map showing land and sea masses, light and dark shades of gray similar to Munsell #4 and #6 in matte finish are quite satisfactory. The lighter gray background should represent the portion of the map of greatest concern (sea or land mass).

Grid lines of matte black paint 1/16 inch in width are readily visible on this type of background and can be seen easily on either shade of gray at distances up to 50 feet or more.

The most satisfactory colors for targets for this type of display are fluorescent paints or papers. Circular targets as small as 7/16 inch in diameter, with simple black patterns, may be seen easily up to 20-foot viewing distance. Typical patterns are shown in the accompanying illustration.

Lettering on such a chart should be matte white to preserve the identity of special figures in other colors. (See p. 2-206 for optimum size for lettering.)

acoustics and noise control

Acoustic treatment of enclosed spaces is directed primarily at the reduction of noise or unwanted sounds and the even distribution of sound energy. For protection from high-intensity noise, the following steps should be taken, preferably in the order listed:

Control the noise at its source.

Create barriers between the source and the listener.

Provide personal protective devices.

Modify procedures to reduce exposure of personnel.

Provide close supervision and examination to detect signs of hearing damage.

Sounds which are distinctly different, intermittent, or diverse in intensity appear to be improved more by acoustic treatment than those which are constant, identical, and in close proximity. It is much easier to shield high-frequency sounds with acoustic barriers than low-frequency sounds.

RECOMMENDED SOUND LEVELS

The sound levels at the left are recommended for the conditions indicated. Levels are measured with a standard sound-level meter incorporating a 40 db frequency-weighting network. (See also Chap. 4, on "Audition.")

	db
recording studio	25
recital hall	30
hospital	35
auditorium	40
classroom	40
offices	45
banks, stores	50
restaurants	50
factories	50–80

Floors made of bare boards magnify impact noises, particularly in long corridors. Wood-block, asphalt, or thick linoleum or cork on concrete will reduce such noise satisfactorily. Carpet with proper padding will absorb airborne sounds and is recommended in areas where expense will warrant such application.

For impact noise, it is important to prevent transmittal through the working space by changing the characteristics of the force transmitted to the radiating material.

Doors opposite each other transmit noise freely; staggering doors will cut down this free transmission. Windows can be designed to eliminate as much as 53 db of noise: a single pane of 21-ounce glass reduces noise by 28 db; 1/4-inch plate glass cuts out 35 db; and a double 21-ounce glass sandwich with a 1-inch airspace gives a 42 db reduction — with 8-inch space, 53 db.[21]

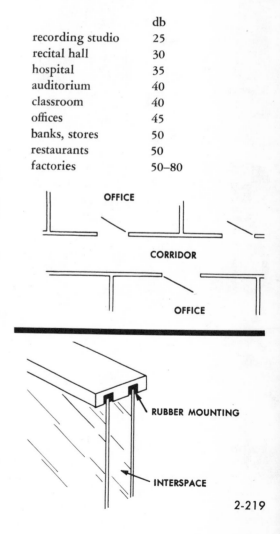

OFFICE

CORRIDOR

OFFICE

RUBBER MOUNTING

INTERSPACE

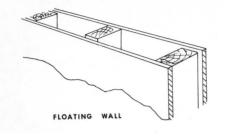

FLOATING WALL

½-in. plaster on wood lath over 2 x 4-in. studs — 42-db loss

⅜-in. plywood on 2x 4-in. studs — 31-db loss

double-strength glass — 28-db loss

Walls and ceilings can be designed to absorb as much as 5 to 10 db and break distracting reverberation by means of materials such as perforated acoustic tile and/or by construction of irregular wall patterns.

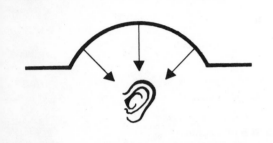

Dome ceilings should be avoided, especially in small enclosures. This type of ceiling tends to focus sound about the listener.

Narrow rooms generally provide better acoustics. Width-to-length ratio of 3:5 is suggested.

The ratio of ceiling height to room width recommended is 2:3, decreasing for very large rooms.

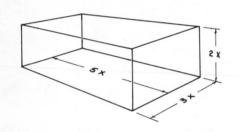

When ventilation fans are required, these should be designed so that fan-tip speed does not exceed 55 ft/sec, and the air outlet velocity is below 1500 ft/min. The fan casing must be rigidly mounted and dampened. Noisy machinery should be shock mounted and isolated from areas where employees are working on other tasks requiring concentration.

Temporary control of factory reverberation may be accomplished with baffle boards of sound-absorbing materials. Also, portable booths can be constructed around certain especially noisy equipments.

Heavy foil damping materials have proven beneficial in reducing typical aircraft fuselage vibration — thus creating a more reasonable cabin environment. It is not the purpose of this section to provide all the details necessary to perform an acoustic treatment analysis, but rather to point out types of treatment which should be considered for various noise problems.

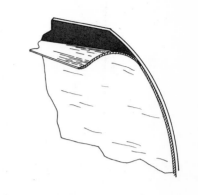

The illustration of the automobile sound treatment shows a variety of acoustic considerations which will promote a reasonable level of comfort for the occupant.

(1) An acoustic blanket under the hood not only absorbs engine noise, but also dampens structural vibration.

(2) Interior upholstery absorbs noise effectively, especially if padding is provided underneath the cover.

(3) Damping material cemented to the roof and headliner material together dampen and absorb noise.

(4) Damping material should be placed on all large metal surfaces, such as the trunk lid.

(5) Heavy undercoating on inner surface of fenders, etc., provides good damping of road noise.

(6) Rubber insulating door-seals also provide a measure of noise reduction.

(7) Shock mounting of mechanical parts prevents rattles.

(8) Tight windows are a definite aid to reduction of noise.

(9) Undercoating applied to the inside of door panels before they are assembled will provide important noise reduction.

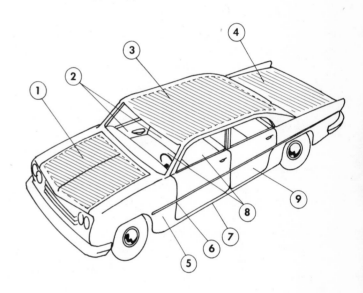

In general, the same type of acoustic treatment works for major appliances which are prone to produce noise: (1) isolate the motor, (2) insulate doors, (3) provide damping on panels, (4) isolate from the floor.

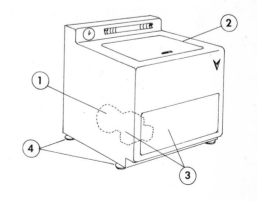

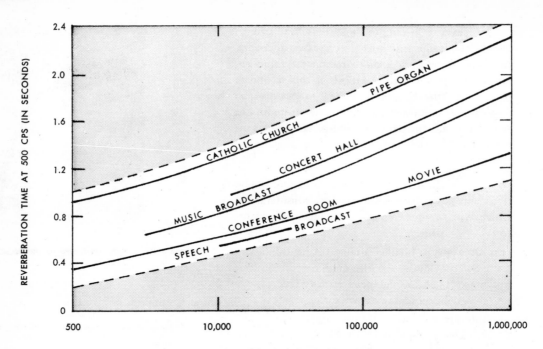

Room volume cu. ft.
Optimum Reverberation times for rooms of various volumes and uses.

(From *Acoustics*, by L. L. Beranek. Copyright 1954.
McGraw-Hill Book Company, Inc. Used by permission.)[22]

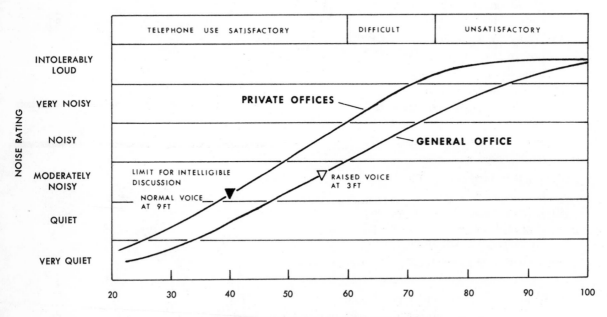

Speech interference levels in db RE 0.0002 microbar (average of
sound pressure levels in bands 600-1200, 1200-1400, 2400-4800 cps)

(From *Acoustics*, by L. L. Beranek. Copyright 1954.
McGraw-Hill Book Company, Inc. Used by permission.)[22]

The diagram at the right indicates qualitative zones of relative comfort in residential rooms. The outer zone is generally uncomfortable or annoying for normal living. The inner zone of maximum comfort also gives optimum conditions for ease and intelligibility of conversation. Contour numbers give per cent of speech sounds which will be heard correctly under average conversational conditions.

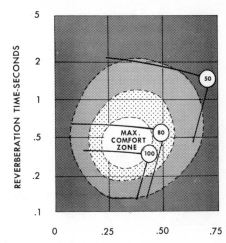

(After Public Administration Service, *Standards for Healthful Housing.*)[23]

Noise control is achieved by means of the following:

Proper planning to segregate sounds.

Design structures to block sound passage.

Isolate vibrating machinery by means of appropriate absorbers.

Utilize absorbing materials.

Ideally, noise control should start with the source of the noise. Selection of quiet equipment and proper mounting is the first step. Motors, oscillating machinery, and fans are a typical source of vibration and noise that can be easily controlled at the source — with much better success than trying to block the noise, or absorb it later.

Separation of noisy machinery from areas requiring quiet cannot always be accomplished. It is also apparent that the worker at the machine still has the problem. A typical problem that can be alleviated by a simple means is the sheet metal shop where metal pieces and parts are allowed to drop from the cutting table. Providing a chute which is covered with rubber mat reduces such clatter and in turn reduces the attendant fatigue caused by such noise.

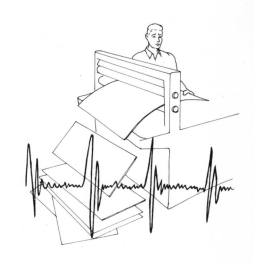

Don't assume that people "get used to such conditions" and that therefore it is not necessary to do anything about it.

RECOMMENDED LIMITATIONS FOR AIRBORNE NOISE ABOARD SHIP

Maximum sound-pressure levels recommended for occasional exposure should be considered in all accessible areas.

Watch stations not requiring speech communication should follow levels tested under Repeated Exposure. (see table below).

Watch stations requiring minimum speech communication should observe the maximum permissible levels recommended under Repeated Exposure (below) and the speech-interference limits given on page 2-225.

Spaces requiring close-up speech communications without strain and with other communication from loudspeakers possible to all parts of the area should maintain speech interference level below 70 db.

Small spaces (less than 5000 cubic feet) requiring speech communication to all parts of the area without strain should maintain a level below 60 db.

For noisy berthing spaces use values given under Noisy Comfort Criterion (below).

For social spaces, such as messing areas, use speech-interference level below 60 db.

Special quiet ship spaces, such as sick bay, should maintain levels given under Quiet Comfort Criterion (below).

LIMITS FOR DEAFNESS-AVOIDANCE AND COMFORT[24]

	MAXIMUM PERMISSIBLE SOUND PRESSURE LEVEL (db above 0.0002 microbar)			
	DEAFNESS-AVOIDANCE CRITERION		COMFORT CRITERION	
OCTAVE BAND	OCCASIONAL EXPOSURE (1 hour or less)	REPEATED EXPOSURE (period of months)	NOISY (people expect noise)	QUIET (people expect quiet)
38- 75	125	115	100	80
75- 150	120	110	95	70
150- 300	120	110	90	60
300- 600	120	105	85	55
600-1200	115	100	75	50
1200-2400	110	95	65	50
2400-4800	105	90	60	50
4800-9600	110	95	55	45

MAXIMUM PERMISSIBLE SPEECH-INTERFERENCE LEVELS

DISTANCE TO THE TALKER (feet)	ACOUSTIC ABSORPTION OF AREA (sabines)	SHOUT (db)	VERY LOUD (db)	RAISED VOICE (db)	NORMAL (db)
½	Any value	90	84	78	72
1	Any value	84	78	72	66
2	Any value	78	72	66	60
4	Below 100	78	72	66	60
	Above 100	72	66	60	54
8 or more	Below 100	78	72	66	60
	100 to 400	72	66	60	54
	400 to 1600	66	60	54	48

NOTE: A sabine is a unit of absorption equal to the absorption of 1 square foot of surface which is totally sound absorbent. As more absorption is present the less interference can be tolerated, because the speech energy is partially absorbed. The above Table is for the male voice — decrease 5 db for female voice. Speech energy below 200 cps or above 7000 cps contributes very little to speech intelligibility.

NOISE LIMITS FOR AVOIDING HEARING DAMAGE — DB

TIME	EARS UNPROTECTED	WITH EAR PLUGS	EAR PLUGS AND MUFFS
8 hrs.	100	112	120
1 hr.	108	120	128
5 min.	120	132	140
30 sec.	130	142	150

Speech within a noise background is intelligible when at least 40 per cent of the *average* speech level is above the spectrum level of the background noise. For this reason the normal voice level, which would be adequate in a quiet room 18 inches from a speaker, must be raised about 12 db in the presence of the masking noise of a DC-3 airplane for speech to be understood in the cockpit.[25]

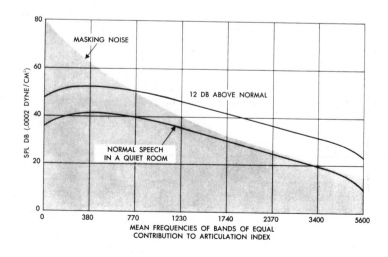

temperature and ventilation

The effects of temperature upon human performance are still not thoroughly understood. However, certain extreme temperatures have proven detrimental to work efficiency. Moderately complex tasks such as problem solving, hand coordination, or visual attention without physical exertion are possible in temperatures as high as 85° F. By increasing the complexity of the task or adding physical or mental strain, however, we lower this maximum slightly.

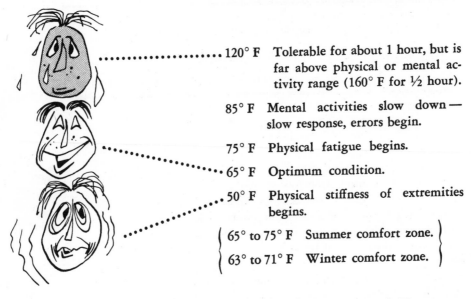

120° F Tolerable for about 1 hour, but is far above physical or mental activity range (160° F for ½ hour).

85° F Mental activities slow down — slow response, errors begin.

75° F Physical fatigue begins.

65° F Optimum condition.

50° F Physical stiffness of extremities begins.

65° to 75° F Summer comfort zone.

63° to 71° F Winter comfort zone.

Humidities between 30 and 70 per cent have been found comfortable by most people.

NECESSARY AIR TEMPERATURE

	BTU EXPENDED PER HOUR	AIR TEMPERATURE NECESSARY (°F) (ASSUMING APPROPRIATE CLOTHING) FOR THERMAL BALANCE AT AIR MOVEMENT RATES[26] OF		
		20 FPM (indoors)	100 FPM	20 MPH (outdoors)
At rest	400	70	75	78
Moderate activity	1000	58	60	63
Vigorous activity	4000	28	30	35

RELATION BETWEEN COMFORT AND
MEAN SKIN TEMPERATURES
(degrees F)

Very hot	98
Unpleasantly warm	96
Indifferently warm	94
Comfortable	93
Comfortably cool	91
Indifferently cool	88
Unpleasantly cool	86
Extremely cold	84

RELATION BETWEEN COMFORT AND
TEMPERATURE OF THE EXTREMITIES
(degrees F)

	Hands	Feet
Minimum	68	73
Tolerable	68–59	73–64
Intolerable pain	59–50	64–55
Numbness	50–	55–

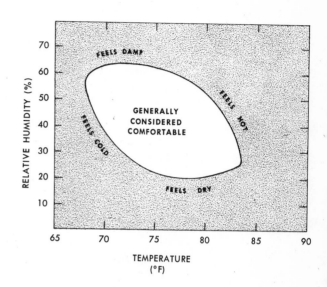

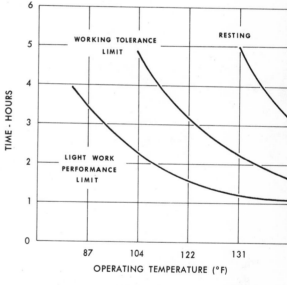

TOLERANCE TO HEAT

In general, one should strive to create an environment which lies within the Generally Comfortable range shown in the chart, above and to the right. However, it is not always possible to do so. Therefore, the next few charts are presented to indicate what may be expected when the subject must endure certain extremes of temperature.

In studies dealing with persons working in extreme temperature conditions, it has been found that the more capable and highly motivated person will be affected more by extremes although incentives often overcome some of the deterioration in performance.

Acclimatization for a reasonable period of time allows a person to overcome some abnormal temperature conditions — especially, heat.

Radiant heating methods have been shown to provide the most ideal approach to heating, because they allow warmth without introducing hot air — which is generally associated with a sense of "staleness."

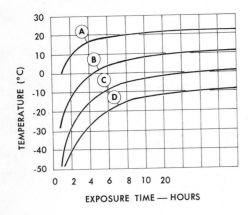

HUMAN TOLERANCE TO EXTREME COLD

Tolerance times for endurance to cold, wearing various clothing, is shown in the chart at the left. Subjects were seated and performed only light work. Air velocity was approximately 200 ft/min, with barometric pressure at 1 atmosphere. (Based on *NASA Life Sciences Data Book.*[27]

A = light coveralls (1 clo.)

B = coverall, jacket, woolen underwear (2 clo.)

C = intermediate flying clothes (3 clo.)

D = heavy flying clothes (4 clo.)

NOTE: Clo. = resistance of clothing to heat flow which permits passage of 1 K cal/m²/hr with temperature gradient of 0.18° C. One clo. is required to maintain comfort, sitting in normally ventilated room at 70° F with humidity less than 50 per cent.

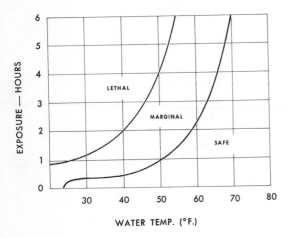

TOLERANCE OF COLD WATER EXPOSURE

The chart at the left shows time of life-expectancy in cold water (no exposure suit). Under the category of "marginal," 50 per cent expectancy of unconsciousness would probably result in drowning.

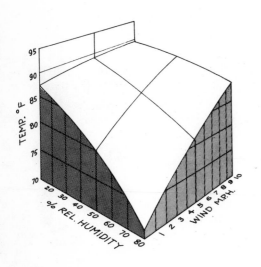

TEMPERATURE-HUMIDITY AND AIR FLOW

The curved surface on the chart at the left represents the "comfort" line. It illustrates how changes in any one of the parameters can maintain a comfort level. For example, with no air movement, comfort exists with temperature at 72° and humidity at 90 per cent. Temperature can rise to 75°, with humidity still at 90 per cent, if the air is caused to move at 2 mph, because the subject still "feels comfortable."

Normal body temperatures vary for different areas of the body, as shown. When air temperature drops below 62° F we enter the zone of "body cooling"; heat losses occur mainly by convection and radiation, slightly by evaporation. Above 78° F the body gains heat by convection and radiation in greater quantities than it can cool itself by these same means, so that the burden of heat dissipation is thrown on the evaporation system. Individuals can adapt to changes as great as 20 per cent in any of the factors in the comfortable temperature range and up to 35 per cent in conditions of extreme cold, but not necessarily in extreme heat — heat actually increases heat production.

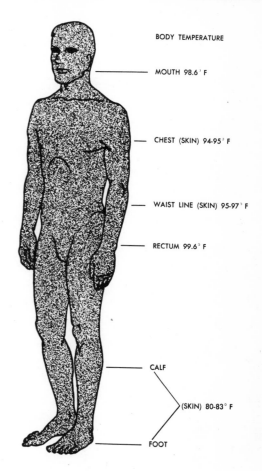

BODY TEMPERATURE

MOUTH 98.6° F

CHEST (SKIN) 94-95° F

WAIST LINE (SKIN) 95-97° F

RECTUM 99.6° F

CALF

(SKIN) 80-83° F

FOOT

TYPICAL COMMERCIAL VENTILATION RATE RECOMMENDATIONS

A 1 cu. ft fresh air per minute per square foot of floor space (average workroom)

B 1½ cu. ft fresh air per minute for heavy work (except when net free space per worker = cu. ft, reduce this amount by 50 per cent)

C ½ cu. ft fresh air per minute per square foot of floor space (average office)

Other typical areas:

Department stores, auditoriums, libraries, schoolrooms, churches, courtrooms, gymnasiums — use B

Museums, railroad station — use C

Hospitals — use A

Operating rooms, lavatories, laboratories — use 2 cubic feet

Kitchens — use 4 cubic feet.

NECESSARY VENTILATION RATE

	OXYGEN CONSUMPTION PER PERSON AT SEA LEVEL (cu. ft per min.)	VENTILATION RATE FOR PERSON TO MAINTAIN CONCENTRATION OF CO_2 BELOW 0.5 PER CENT (cu. ft per min.)			
		SEA LEVEL	5000 FT	10,000 FT	15,000 FT
At rest	0.008	1.2	1.4	1.7	2.1
Moderate activity	0.028	3.9	4.7	6.7	6.9
Vigorous activity	0.056	8.7	9.7	11.7	14.5

VENTILATING GARMENTS

High-performance aircraft, space vehicles, and other special operational situations sometimes require that operators wear special garments to protect them from the extreme heat generated by the vehicle. Ventilating garments should be designed to provide an even distribution of air over the entire body in order to allow equal evaporation of body perspiration. The ventilating air must be dry, with 5 to 7 mm Hg water vapor pressure — temperature to be maintained between 60° to 90° F.

RESPIRATION

The normal breathing rate of an adult is between 14 and 20 respirations per minute. If we take an average rate of 16, then the air required for normal breathing would be about 8 liters (0.28 cubic feet) per minute. At sea level the oxygen content of the air is approximately 21 per cent. At 15,000 feet, it is approximately 12 per cent. The CO_2 content in an inclosed air space occupied by personnel should be not greater than 0.5 per cent. Between 1 and 2 per cent concentration in inspired air is not noticeable, although it may cut down a person's efficiency. When more than 3 per cent CO_2 is present, an individual will notice slight effort in breathing; when between 5 and 10 per cent CO_2 is present, a person will breathe heavily and tire quickly; more than 10 per cent CO_2, if present for any length of time, will be fatal.

Pressurized cabins are required on aircraft which expect to fly for extended periods above certain altitudes. Although people have become conditioned over a period of time to the rarified atmospheres of high mountainous areas, such as in South America, the normal passenger or crew member of aircraft which fly at extremely high altitudes cannot survive without adding oxygen to his environment. The chart on the next page illustrates the tolerance limits for various altitudes.

HUMAN REQUIREMENTS AND PERFORMANCE LIMITS FOR VARIOUS ALTITUDES

5,000 ft	Maximum for normal night vision without supplemental oxygen supply
8,000 ft	Oxygen should be used for routine operations
10,000 ft	Maximum without routine use of oxygen
18,000 ft	Maximum for emergency without use of oxygen
20,000 ft	Cabins should be pressurized
25,000 ft	Consciousness without oxygen is limited to approximately 116 seconds
30,000 ft	Positive pressure-breathing is required to supplement oxygen
35,000 ft	Maximum for demand-type oxygen systems
40,000 ft	Time of consciousness without oxygen is approximately 23 seconds
45,000 ft	Partial pressure suits are required for regular flights
50,000 ft	Maximum for emergency use of pressure-breathing demand-oxygen

Time of useful consciousness and unconsciousness for various altitudes following a sudden loss of oxygen is shown in the graph at the right.

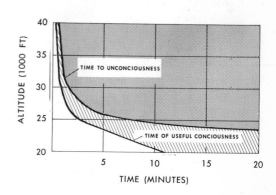

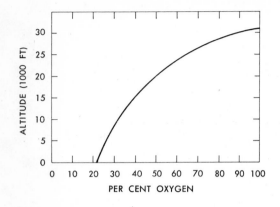

Per cent of oxygen required in the inspired air for various altitudes in order to maintain a normal alveolar oxygen tension of 28 mm Hg is shown in the graph at the left.

With the advent of manned space flight, hermetically sealed cabins were required to provide a normal "earth environment" for space crews. Such cabins require zero leakage of atmospheric gases at a pressure differential of 14.7 psi. Although early space vehicles have used lowered pressures with enriched oxygen environments, certain hazards are involved, particularly fire. Therefore sea-level conditions are recommended:

Total atmospheric pressure, 14.7 ($\pm$ 2 psi)

Oxygen concentration, 30% ($\pm$ 10%)

Nitrogen concentration, 70% ($\pm$ 10%)

Carbon dioxide concentration, 0.03%

Noxious fumes or gases concentration should be below detectable levels

Relative humidity, 35% ($\pm$ 10%)

Temperature, 70° F ($\pm$ 10° F)

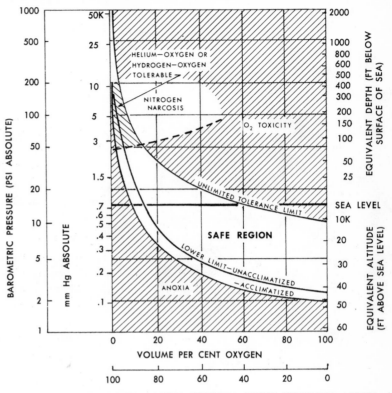

VOLUME PER CENT INERT DILUENT: NITROGEN, HELIUM, HYDROGEN, ARGON

The barometric pressures above and below 1 atmosphere (sea-level pressure — 760 mm Hg absolute or 14.7 psia) which are safe for continuous human exposure with air either enriched or reduced in oxygen content are shown in the graph above. At about 3 atmospheres pressure, normal air with 20 per cent O_2 becomes unsafe because of the danger of oxygen toxicity. At pressures below 1 atmosphere, oxygen enrichment is needed to combat anoxia. The amount of enrichment needed can be reduced by acclimatization to low oxygen tension.[27]

Toxicity is, of course, an extremely important factor in the development of space-cabin environmental systems. Toxic contaminants which may create a hazard to the human are presented in the section on Safety, p. 2-263.

vibration

The more powerful our machinery becomes, the more disturbed we are by its vibration. This high-frequency, low amplitude oscillation not only affects the physiological well-being of the operator, but is often detrimental to mental and physical tasks. Depth perception fails with frequencies between 25 and 40 cycles per second, and also again between 60 and 90 cycles per second. Binocular acuity is affected more than monocular acuity. Reading speeds are reduced by vertical vibration at low frequency, and increased illumination is necessary. Seated operators are more adversely affected by vertical vibration, standing operators by horizontal oscillations.

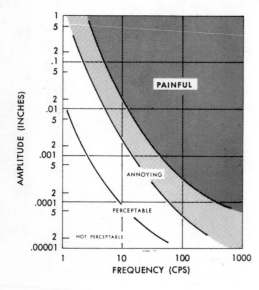

The human body reacts to vibration and resonating stimuli much the same as does a mechanical system of masses and springs. When the resonant stimulus approximates the natural human — body resonance of about 5 cycles per second, the person concerned finds this quite disagreeable.

Resonant frequency of the human body should be considered in the design of vehicles and vehicle seating: i.e., avoid amplifying the effect on the body through damping.

Pelvic region, 4–6 cps

Abdominal mass, 4–8 cps

Head (relative to shoulders), 30 cps

TYPICAL EFFECTS OF VIBRATION ON HUMAN BEINGS[28]

RESPONSE	EFFECT[a]	FREQUENCY (cps)	DISPLACEMENT (inches)
Respiration control	−	3.5–6.0	.75
	−	4.0–8.0	.14–.61
Body tremor	+	40.0	.065
	+	70.0	.03
Hand tremor	+	20.0	.015–.035
	+	25.0	.035–.055
	+	30–300	.02–.20
	+	1000	.008
Aiming	−	15.0	.07–.12
	−	25.0	.035–.055
	−	35.0	.03–.05
Hand coordination	−	2.5–3.5	.50
Foot pressure constancy	−	2.5–3.5	.50
Hand reaction time	+	2.5–3.5	.50
Visual acuity	−	1.0–24	.024–.588
	−	35.0	.03–.05
	−	40.0	.065
	−	70.0	.03
	−	2.5–3.5	.5
Tracking	−	1.0–50	.05–.18
	−	2.5–3.5	.5
Attention	−	2.5–3.5	.5
	−	30–300	.02–.20

[a] + = increase, − = degrades

Reaction to sinusoidal, whole body vibration in the vertical axis (taken on a hard seat with subject restrained by seat belt) is shown in the graph at right (after Parks[29]).

A = alarming

B = extremely annoying

C = mildly annoying

D = definitely perceptible

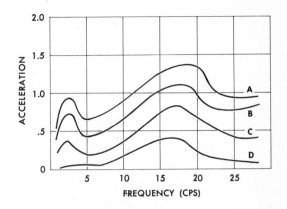

G-FORCES

The term g-force is applied to the acceleration due to gravity. A body stationary to the earth is subjected to a downward pull which is equivalent to a linear acceleration of one g.

EFFECTS OF PROLONGED G

2 g — visual acuity is reduced
4 g — gross body movement is difficult
8 g — respiration becomes difficult
10 g — difficult to hold head up, can't move limbs
12 g — breathing difficult without mechanical help
14 g — vision begins to fail

TRANSVERSE

2 g — visual acuity reduced
4 g — peripheral blindness, limb movement difficult
5 g — temporary blindness and loss of body control
6 g — unconsciousness

POSITIVE

2 g — diminished vision, + head pains
3 g — conjunctival hemorrhage, red-out, and mental confusion
4 g — probable hemorrhage and retinal bleeding

NEGATIVE

TOLERANCE LIMITS

5 negative g for 0.5 second
5 positive g for 20 seconds
10 negative g for 0.01 second
10 positive g for 2 seconds
20 positive g for 0.15 second

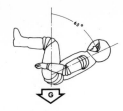

CONTOURED ASTRONAUT COUCH

Tolerance to g-forces can be increased to a measurable extent by placing the subject so that acceleration forces are transverse to the long axis of his body. The illustration at the left indicates the optimum position for maximum tolerance.

In addition, it is important to distribute the force as evenly over the body as possible — but at the same time to contain the fleshy portions so that they cannot be deformed by the force. Recent studies have also shown that increased tolerance will be obtained by the use of positive pressure-breathing.

Experimental use of water immersion techniques have also demonstrated remarkable increases in g tolerance — as yet, however, not for practical purposes.

Where critical g levels are anticipated, use auditory rather than visual signals. Reaction time to auditory signals is shorter, and they can often be heard even after the subject has begun to black out.

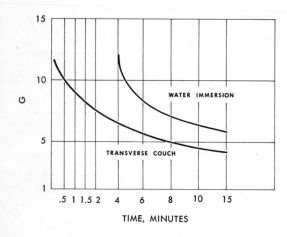

As one would expect, g forces restrict the ease with which a person can move his arms, legs, head, etc. For example, he cannot move his head away from the headrest if more than 4 g are acting against his head, or he can't raise an arm off the armrest if more than 8 g are acting against the arm. He can't raise a leg against more than about 3 g, although he can still perform limited wrist motion even against 25 g. Armrests and controls should be placed very close to the operating position if extreme forces are expected.

In addition to the typical g forces just discussed, another force problem is faced which creates physical difficulties for the human operator. This is called Coriolis — which is the component of force present whenever movement takes place within a rotating vehicle. A typical case in point might occur in a rotating space station, the rotation being provided to create artificial gravity.

In such a case, the Coriolis force will affect the occupants of the space station differently, depending upon the direction in which they are moving, and also their distance from the hub of the spin axis.

If a vehicle had a 20-foot radius and was spinning to simulate a 1.0-g field, a 150-lb man climbing a ladder from the periphery of the station to the hub at 3.5 ft/sec would experience a 41-lb. force, which is in the same direction as that of the rotation.

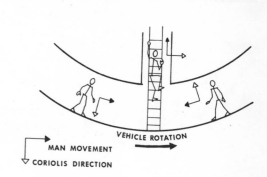

VEHICLE ROTATION

MAN MOVEMENT

CORIOLIS DIRECTION

In the illustrations below are shown typical design considerations to overcome deleterious effects of Coriolis.

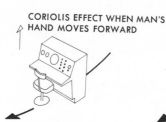

CORIOLIS EFFECT WHEN MAN'S HAND MOVES FORWARD

LOCATE CONSOLE ATHWARTSHIP SO THAT TYPICAL LATERAL HAND MOVEMENT ISN'T DISTURBED

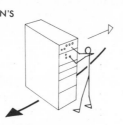

LOCATE TALL RACKS SO THAT ACTION OF PULLING OUT CHASSIS ISN'T INFLUENCED BY CORIOLIS

LOCATE PLANE OF LADDER SO THAT CORIOLIS WON'T THROW MAN BACKWARD

IF BUNK IS ORIENTED WITH FOOT TOWARD DIRECTION OF ROTATION, OCCUPANT CAN RAISE UP OUT OF BED EASIER

SUBGRAVITY AND WEIGHTLESSNESS

In the weightless environment, all loose objects, including man, "float"! Once an object is put in motion, it will continue that motion until it is deliberately stopped, either by some propelling device or mechanical restraint, or because it strikes another object. The designer must consider the problems created by this phenomenon and provide methods for attenuating the ill effects which may occur. Although brief moments of weightlessness occur in certain types of aircraft maneuvers, the most difficult problems occur in space operations. The following list of typical problems pertains to space-vehicle design:

PROBLEM AREAS IN THE WEIGHTLESS STATE

Without special propulsion or restraint devices, a man cannot move himself from one point to another except by "shoving off" from a solid surface. Alternately, he cannot stop himself except by bumping into another solid surface. If he does not have something to hold on to at the stopping point, he may continue to bounce from one solid surface to another.

Once in a "floating state," a man may induce a tumbling motion in his body which he cannot correct or stop without special propulsion or stabilization devices — or by striking or holding on to solid surfaces.

If men are outside the parent space vehicle, they must be tethered to the vehicle at all times!

It is possible for a man to become suspended (out of reach of any solid object or surface) so that he cannot move himself at all!

If a man should get himself into an uncontrolled tumbling state, he will be subject to severe sensory and cognitive disorientation (and probably nausea) and be unable to function satisfactorily even after tumbling has stopped unless the tumbling can be halted almost immediately after it begins.

Uncontrolled motion of a man leads to probability of his striking other objects (often quite hard) and causing injury to himself or damage to his protective garments or to equipment. Puncturing or tearing of protective garments may expose the man to even greater hazards.

DESIGN SUGGESTIONS

Cabin configuration should be sufficiently small that crew members are within reach of some solid object or surface, or they should be provided with some means for preventing their becoming hopelessly suspended in the middle of the compartment. Provide a safety line or a portable propulsion device if necessary.

All solid objects such as bulkheads, consoles, seats, etc., should be free of sharp corners or projections which are unguarded. All controls, switches, handles, etc., should be inset in wall or panel surfaces so that they cannot be struck accidentally. When controls are inset, sufficient clearance must be provided for access and operation with pressurized gloves.

Handrails and handholds should be provided at strategic points throughout the space vehicle to aid the astronaut in maneuvering his body and also for stabilizing himself for applying force on controls, etc. Tools which apply torque should be designed with a method for stabilizing the tool, so that the man's turning motion won't cause him to rotate instead of the tool. The motion loop must be closed at both ends of the tool!

All objects which we normally expect to lie on a horizontal surface in the 1-g gravity state must be secured; otherwise they will float. Consider such items as pencils, papers, books, communication and oxygen lines, etc.

Seat belts should be provided on all seats. Straps or coverlets should be provided on all bunks or beds. If a man is expected to apply large forces to a control while standing, he should have foot stirrups on the floor, spaced about 12 to 14 inches apart.

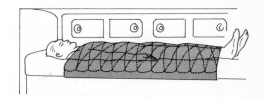

Provide "squeeze" containers for all liquid or semi-liquid foods and water for drinking.

Facilities for personal washing, such as sinks and showers, should be designed so that the water is always captive.

Provide methods for capturing such debris as dust, dirt, whiskers, etc., so that they cannot drift into the environmental system of the space vehicle.

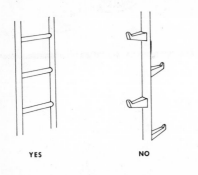

YES   NO

Ladders which may be installed in space vehicles to aid in boarding on the earth's surface may not necessarily be appropriate for assisting crewmen in the weightless environment in space. Make sure there are no "open" rungs which can snag clothing or personal equipment, or which could puncture the man or his equipment.

All hatches and equipment doors should have provisions for securing in the open position as well as for closing.

All storage areas should be designed so that their contents are held captive within the area and cannot "float" out of a cabinet or drawer.

radiation

Human beings should not be exposed to certain types of radiation for very long. The recommended exposure limit for microwave radiation which would be typical of radar installations should not exceed 0.01 milliwatts/cm² per working day. Layout of such installations must preclude exposure of personnel as much as possible by routing them away from the hazard or providing barrier protection.

Manned space vehicles must be constructed in such a way that personnel are protected from ionizing radiation. Maximum exposure limits are shown below.

MAXIMUM IONIZATION RADIATION EXPOSURE LIMITS[30]

IONIZING RADIATION OF ANY TYPE, OR COMBINATION OF TYPES	PERMISSIBLE REM[a] PER CALENDAR QUARTER (WITHOUT COMPLETE MEDICAL HISTORY)[b]
Whole body	1.25
Head, trunk, blood-forming organs, eye-lens, and gonads	1.25
Body extremities	18.75
Skin	7.50
Acute accidental single exposure (either internal or external to the body)	25.0 (or more in extreme cases)

[a]REM = Roentgen equivalent(s), man.

[b]If a medical record is available, a higher exposure, 80 per cent of the limit in effect, is permissible: 3/REM/quarter, provided no more than 5 ($n-18$) REM total accumulated dosage has been met (where n is the age of the subject).

SHIELDING RECOMMENDATIONS FOR IONIZATION
RADIATION PROTECTION[30]

RADIATION TYPE	RANGE OF RAYS IN AIR	SHIELD MATERIAL	
		TYPE	THICKNESS
Alpha particles (4 million electron volts)	2.8 cm	Aluminum sheet Paper Ordinary clothing	1/64 inch 1/64 inch 1/64 inch
Beta particles (3 million electron volts)	13.0 meters	Lead Aluminum Pyrex Lucite Water	1.4 mm 5.3 mm 6.6 mm 12.4 mm 14.8 mm
Gamma rays (4 million electron volts)		Shielding is accomplished by reducing intensity of incident gamma radiation by scattering interactions within a shield (probability of completely absorbing the nuclei of atoms in a shield is slight). Thickness of material required to reduce radiation to one half is called the half-value layer. Half-value layers for typical materials are: Lead 0.3 inch Iron 0.5 inch Aluminum 2.7 inch Concrete 2.7 inch Water 8.3 inch	
Neutrons		Since gamma radiation is produced in the process of neutron attenuation, shielding against neutrons should also include shielding against gamma radiation. An effective material is cement mixed with iron shot. However, beryllium-lithium combinations are best for lightweight applications, such as in aircraft, space craft, or remote handling equipment.	

fatigue

Fatigue is a complex factor which includes actual physiological changes in the body, a resulting feeling of weariness in the individual, and lowered efficiency in his performance of tasks. The most effective ways to combat fatigue are: (1) provide adequate caloric input for the body, (2) simplify the task (i.e., keep motions simple, distribute the load between hands or hands and feet), (3) keep force requirements well below tolerance limits, (4) reduce the number of distracting influences (i.e., noise, vibration), (5) maintain an optimum physical environment (i.e., in temperature, humidity, ventilation, acceleration, pressure, etc.) and (6) provide adequate rest periods.

Average intake requirement in calories per day:

For sedentary activities, 2400

Light manual labor, 2700

Medium manual labor, 3000

Heavy manual labor, 3600

Type of work determines the length of time an operator can efficiently perform his duties.

Description of Work	RECOMMENDED TIME LIMITS
Task which requires low level motor skills, is highly repetitive and devoid of critical decisions	Up to 12 hours
Highly redundant task using standard procedures, moderate responsibility, and limited manual precision	Up to 8 hours
Heavy, continuous physical labor interspersed with suitable recess	Up to 6 hours
Fairly responsible, decision-making task on a continuous, but random basis	Up to 4 hours
Critical, but monotonous vigilance task	Up to 2 hours
Extremely accurate motor skill with critical reaction time — no time to relax	Up to 30 minutes

NOTE: The time limits suggested above are subject to variations including proper insertion of rest periods or changes in task routines. Work-rest cycles are normally based on a 24-hour day, and as such will reflect variations during this period. It is important to consider the normal variations in planning critical tasks; i.e., efficiency normally drops off about 10 o'clock in the forenoon, and once again in midafternoon, followed by an end spurt just before the worker knows his work period is over. Although we are normally oriented to an 8-hour workday, with 8 hours for sleep, people can adapt to other cycles quite easily.

PASSENGER DENSITIES VS TRIP DURATION[31]

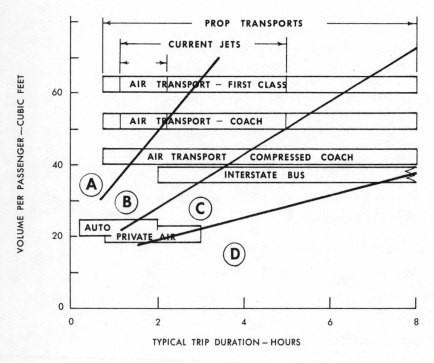

A PLUSH

B COMFORTABLE

C CONFINED

D RUGGED

One of the many factors which contribute to fatigue may be found in the space provided for passengers in transportation vehicles. In the illustration above, an estimate of volume per passenger vs duration of exposure has been estimated. Such estimates are based upon experience rather than on the basis of research evidence. One major aircraft manufacturer uses the following typical standards: nominal design compartment-volume per passenger, 50.5 cubic feet; compartment contents proportioned 77.5 per cent for seating, 3 per cent for door aisles, 6 per cent for coatracks, and 7.5 per cent for buffets; seat spacing between seat rows, 38 inches.

WORK PROGRAMMING is an essential consideration in minimizing potential fatigue build-up. Although most persons are conditioned to a normal 8-hour workday, with the rest of the 24-hour cycle devoted to a combination of rest and recreation, it is perfectly feasible to create other work-rest cycles which maintain useful work levels.

With the advent of space travel, the normal day-night cycle has been speeded up to the point that it has little if any bearing on the regulation of work and rest periods. Man can adapt himself to a diurnal cycle within the range of 18 to 28 hours. Within the range, the human body-temperature curve adjusts satisfactorily. In the illustration below are shown different possibilities for work-rest scheduling.

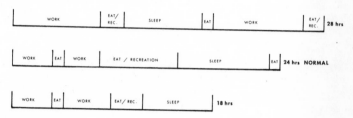

Some of the factors to consider in creating work-rest cycles for multi-crew systems include the following:

Don't plan for a man to step into a work period directly from the sleep period.

There should be an overlap for changes of duty crew-members.

Operator efficiency is at a low ebb, for about an hour after eating — owing to the energy required for digestion.

Owing to the nature of some emergency hazards and the duties associated with overcoming the emergency, it may be necessary to stagger sleep periods so that more than one crew member is awake at the same time.

If rest and duty areas cannot be isolated, plan the length of sleep time to allow for difficulty in getting to sleep.

Minimum sleep duration should be at least 6 hours.

Maximum time without sleep for emergency conditions should not exceed 36 hours.

Plan the cycle so that crew members who expect to perform critical tasks at a particular time will have had sufficient rest just before this event (e.g., landing an aircraft or preparing for re-entry of a space vehicle).

Lifting and carrying heavy packages is fatiguing, and may be injurious. The recommended weight limits illustrated below and opposite take into account not only the height to which the package is lifted, but the size and shape of the package. These weights are not necessarily the maximums which could be lifted. Rather, they are weights which could be lifted by the average man over and over again — typical of actual working conditions. It should be noted that these packages do not have handles, and they are assumed to be well balanced.

RECOMMENDED WEIGHT LIMITS FOR PACKAGE DESIGN

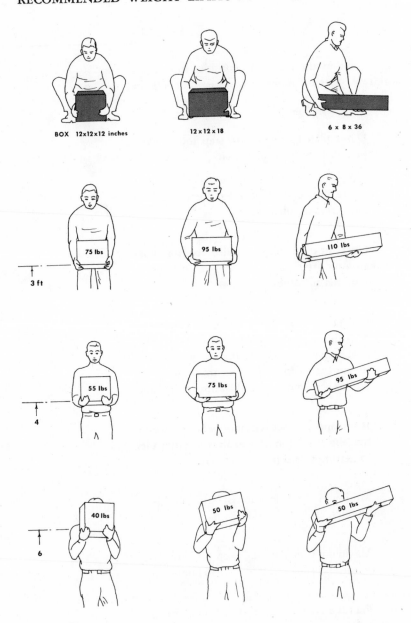

BOX 12x12x12 inches   12 x 12 x 18   6 x 8 x 36

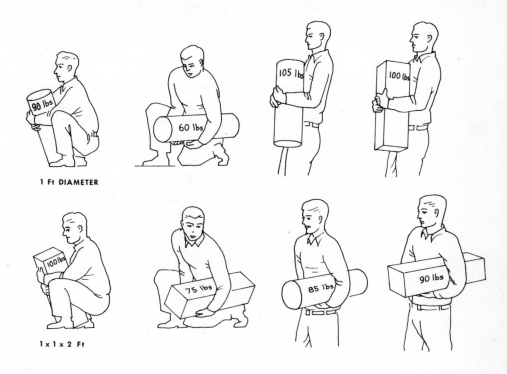

1 Ft DIAMETER

1 x 1 x 2 Ft

Don't *"create"* fatiguing tasks!

Consider the position the operator will have to assume in order to perform the operation or task. If the operator or technician has to hold his hands above his head for any length of time, he will become extremely fatigued.

If he has to crouch, bend, or squat, he will soon become stiff, and this will contribute to his becoming less efficient.

If an operator has to hold a heavy weight while performing a precision operation, (e.g., supporting the weight of a heavy component which he is trying to connect to critical pins or leads), the stress of the combined task becomes quite fatiguing and he is apt to commit an error.

Design the operator's task so that he does not have to perform a continuous reaching movement. This type of operation causes fatigue both from the stress of reaching and the strain of maintaining body balance.

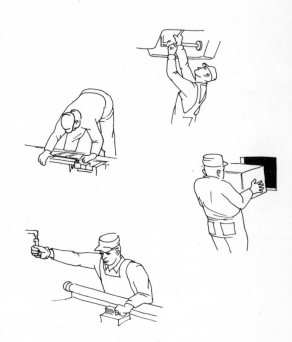

design for safety

It has often been said, "Safety is everybody's business." Another often quoted statement, referred to as "Murphy's Law," is: "If it is possible for it to be done wrong, someone will do it sooner or later." Every designer should take it upon himself to create designs (and tasks) which do not lead to accidents, personal injury, or damage to equipment. The following check list is provided as a reminder of some of those things which are most often responsible for personnel injury.

SAFETY HAZARD CHECK LIST FOR DESIGNERS

STUMBLING OR TRIPPING — This type of hazard is caused by allowing objects to be placed in the direct path of people. It is amplified when illumination is poor, or people have to traverse the pathway with their arms loaded with equipment, or they have to hurry through the area.

SLIPPING — Surfaces which are highly polished or become very slick when wet, and areas subject to oil drippings, etc., invite disaster!

BUMPING THE HEAD can be caused by low overhead or objects which have been placed too low. If low overheads or equipment cannot be avoided, these should be well marked, padded, and illuminated. Personnel should wear protective headgear. Another type of head injury comes from things being dropped from above. Screens should be provided to catch falling objects — or in the case where construction is underway, hard hats should be worn by all personnel in the area.

BUMPING SHARP CORNERS OR EDGES — All projecting corners or edges should be eliminated from equipment if there is any chance of a person's body coming in contact with the equipment. If the projections cannot be removed or the corners radiused, these should be padded to reduce the possibility of injury.

SNAGGING — Catching the body or clothing on parts of equipment or metal trim may cause injury directly or even indirectly if the person is momentarily thrown off balance and into some even more dangerous situation.

ELECTRICITY — Burns or even death may result from the human body shorting across uncovered electrical leads. One must consider not only the insulation of wiring and electrical parts, but also other metal surfaces and floor. Special care should be taken to anticipate the possibility of liquids falling on wiring, thus causing shorts. Even a light electrical shock could cause a person to react in such a way as to injure himself in jumping back from the shock point and striking other equipment, or falling off a work stand.

BURNS from hot metal, glass, liquid, steam, air, or acid should be anticipated in the design of all equipment and work stations.

PINCHING OR MASHING — Anticipate the possibilities of the worker or user catching his hand in a door, or between a chassis and cabinet, or letting a heavy component down on fingers because of lack of adequate handles. Even tools and the location of tool attachments must be considered in their potential for pinching fingers, cracking knuckles, etc.

FALLING — When there is a possibility of causing a worker or operator to lose his balance because of equipment motion, it is the responsibility of the designer to provide security against this — guard rails, safety belts, handholds, non-slip flooring, etc.

ACCELERATION — Acceleration, deceleration, impact shock, and oscillation are all considerations which the designer must face. These should be limited to the ranges which can be withstood by human beings. Seats should be provided which distribute loads. Restraints should be provided to stabilize the body. Absorption materials should be provided to attenuate the transmitted energy.

NOISE — Deafness-avoidance criteria must be adhered to in all cases. In addition, noise may lead to a worker not hearing another safety signal, or the eventual fatigue produced by continuous noise may lead to increased carelessness.

BRIGHT LIGHT — Flash blindness is a consideration in certain military operations. In addition, temporary blindness from a bright light may cause the operator to miss other important signals which lead to even more hazardous conditions. The nuclear age has also introduced the problem of retinal burns from rockets, nuclear explosions, etc.

TOXIC SUBSTANCES — Materials or substances which are toxic to the skin or through chemical reaction create fumes which may be poisonous must be avoided.

ATMOSPHERE AND PRESSURE — Not only should these environmental conditions be maintained within normal human tolerance ranges, but due consideration must be given to the potential hazard of such conditions being borderline — causing a reduction in human efficiency and leading to the man endangering his own life because of poor reaction to operating conditions.

TEMPERATURE — Hot or cold environments as well as hot or cold materials are hazards which must be anticipated and guarded against in design. Sweat on the hand may lead to an accident. Stiffness in the fingers may cause a man to drop a tool or component.

PHYSICAL STRAIN — Lifting a component which is too heavy can cause a rupture, or cause the operator to drop the item on his fingers or foot.

RADIATION — Protection from electromagnetic and particulate ionizing radiation is important not only in space, but also in design and location of radar equipment.

EXPLOSION AND FIRE — Although these hazards are among the most common, too many designers give too little thought to the cause and prevention of such hazards.

NOTE: All designers should perform a complete hazard analysis of each design problem to determine all safety hazard possibilities — and then take steps to design these hazards out of their hardware!

SAFETY CONSIDERATIONS FOR SPECIFIC DESIGN APPLICATIONS

HOMES

Controls for heaters, stoves, etc., should be located or designed so that small children cannot turn them on.

Sufficient landing area should be provided at the head of a stairway so that no one can inadvertently step through a door and miss the stairs.

All heating units should be located, insulated, or guarded so that small children (or adults, for that matter) cannot touch hot surfaces.

Sufficient illumination should be provided in all hallways, stair wells, and door thresholds so that people will not stumble because they cannot see.

Overhead clearance in stair wells must be sufficient to prevent people from bumping their heads. This also applies to cabinets — especially over serving tables.

All swinging doors should have observation windows so that people approaching the door can see another person approaching from the other side.

All outside doors should open to the outside. Inside doors should not open into passageways.

Handrails should be provided on all stairways.

All staircases should be designed to recommended rise and tread dimensions to minimize stumbling.

All electrical outlets or switches should be located far enough from showers or bathtubs so that occupants cannot reach the switches while standing in the shower or tub.

Water heaters should be located so that, in the event of leakage, water will not flood the house — and especially not get to any electrical wiring. All water heaters should have automatic shutoffs to isolate gas or electric input to the heater.

Where garages are attached to the house, fire-retardant walls and doors should be provided.

Floor heating vents should be insulated so that persons with bare feet will not be burned walking across them.

Fluorescent light fixtures must be protected from accidental breakage.

Sharp corners on cabinetry should be avoided, especially where it is exposed in a passageway or immediately adjacent to a doorway.

Window glass may focus and concentrate sunlight to cause spontaneous combustion. Locate windows to avoid such possibilities or provide protection by means of roof overhang, etc.

Provide sufficient clearance between doors and adjacent passageway walls so that people cannot be caught between the opened door and the wall.

Provide handles on sliding doors so that people won't pinch their hands when closing the doors.

Avoid use of flooring materials which become slippery when wet — or provide suitable non-skid materials on top of the regular material.

INDUSTRIAL FACILITIES

Provide guard rails or other protective devices around dangerous (moving) machinery, fabrication areas, moving vehicles, etc. Apply appropriate color codes for these and associated safety and emergency equipment.

Provide safety shutoff controls — located in the most accessible position — for all hazardous machinery and equipment.

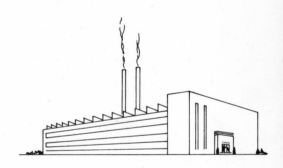

Provide good "seeing conditions," such as highly reflecting ceilings, walls, floor, workbenches, etc., with proper illumination levels of diffused light. Use standard color coding of tools, machinery, fixtures, safety devices, signs, instructions, labels.

Provide suitable lifting and carrying devices to minimize chance of workers lifting materials or components which are too heavy.

Provide protective eye shields and clothing where flying particles are apt to injure workers.

Provide suitable containers for explosive, combustible chemical-material storage or waste disposal.

Provide emergency stations at strategic points to provide first aid to injured workers.

Provide visual and aural warning systems for hazardous work areas.

Provide suitable emergency equipment for fighting fire or taking care of chemical or radiation accidents.

Provide suitable flooring for isolation of the worker from electrical shock, vibration, collection of chemical or liquid spillage, etc.

Incorporate self-locking or other fool-proof devices on elevating stands and work platforms to prevent inadvertent collapse.

Design work stands so that they have a low center of gravity or can be anchored securely against tipping.

Provide guard rails around all floor openings or raised work areas.

Provide for flushing or neutralizing harmful materials which may be spilled.

Provide adequate signs for identifying and instructing: i.e., weight or capacity, jack points, pipeline or container contents, high voltage, very hot or cold surfaces or materials, "No Smoking," "Explosives," "Radiation," etc.

Design fixtures and jigs in such a way that head bumping, clothing snagging, or bumping into sharp corners or edges is minimized.

Provide adequate ventilation and exhaust systems in all areas subject to considerable dust or fumes.

Lay out all work areas in such a manner that personnel can evacuate the area quickly and safely.

GROUND VEHICLES

Provide maximum possible unobstructed visibility in all directions for the vehicle operator.

Place all normal and emergency operating controls within reach so that the operator does not have to leave his normal eye-reference position for "seeing out" of the vehicle. This should include auxiliary items such as ashtrays, cigar lighters, and radio controls.

Arrange controls or code them in such manner that the operator will not select the wrong control accidentally.

Eliminate, rearrange, or inset, all controls or other protruding devices to prevent the operator or passengers from bumping into them or snagging a coat sleeve on them at any time — both under normal or emergency conditions. This includes door and window handles, handles to glove compartments, etc.

Avoid use of materials which will shatter or break off (leaving sharp edges) in the event of an accident.

Use only non-combustible or fire-retardant materials in the construction or finishing of the vehicle.

Provide adequate grounding for all electrical wiring and components.

Provide fire barriers between power plant and fuel tanks and passenger compartments.

Design door frames and door fastenings so that doors will not open accidentally (consider frame distortion in event of accident), and so that occupants can always open doors to get out quickly in an emergency.

Provide energy-absorbing materials on all surfaces which may be struck by occupants in the event of a sudden stop or an accident. Consider the possibility of the vehicle rolling over.

Provide restraining devices for occupants — i.e., seat belts and shoulder harness (securely fastened to the primary vehicle frame).

Provide clearance for feet, knees, head. For example, legs have been broken because they slid beneath the seat in front of the occupant, or knees have been crushed under a low dashboard.

Seats must be anchored securely against inadvertent movement during sudden stops. All adjustments on seats should be designed so that they will not become disengaged accidentally.

Provide easily accessible hand fire-extinguishers.

Provide turn signals (both inside and out). There should be some means of telling from the inside of the vehicle when the signal lights are burned out.

There should be an indication inside the vehicle when other exterior lights are burned out — particularly headlights and taillights.

Provide some warning indicator to let the driver know when a door is not securely closed.

Provide safety door-locks to prevent small children from inadvertently opening the doors.

Design the steering wheel so that the driver cannot be impaled on it in the event of a crash.

Provide door stops to hold doors open while passengers get into or out of the vehicle — to prevent a door falling shut on a leg or arm.

Locate all operating displays so that the operator doesn't have to take his eyes too far from his view of the road, and so that his view is not obstructed by the steering wheel or other controls. Instruments should also be arranged so as not to reflect on the windshield at night and so that daylight sun does not mask the display, making it unreadable.

Be sure there is no brightwork in the field of view of the operator, which could reflect sunlight and cause temporary blindness.

Provide a windshield clearing system which is extremely reliable and easy to maintain. Windshield wiper systems which vary in speed owing to motor pull should be avoided.

Design "ease of maintenance" into the vehicle to minimize chance of poor servicing, inadequate inspection, or lack of thoroughness owing to difficulty in performing maintenance, service, or repair.

Provide tire-changing equipment which minimizes the possibility of the vehicle falling on the person trying to change the tire.

All vehicle surfaces, edges, trim, etc., should be designed so that a person working on the vehicle (cleaning, repairing, servicing, etc.) cannot snag or cut himself.

GROUND-SUPPORT TRAILERS

When internal combustion engines are part of the equipment, route exhausts to prevent accumulation of carbon monoxide in areas occupied by personnel.

Provide ventilation in enclosures of 35 to 40 cubic feet per minute.

Provide cross-ventilation in vans or trailers containing test equipment, particularly if the equipment gives off heat.

When equipment may involve exposure of personnel to dangerous gases, provide warning signals to indicate when dangerous concentration is approaching.

Use materials that do not produce hazardous environments under severe operating conditions — lead, cadmium, polytetrafluoroethylene, etc. Other materials may liberate substances which are, or may combine with the atmosphere to become, combustible or corrosive.

Point exhaust pipes of internal combustion engines upward to lessen danger of igniting flammable liquids which could have collected on the ground or floor.

Provide warning lights to indicate fire or excessive heat in areas which may not be visible to the driver of the vehicle.

Provide suitable fire extinguishers in the driver's compartment in a quickly accessible place. Similar extinguishers should also be available in the trailer.

Locate away from exhaust pipes any fabrics or insulating materials which are susceptible to oil soaking.

Route fuel, hydraulic, or any other lines containing flammable fluids away from hot exhaust pipes.

Attach flame arresters on exhaust when the vehicle may be operated in areas where flammable or explosive vapors and fumes might collect.

Equip trailers with electrical "breakaway" brakes which function automatically in the event the trailer begins to roll on a slope.

Provide insulation on tool handles which may be used near voltages in excess of 50 volts.

Provide tools which are spark resistant if they are to be used in areas subject to fire or explosion hazards.

All doors of trailers which may be occupied should be openable from inside as well as out.

All trailers should have braking systems of their own—operable from the prime-mover driver's position.

Warning indicators should be provided in the prime-mover's cab to notify him of any safety hazard occurring in the trailer while moving on the road. These might include fire, excessive sway, etc.

Air conditioning should be provided in trailers (occupied by personnel) used in extremely hot climate.

Adequate heating should be provided in trailers (occupied by personnel) used in extremely cold climates.

AIRCRAFT

PILOT COMPARTMENT:

Provide maximum possible outside visibility.

Locate all in-flight operating controls within easy reach so that the pilot's eyes do not shift from the basic eye-reference point when he moves to reach for a control.

Arrange controls so that they cannot be inadvertently dislodged, or so that they do not obstruct visibility of critical instruments or displays.

Arrange all visual displays so that they can be seen from the pilot's normal position. Provide maximum legibility for the expected viewing distance and eliminate all possible ambiguities of reading or interpretation.

Make sure all control motions are compatible with the expected response of the aircraft and displays, and with the functional response of other informational devices.

Provide optimum feedback from all control actions.

Provide adequate seating and restraint for the support and safety of the crew — including appropriate escape facilities.

Provide a reliable environmental system with emergency backup.

Provide adequate windshield clearing and defogging systems.

Delethalize cockpit interior to minimize crew injury in event of crash.

Provide adequate exits for ground escape.

Provide survival equipment, clothing, and rations for appropriate military aircraft on overseas missions.

Provide adequate illumination in the cockpit — consider the problems of reflection on windshields at night, as well as sunlight reflection on instrument faces in daylight.

Arrange seats and control consoles for easy ingress and egress to all work stations. Consider particularly the possibility of snagging clothing, thus throwing the person off balance and into another crew member or causing him to dislodge a critical flight control.

PASSENGER COMPARTMENT:

Provide seats and restraints which will minimize crash injury for both passengers and stewardesses. Emphasis should be placed on secure tiedowns which cannot break loose upon impact, and energy-absorbing materials to prevent puncture wounds.

Provide adequate illumination for both normal and emergency movement of personnel — in the cabin generally, at exits, on escape chutes and survival and fire-fighting equipment.

Provide sufficient number of strategically located exits to allow all occupants to deplane in the minimum time. Design exit-opening devices so that they are foolproof. Consider all potential conditions and positions of the aircraft at the time of ditching.

Provide escape devices and equipment for both land and water ditching. Consider all conditions and positions of the aircraft at the time of ditching.

Provide storage of emergency equipment which is easily identifiable and available to all occupants (passengers as well as crew).

Provide reliable emergency environmental systems — oxygen, pressure, lights, etc.

Provide adequate tie-down systems for cargo to prevent shifting or breaking loose.

Don't design accessories, trim, or other devices in such a manner that they can break loose in event of rough weather or crash landing.

Design buffet facilities and lavatory equipment so that nothing can break loose in flight or during crash landing.

Choose or treat all interior materials for fire resistance.

GENERAL:

Exterior running lights should be designed and located to maximize conspicuousness of the aircraft at night.

Provide taxi, landing, and inspection lights which maximize pilot's ability to perform all phases of night operations safely (take precaution against annoying or blinding back-scatter and glare).

Provide complete fail-safe warning systems which will give maximum chance for recovery from such emergencies as engine fire or failure, landing-gear malfunction, unsecured hatchets or doors, cabin-pressure loss, etc. (Consider ordnance equipment for military aircraft.)

Provide adequate electrical grounding for both airborne and ground servicing.

Consider all hazards to maintenance personnel: i.e., protection from sharp corners on wings, empennage, and fuselage, and possibility of power-controlled doors closing accidentally, explosion of tires, rupture of high-pressure lines, landing-gear collapse, ingestion into jet intakes, being struck by propellers, etc.

MISSILE BASES

Use conspicuous placards to indicate high voltage, extremely cold or very hot equipment, etc.

For operation of switches or controls which initiate hazardous operations, such as ignition, crane moving, etc., provide for the prior operation of a related or a locking control. Where practicable, the critical position of such controls should activate a warning device in the affected area.

A hazard alerting device should be provided to warn personnel of impending or existing hazards (fire, presence of combustible or asphyxiating gas, radiation, etc.).

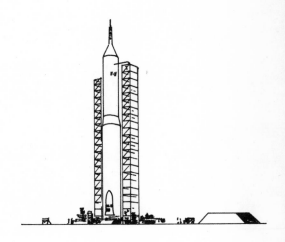

Provide a guard on all moving parts of machinery and transmission equipment, including pulleys, belts, gears, blades, etc., in which personnel may become injured or entangled.

Incorporate self-locking or other foolproof devices on elevating stands and work platforms to prevent accidental or inadvertent collapse.

Employ some form of anchor or outriggers on stands with high centers of gravity.

When applicable, distinctly mark the center of gravity of equipment.

Provide handrails on platforms and stairs, and around floor openings or wherever personnel may fall from an elevation.

Provide automatic shutoff devices on fuel service equipment to prevent overflow and spillage.

Provide portable hand-operated fire extinguishers in areas where fire hazards exist or may be created.

Design all emergency doors and exits so that they are readily accessible, unobstructed and quick-opening. Design the door or hatch to open by a single motion of hand or foot.

Eye baths, showers, and other first-aid equipment should be readily available in areas where toxic materials are handled.

Provide for neutralization or flushing of harmful materials spilled on equipment or personnel.

Specifically identify areas of operation or maintenance requiring special protective clothing, tools, or equipment such as insulated shoes, gloves, or suits, or non-sparking tools. Appropriate action should be taken to insure the availability of such items concurrently with the complete development of the hardware, and storage facilities which must be provided for them.

Incorporate "No Step" markings where applicable.

Indicate weight capacity on stands, hoists, lifts, jacks, and similar weight-bearing equipment to prevent overloading.

Jacking and hoisting points should be conspicuously and unambiguously identified.

Wiring should be routed through plugs and connectors so that removal of a plug or connector does not expose hot leads.

Insure that all pipelines — liquid, gas, steam, etc. — are clearly and unambiguously labeled or coded as to contents, including any specific hazard properties.

ISOLATED MILITARY STATIONS

Provide emergency power systems to prevent any interruption of operations.

Design station quarters so that each element can be isolated in event of fire.

Provide warning system to alert all personnel — regardless of where they are located.

SHIPS

Provide compartmental isolation to contain and control fire, explosion, flooding, etc.

Provide auxiliary power.

Provide guard rails on all open deck areas traversed by personnel.

Provide warning systems both for on-board personnel and for alerting adjacent vessels.

Provide escape systems for abandoning ship. Include survival equipment: food, water, communications gear, foul-weather clothing, sun-protection equipment, first-aid supplies, flashlight, signal lights, etc.

Design all overhead (including hung equipment and piping) facilities so that personnel will not strike their heads. Where this is not possible, make sure such areas are well marked, illuminated, and where possible, padded. NOTE: Warning signs must be seen "in time"!

Provide non-skid material on all decking, stairs, and ladders which are subject to becoming wet and slippery.

Hatch doors should be designed so that they can be held open mechanically (even in heavy seas) and will not slam shut on personnel trying to go through.

Helmsman's position should be located such that he has unobstructed view in all directions whenever possible. On large vessels where this may be impossible, there should be auxiliary stations where other personnel can observe the areas not seen by the helmsman or skipper. Adequate communication (including backup system) must be available between stations.

SPACE VEHICLES AND STATIONS

Design environmental system (including backup) to maintain normal earth-bound environment. Provide instantaneous warning of failure of any element.

Provide continuous biomonitoring of all occupants.

Provide adequate seating and restraints for attentuation of access accelerations during launch, re-entry, landing, tumbling, etc.

To overcome problems of weightlessness, provide "assist" devices (handholds and footholds), eliminate sharp corners and edges, imbed protruding controls, etc.

Consider Coriolis effects on human locomotion and dexterity (in case of a rotating, artificial g station).

Provide adequate protection from solar flare radiation.

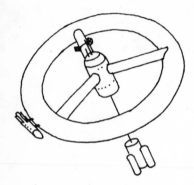

Provide quick and simple detection and location system for meteoroid punctures.

Provide eye protection at all windows from direct sunlight.

Provide adequate escape and survival system for all conditions to be encountered: space, airborne, water, land, etc.

Provide safety lines for all personnel performing outside the space vehicle or station.

Provide compartmental isolation in the event of fire, explosion, pressure loss, etc.

Provide independent power systems to maintain uninterrupted operation of any part of the vehicle or station left intact in the event of a partial accident or station damage.

HOSPITALS

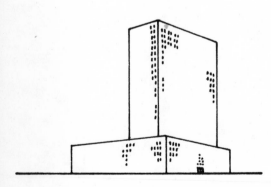

Provide emergency power source (independent of the primary power system).

Provide emergency illumination in critical areas (i.e., operating rooms, etc.).

Provide compartmental or area isolation in the event of fire or other disaster.

Provide for emergency evacuation of non-ambulatory patients.

Handrails should be provided in all passageways, stairs, etc.

All floor materials should be such that they cannot become slippery through use of polishes or waxes.

Sharp corners or edges and protruding cabinets or equipment should be avoided in design or equipping of hospitals.

SAFETY

RESPIRATION SAFETY RECOMMENDATIONS

MAXIMUM ALLOWABLE CONCENTRATION OF COMMON GASES, VAPORS, DUSTS, AND FUMES IN THE BREATHING ATMOSPHERE[32,33]

Dusts:[a]

Asbestos	5.0
Cement	15.0
Organic	50.0
Silica	
above 50% free SiO_2	5.0
5 to 50% free SiO_2	20.0
below 5% free SiO_2	50.0
Pottery	4.0
Silicon carbide	50.0
Mica	
below 5% free SiO_2	20.0
Soapstone	
below 5% free SiO_2	20.0
Slate	15.0
Portland cement	50.0
Talc	20.0
Nuisance dust	50.0

Gases and vapors:[b]

Acetone	1000.0
Ammonia, anhydrous	100.0
Amyl acetate	200.0
Amyl alcohol	100.0
Analine	5.0
Arsine	1.0
Benzene (benzol)	25.0
Butenol	50.0
Butyl acetate	20.0
Carbon disulfide	20.0
Carbon dioxide	5000.0
Carbon monoxide	100.0
Carbon tetrachloride	25.0
Chlorine	1.0
Chlorine trifluoride	0.1
Chloroform	100.0
Dichlorobenzene	50.0
Dichlorethyl ether	15.0
Ether (ethyl)	400.0
Ethyl alcohol	1000.0
Ethyl bromide	1700.0
Ethyl chloride	70.0
Ethylene dichloride	100.0
Ethylene oxide	50.0

Fluorine	0.1
Formaldehyde	20.0
Gasoline	500.0
Hydrochloric acid	10.0
Hydrogen chloride	5.0
Hydrogen cyanide	20.0
Hydrogen fluoride	3.0
Hydrogen peroxide	1.0
Hydrogen sulfide	20.0
Methyl alcohol (methanol)	200.0
Methyl bromide	30.0
Methyl chloride	500.0
Monochlorbenzine	75.0
Naptha (coal tar)	200.0
Naptha (petroleum)	500.0
Nitric acid (fuming)	5.0
Nitrobenzene	5.0
Nitrogen dioxide	5.0
Ozone	0.1
Phosgene	1.0
Phosphine	0.05
Phosphorus trichloride	1.0
Propyl alcohol (isopropyl alcohol)	400.0
Sulfur dioxide	5.0
Tetrachlorethane	10.0
Tetrachlorethylene	200.0
Toluol	200.0
Trichlorethylene	200.0
Turpentine	100.0
Xylol (coal-tar naptha)	100.0

Metallic dusts and fumes:[c]

Aluminum oxide	50.0
Cadmium	0.1
Chromic acid	0.1
Lead (or lead compounds)	0.15
Manganese	6.0
Mercury	0.1
Zinc oxide	15.0
Chlorodiphenyl	1.0

Smoke:

40% density (i.e., 60% light visible through it)

[a] Dusts: million parts per cubic foot. [b] Gases and vapors: parts per million. [c] Metallic dusts and fumes: milligrams per cubic meter.

2-263

references

1. Lichtenstein, M., and Woodson, W. E. *A Human Engineering Evaluation of an Experimental Dial Index Design* (Navy Electronics Laboratory, Internal Technical Memorandum no. 94) 27 July 1953.

2. Baker, C. A., and Grether, W. F. *Visual Presentation of Information* (Air Force. Wright Air Development Center, Technical Report no. 54-160) 1954.

3. Bowen, H. M. *et al. Optimum Symbols for Radar Displays* (Office of Naval Research, prepared by Dunlap and Associates, Contract no. Nonr 2682(00)) 1 September 1959.

4. Fogel, L. J. "A New Concept: The Kinalog Display System" *Human Factors* vol. 1, no. 2, April 1959, pp. 30-37.

5. Wright, L. C. *The Air Force Program for Improved Flight Instrumentation* (Air Force. Wright Air Development Center, Technical Report no. 56-582) November 1956.

6. The Bendix Corporation, Eclipse-Pioneer Division, *The Bendix Propulsion Data System: Information Brochure* (Publication no. 6111-24).

7. Cornell Aeronautical Laboratory, *Pocket Data for Human Factor Engineering* (Cornell University, Buffalo 21, N.Y.) 1958.

8. Bradley, J. V. *Control-Display Association Preferences for Ganged Controls* (Air Force. Wright Air Development Center, Technical Report no. 54-379) August 1954.

9. Hunsicker, P. E. *Arm Strength at Selected Degrees of Elbow Flexion* (Air Force. Wright Air Development Center, Technical Report no. 54-548) 1955.

10. Thomson, R. M. *et al. Arrangement of Groups of Men and Machines* (Office of Naval Research, ONR Report no. ACR-33) December 1958.

11. Randall, F. E. *et al. Human Body Size in Military Aircraft and Personal Equipment* (Air Force. Air Materiel Command, Technical Report no. 5501) 10 June 1946. (PB 33108)*

12. National Safety News "Stairs and Ramps" *National Safety News* vol. 51, no. 3, March 1945, p. 106.

13. Illuminating Engineering Society Committee on Residence Lighting "Functional Visual Activities in the Home" *Illuminating Engineering* vol. 46, no. 7, July 1951, pp. 375-382.

14. American Standards Association *American Standard Practice for Industrial Lighting* (sponsored by Illuminating Engineering Society; American Standards Association, Report no. A11.1) 1952.

15. Farnsworth, D. *Developments in Submarine and Small Vessel Lighting* (Submarine Base, New London. Medical Research Laboratory, BuMed Project NM 002 014.02.01; Report no. 209) 8 September 1952.

16. Air Force–Navy Aeronautical Bulletin *Plastic Lighting Plate Marking and Control Design* 16 March 1953.

17. Faber Birren Company *Application of Color to Shore Establishments for the United States Navy Bureau of Yards and Docks* Faber Birren Company, 500 Fifth Avenue, New York, 1948.

18. Department of the Navy, Bureau of Yards and Docks *Design Manual: Architecture NAVDOCKS DM-1* February 1962.

19. General Services Administration, Federal Supply Service, Standardization Division, Specifications and Standards Branch, *Federal Standard No. 595: Color* (Federal Supply Service, Washington 25, D.C.) 1 March 1956.

20. Air Force, Ballistic Missile Division *Gas and Fluid Line Identification for Use in Missile and Space Systems* (Ballistic Missile Division, Inglewood, Calif., AFBM Exhibit no. 58-20) 7 October 1958.

21. Bagenal, H. *Practical Acoustics and Planning against Noise* Chemical Publishing Company, 1942.

22. Beraneg, L. L. *Acoustics* McGraw-Hill, 1954.

23. Committee on the Hygiene of Housing *Standards for Healthful Housing: Construction and Equipment of the Home* (Public Administration Service, Special Publication no. 56) 1951.

24. Strasberg, M. *Criteria for Setting Airborne Noise Level Limits in Shipboard Spaces* (Bureau of Ships, Report no. 371-N-12) 15 July 1952.

25. Beranek, L. L. "Airplane Quieting. II. Specification of Acceptable Noise Levels" *Transactions of the American Society of Mechanical Engineers* vol. 69, February 1947, pp. 97-100.

26. Winslow, C. E. A., and Herrington, L. P. *Temperature and Human Life* Princeton University, 1949.

27. Paul Webb Associates (comp.) *NASA Life Sciences Data Book* (National Aeronautics and Space Administration, Office of Manned Space Flight, Washington 25, D. C.) June 1962.

28. Linder, G. S. "Mechanical Vibration Effects on Human Beings" *Aerospace Medicine* August, 1962, pp. 939-950.

29. Parks, D. L. "Defining Human Reaction to Whole-Body Vibration" *Human Factors* vol. 4, no. 5, October 1962, pp. 305-314.

30. Barbiere, R. E. *et al. A Radiobiology Guide* (Air Force. Wright Air Development Center, Technical Report no. 57-118-1) 1958.

31. Shipps, P., and Frick, J. "Passenger Density and Accommodations as Factors in Supersonic Transport Design" Preprint of paper prepared for Society of Automotive Engineers, National Aeronautic Meeting, 1961.

32. Altman, J. W. *et al. Guide to Design of Mechanical Equipment for Maintainability* (Air Force. Aerospace Systems Division, Technical Report no. 61-381) August 1961.

33. Breeze, R. K. *Space Vehicle Environmental Control Requirements Based on Equipment and Psychological Criteria* (Prepared by North American Aviation, Inc. Air Force. Aerospace Systems Division, Technical Report no. 61-161) December 1961.

*Items for which PB numbers are given . . . Washington 25, D.C.

vision

Visual impressions depend upon light and upon its receptor, the eye. The visual processes enable us to perceive form, color, brightness, and motion. It has been estimated that 80 per cent of our knowledge comes to us by way of the eye.

The light-sensitive part of the eye is generally conceded to be an extension of the brain and its neural network is nearly as complex as that of the brain. Before the visual impression is attained, light energy must set off a chain of chemical, neural, and "mental" processes. The impressions transmitted through the eyes are carried to the visual centers of the brain for integration, evaluation, and interpretation.

This chapter attempts to impart to the reader some insight into major aspects of this visual system — its anatomy, physiology, and psychology. It contains fundamental information upon which many of the recommendations of the preceding chapter are based.

STRUCTURE OF THE EYE

Through the eyes, which work somewhat as do our modern cameras, are transmitted our visual impressions of the world.

The EYE MUSCLES keep the eyes properly fixated upon the object to be seen; they move the eyeball up or down, right or left.

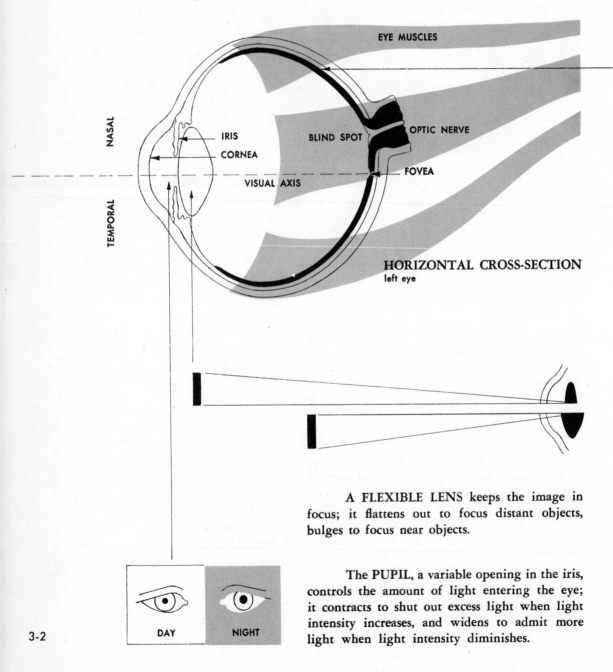

HORIZONTAL CROSS-SECTION
left eye

A FLEXIBLE LENS keeps the image in focus; it flattens out to focus distant objects, bulges to focus near objects.

The PUPIL, a variable opening in the iris, controls the amount of light entering the eye; it contracts to shut out excess light when light intensity increases, and widens to admit more light when light intensity diminishes.

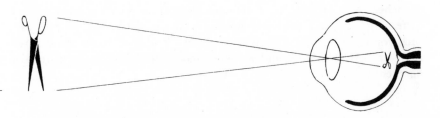

The RETINA receives light reflected from the object; this light, having been refracted by the lens, forms an inverted image on the retina. The light-sensitive neural receptors in the retina are called rods and cones.

The inverted image is converted to nerve impulses which are carried by the optic nerve to the brain. The pattern of impulses set up by the image on the retina causes a corresponding pattern of nerve impulses reaching the brain; these impulses are the basis from which the brain "sees" an upright image. Neural fibers from the right and left halves of each retina go to the optic center of the corresponding sides of the brain, as shown on the diagram.

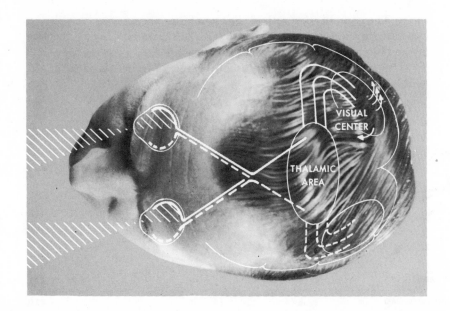

FUNCTIONS OF THE EYE

accommodation

Accommodation is the action of focusing the lens on near or distant objects. Because the lens loses its elasticity with age, a child, who can focus on an object as near as 2.4 inches, will grow into an adult of, say, 40, who generally cannot focus on an object nearer than 6 inches. This hardening-of-the-lens condition which occurs with increasing age and prevents normal accommodation is known as presbyopia. Objects at distances of about 20 feet or more are essentially at optical infinity and no accommodation is necessary to focus on them.

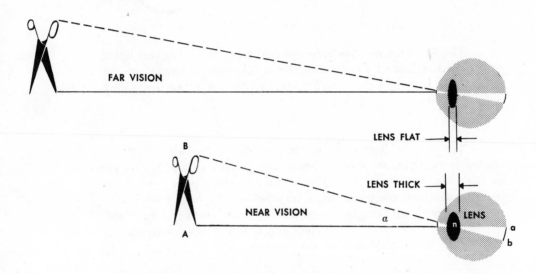

The size of the retinal image of an object may readily be calculated by means of the equation $AB/ab = An/an$, when the size of the object and its distance from the eye are known. Take *an* as 0.8 inch. Image sizes, however, are usually given in terms of visual angle, in this case, angle a.

AMPLITUDE OF ACCOMMODATION

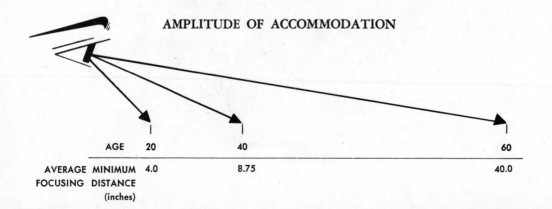

AGE	20	40	60
AVERAGE MINIMUM FOCUSING DISTANCE (inches)	4.0	8.75	40.0

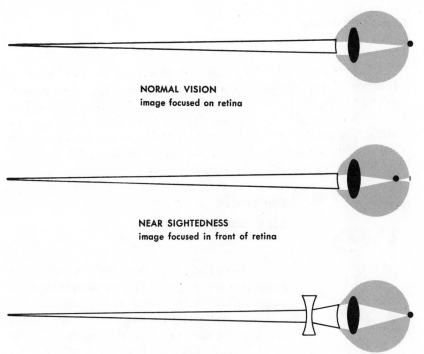

NORMAL VISION
image focused on retina

NEAR SIGHTEDNESS
image focused in front of retina

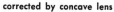

corrected by concave lens

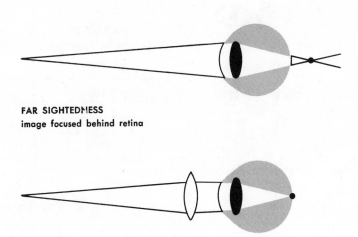

FAR SIGHTEDNESS
image focused behind retina

corrected by convex lens

    Other abnormal conditions commonly referred to are myopia (near-sightedness) and hyperopia, the opposite condition (far-sightedness). These conditions are usually correctable by the use of optical lenses, a procedure ordinarily called "refraction" by the oculist.

convergence

Convergence, the act of aiming both eyes at the same point, is a function of the eye muscles and lens together. The average time required to aim the eyes and focus them on a new point displaced in distance is about 165 milliseconds. This act is called fixating or re-fixating. The average length of these fixations (in reading, for example) is about 200 milliseconds. Beyond a distance of about 20 feet, convergence needed in order to fixate is negligible.

saccadic
eye movement

According to Woodworth, saccadic eye movement is a simple, conjugate movement without complication by change of convergence. It is a coordinated motion of both eyes, even though one may be screened from the object. A movement over a space of five letters of ordinary print, at a reading distance of 1 foot, takes 15 to 20 milliseconds. The accompanying table[7] (see list of references, p. 2—29) shows durations of movements of various extents. A movement of 20 degrees corresponds to about 4 inches on a page 1 foot from the viewer.

EXTENT OF MOVEMENT (degrees)	DURATION OF MOVEMENT (millisec)
10	40
20	55
30	80
40	100

visual field

The visual field is the area, measured in degrees, which can be seen by the fixated eye.

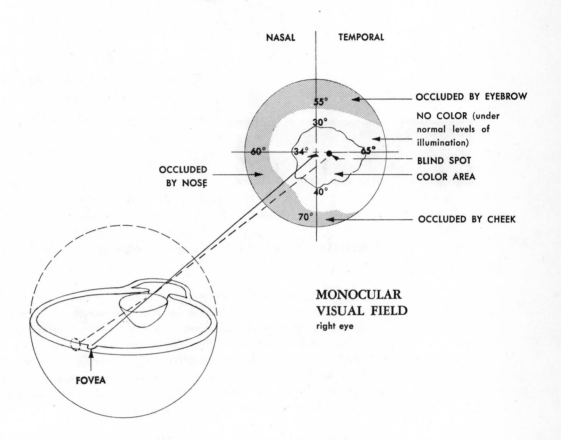

NASAL   TEMPORAL

OCCLUDED BY EYEBROW

NO COLOR (under normal levels of illumination)

BLIND SPOT

COLOR AREA

OCCLUDED BY NOSE

OCCLUDED BY CHEEK

55°
30°
60°   34°   65°
40°
70°

FOVEA

MONOCULAR VISUAL FIELD
right eye

BINOCULAR VISUAL FIELD

94°   94°

0°

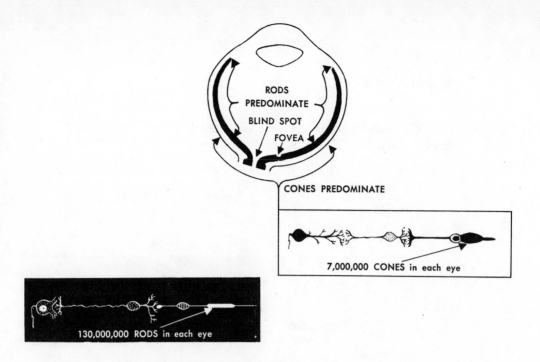

RODS PREDOMINATE
BLIND SPOT
FOVEA

CONES PREDOMINATE

7,000,000 CONES in each eye

130,000,000 RODS in each eye

characteristics of rods and cones

Rods belong to a system which can perceive only black, white, and shades of gray. Cones belong to a system which permits color perception when the illumination is above a very low minimum intensity, below which no color can be perceived. Areas in which rods and cones predominate respectively are shown in the horizontal cross section of the eye above. The fovea contains only cones. The blind spot is the point at which the optic nerve enters the retina; neither rods nor cones are present there to receive visual stimulation.

When the illumination is above approximately 0.01 lumen per square foot, the photopic (cone) system of vision is used; when it is below approximately 0.001 lumen per square foot, the scotopic (rod) system is used. Illumination between 0.01 and 0.001 lumen per square foot establishes a condition to which both systems respond; we use this "mesopic" vision at twilight and dawn, when we can see color in the sky but see objects on land only in shades of gray.

Adaptation is the process by which the eyes become accustomed to changes in the level of illumination impinging upon them. In dark adaptation, a substance called "visual purple" begins to build up as soon as the light is taken away; rods respond when this substance is activated by light. The time it takes for us to accustom (not completely adapt) ourselves to a darkened room is about 15 minutes — actual time for complete dark adaptation (rods) is about 30 minutes or more. The rate depends on the intensity of the previous light. Light adaptation (cones) is much quicker, requiring only a few seconds.

The eye is sensitive to only a narrow band of wavelengths; the visible spectrum consists of wavelengths lying between the long infrared waves and the short ultraviolet waves. Within this range, not all wavelengths are equally effective in stimulating the retina. As light levels are decreased, the relative luminosity of colors changes, because of a gradual transition from cone to rod vision and the fact that sensitivity of these two systems to the wavelengths of the visible spectrum is different, as shown in the accompanying graph.[12]

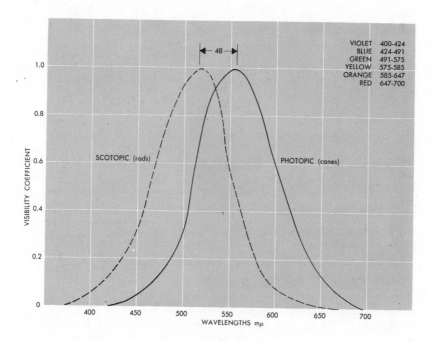

The ordinate is the reciprocal of the energy which is just visible for each wavelength of light (scotopic vision) or which matches a moderately bright standard light (photopic vision). The curves are adjusted to a common scale by making the maximum of each curve equal to one. On an absolute scale of intensities, the rod curve would fall far below that for cones. Note how relative luminosity increases for the lower wavelengths (to the left of where the photopic and scotopic curves cross) as one passes to lower light levels. Green, blue-green, and blue are visible (not necessarily as color) at lower intensities than colors of longer wavelengths.

When illumination is restricted to wavelengths longer than 620 millimicrons (red), adaptation of the scotopic (rod) system will be in large measure maintained, since mainly the photopic (cone) system is excited by this light. Because of this, it is advisable to illuminate aircraft instruments with red light.

INTENSITY RELATIONSHIPS

The minimum intensity of light that can be seen, after complete dark adaptation, is called ABSOLUTE THRESHOLD of vision. It takes only an extremely minute quantity of light to excite the eye — roughly only 1/1,000,000,000 of a lambert. It has been theoretically calculated that as few as half a dozen quanta, or less, of light reaching the retina have a good probability of yielding a visible sensation. The absolute threshold, however, is not of major concern here. The problem is that of detecting a light against a background of lower level. The ratio of light intensity to background intensity is the CONTRAST RATIO. The minimum ratio at which the light can be seen is called the CONTRAST THRESHOLD.

	LOG OF ILLUMINANCE JUST VISIBLE AT EYE (FT-C)	LOG OF BACKGROUND BRIGHTNESS (ML)
PHOTOPIC	—5	4
	—6.25	2
	—7.60	0
MESOPIC	—8.3	—2
	—8.8	—4
SCOTOPIC	—9.6	—6
	—9.8	TOTAL DARKNESS

A light of low intensity may be clearly seen against a dark background. To be seen against a bright background, however, the light must have much higher intensity, as shown by the chart.

Visibility of light depends not only on contrast between field and background luminances, but upon area (visual angle) of the light surface being observed. The diagram below[2] shows the effect of field size on its visibility when the background is completely dark. The numerical values shown are for different diameters (given in minutes of arc) of surface at the same distance from the eye.

As brightness diminishes, size must increase to be seen.

JUST VISIBLE BRIGHTNESS (LOG FT-L)	—2.2	—2.7	—3.25	—4.5	—4.75	—5.6	—5.8
DIAMETER OF SURFACE (MIN ARC)	0.3	0.6	1	6	10	60	100

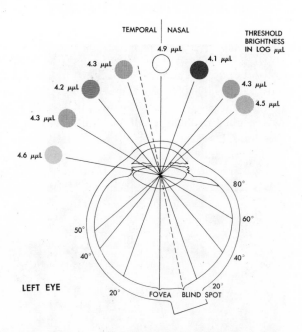

The above illustration[17] shows the sensitivity of different parts of the retina at night. The greatest sensitivity is shown to be about 40 degrees from the fovea on the nasal side of the retina and about 20 degrees from the fovea on the temporal side.

In order to see short flashes of light we must have much more intense light than we need to see longer flashes. Below 0.10-second duration, isolated flashes are equally visible if they contain equal energy.

Threshold visibility for a short flash of light depends on the total energy in the flash: the intensity of the flash multiplied by the duration. Thus the shorter flash must be at a greater intensity than the longer one in order to be visible. This reciprocal relationship between intensity and time, however, holds only up to a critical duration of about 0.1 second. For flashes longer than 0.1 second, threshold visibility depends on intensity alone and is independent of time. In the graph below, the horizontal line shows the range of durations within which the product of intensity and time is constant.[9]

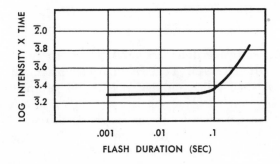

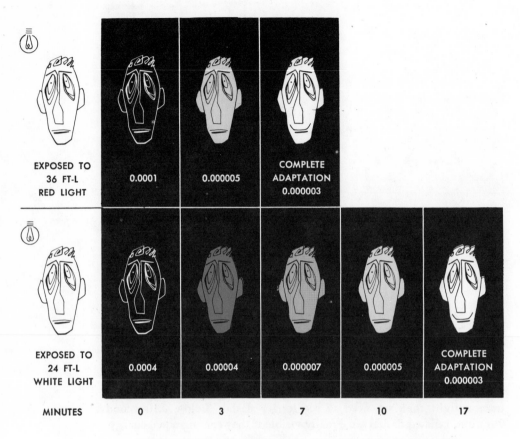

EXPOSED TO 36 FT-L RED LIGHT	0.0001	0.000005	**COMPLETE ADAPTATION** 0.000003		
EXPOSED TO 24 FT-L WHITE LIGHT	0.0004	0.00004	0.000007	0.000005	**COMPLETE ADAPTATION** 0.000003
MINUTES	0	3	7	10	17

BRIGHTNESS OF JUST VISIBLE LIGHT (FT-L) INDICATED IN SQUARES

The intensity of the dimmest light which can just be seen is shown as a function of time in the dark following the original exposure periods to red and white light of the brightnesses indicated.[11] Data are for the averages of ten subjects. The subject exposed to red light regains his response to fainter light sources more quickly than does the subject exposed to white light and reaches the level of "complete" adaptation much sooner also.

The just noticeable difference (JND) between two intensities is termed the DIFFERENCE THESHOLD. The magnitude of this threshold depends somewhat on the wavelengths of the lights for which luminosity-difference judgments are being made. It depends more, however, on the intensity of the standard with which another intensity is being compared. In the normal intensity range, contrast sensitivity improves when light levels are raised.

The ratio between the brightness of a central display field and the brightness of an area surrounding it has an important effect upon brightness discriminations for fine details of the visual task within the display field.[6] As the surrounding-area brightness approaches that of the display field, brightness difference sensitivity within the display field improves. Best differential brightness sensitivity for traces on a cathode ray tube (scope), for example, is obtained when the brightness of the area surrounding the scope is about equal to that of the scope itself. When surround brightness exceeds scope brightness by a factor of more than ten, differential brightness sensitivity on the scope is impaired. The same effect holds, although to a considerably smaller extent, when surround brightness is less than that of the scope. These effects apply to any display which requires fine differential brightness judgments.

FLICKER-FUSION FREQUENCY is the point at which successive light flashes blend into a continuous light; it increases with increasing flash intensities and with decreasing proportion of the light-dark cycle occupied by the flash. It reaches 50 to 60 cycles per second at high intensities. When a flickering light — on 50 per cent of the time, off 50 per cent — flashes at the rate of 10 cycles per second, it appears to be twice as bright as a steady light of the same intensity. This phenomenon is of interest because it occurs at the same frequency as the brain's alpha-rhythm, a fluctuation around 10 cycles per second in the brain's electrical potential. The brightness enhancement may possibly be due to synchrony of impulses from visual stimuli with brain alpha waves.[1] The graph indicates the brightness of a flickering light with a light-dark time ratio of 1 to 1 and at rates of 0 to 20 cycles per second, as compared with the brightness of a steady light, and also shows the relationship of the 10-cycles-per-second point with the alpha-rhythm pattern.

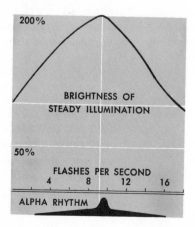

3-13

ACUITY

Visual acuity can be defined and measured in several ways, with different results, depending upon the conditions of its measurement. One of the more commonly used standards is that acuity is the reciprocal of the visual angle in minutes subtended by the smallest discriminable visual detail at the nodal point of the eye, for all practical purposes the center of the lens.

The resolving power of the eye is the ability of the eye to detect small objects and distinguish fine detail. It varies greatly, depending upon the object, spectral distribution of radiant energy, luminosity of background, contrast between object and background, duration of the visual stimulus, and the criterion used to determine whether the object is or is not seen.

There is a marked relationship of visual acuity with the number of rods and cones and their distance from the fovea. Because the fovea (the central area of the retina, on which light from fixated objects falls) contains only cones, acuity is best there under photopic light conditions and poorest there under scotopic seeing conditions.[16,18]

The relationship between field brightness and minimum perceptible brightness difference (which is, in fact, a measure of acuity) for the rods and cones, is shown. Note that there is no appreciable change in sensitivity of the cones, which are used in daylight, while extreme change occurs in the sensitivity of the rods, used in darkened situations.[10]

At lowest intensities of light, the eye can just see a line whose thickness subtends a visual angle of about 10 minutes, while at high intensities, the just-resolvable line subtends less than 1 second of visual angle — less, in fact, than the width of an individual cone in the retina. All experimenters are agreed on the increase of visual acuity with increased illumination. Speed of recognition increases with increased illumination as well. When rapid discrimination of very small objects is required, high intensities of light and large contrast between background and object are necessary.

The relationship between contrast and size for threshold visibility of a standard parallel-bar test object under a brightness level of 30 millilamberts is indicated. As contrast is increased, minimum size and spacing between parallel bars may be decreased without rendering the spacing invisible. As contrast is decreased, size must be increased, especially for lower contrast percentages, in order to maintain threshold acuity.

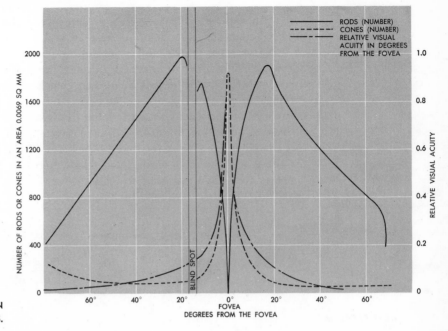

THE RELATIONSHIP
OF VISUAL ACUITY
TO THE DISTRIBUTION
OF RODS AND CONES.

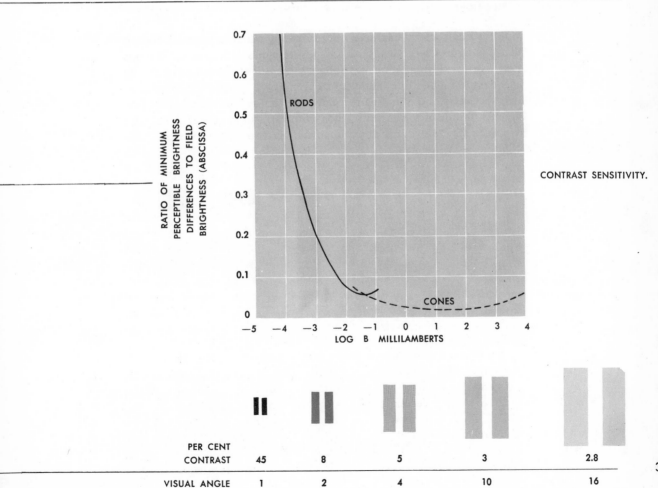

CONTRAST SENSITIVITY.

PER CENT CONTRAST	45	8	5	3	2.8
VISUAL ANGLE MINUTES	1	2	4	10	16

ACUITY AS A FUNCTION OF SIZE AND CONTRAST.

An experiment of a threshold nature was conducted to determine whether the amount of increase in visual acuity, with increase of brightness on targets, differs more for persons with initial subnormal acuity than for those with initial normal acuity. The subjects located checkerboard targets under six levels of target brightness varying from 3.16 to 1000 foot-lamberts. It was found that the subnormal group gained significantly more in visual acuity terms with an increase in target brightness than did the normal group. The data show that adequate light for seeing detail is between 10 and 30 foot-lamberts for those with normal vision, somewhere between 30 and 40 foot-lamberts for subnormal subjects. All twelve subjects in each group, age 20 to 25 years, were tested monocularly.[13]

BACKGROUND BRIGHTNESS LEVEL 0.075 FT-C

WAVELENGTH Mμ	485	520	590	625	665
VISUAL ACUITY (PER CENT)	52	70	75	68	63
	BLUE LIGHT		YELLOW LIGHT		RED LIGHT

Visual acuity has been tested under different spectral illuminants. C-figures were used, with exposure times of 1 second.[8] In this study, yellow illumination was found to permit the best acuity. Given adequate ambient illumination, however, there is negligible relationship between the illuminant color and acuity for black-and-white figures. Luminance contrast, color contrast, illumination level, and exposure time are much more important factors in acuity than color of illuminant.

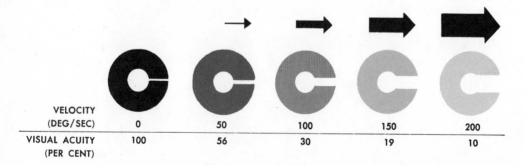

VELOCITY (DEG/SEC)	0	50	100	150	200
VISUAL ACUITY (PER CENT)	100	56	30	19	10

When a visual image passes over successive receptor elements of the retina, that stimulus is perceived to be in motion. Visual acuity, for Landolt-ring test stimuli moving on a horizontal plane around the observer's head, decreases with increasing angular velocity of the test object. The illustration[15] shows that the gaps must increase in size in order to be distinguished at the higher speeds. It was also shown that an object such as the Landolt ring seen 30 degrees from the line of vision is perceived only 60 per cent as well when in motion as when stationary.

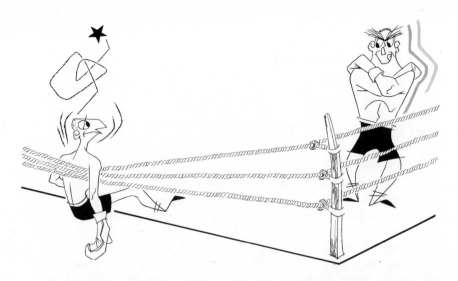

Visual acuity is affected by body vibration. One study[6] showed it to be slightly reduced when the head or the platform was vibrated, with a 0.001-inch amplitude, over a range of 10 to 130 cycles per second.

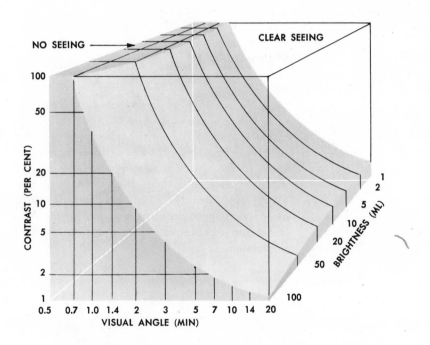

This curved three-dimensional surface[14] shows the relationship among visual angle, contrast, and background brightness. When a combination of these factors falls on a point below the curve, we cannot discriminate, while a combination falling on a point above permits easy seeing.

OTHER FEATURES
OF SEEING

summation and interaction

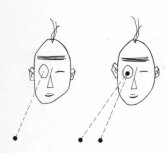

The retina is composed of complex neural interconnections which may produce a summation effect between closely adjacent receptors (retinal summation). Thus, two test patches of light, either of which is below the threshold of vision, may become visible if presented simultaneously to adjacent parts of the retina. The threshold of a light may be lowered by increasing its area, because more interconnected receptors are stimulated. Another type of interaction may take place between the two eyes (binocular interaction) as a result of processes occurring in higher neural centers, including the brain. This phenomenon accounts for the slightly increased probability of binocular detection of small amounts of light as compared with monocular detection of the same amount of light. These and similar phenomena may alternatively be explained by physical optics, the mechanics of the eye, or probability theory.

stereoscopy

When an object is fixated, a different view of it is seen in each eye. This feature of binocular vision is a major cue for the perception of depth. In the instrument known as the stereoscope, views of the object as seen by each eye are presented separately to them. Both two-dimensional views may then be fused, resulting in three-dimensional perception of a single object. Very fine differences between views can give this depth impression.

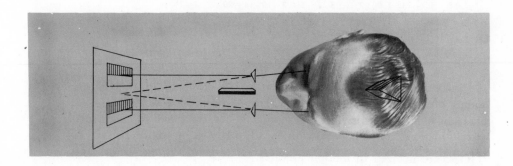

single and double images

When an object is fixated, it is, of course, seen as a single image. Most other features of the visual field are, however, "seen" double, although our experience has taught us to disregard this impression. Many people are not even aware of the existence of double images. One can easily demonstrate them, however, by fixating on a pencil held in front of the eyes. A second pencil held behind the first is seen double.

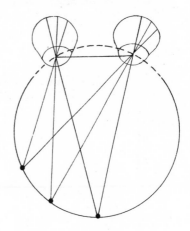

For every fixation point in the horizontal plane there is a circle passing through that point and through the optical centers of the two eyes; with the exception of points very close to the eyes any point on or near this circle, including, of course, the fixation point, is seen singly.[3] Points off the horizontal plane may also be seen singly; these points fall on rather complex curves with reference to the fixation point. Points on the plane but not on the circle are seen as double.

apparent motion

Lights presented in succession at the proper time interval, distance from each other, and intensity, give the impression of movement from one to the other.

If the second flash is more intense than the first, a backwards motion from the second to the first flash may be seen.

With alternate presentation of certain shapes in appropriate positions, the object may appear to move through three dimensions.

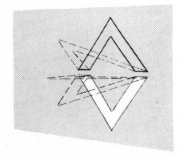

These effects, known as APPARENT MOTION, are utilized in motion pictures.

optical illusions

Although perception of the characteristics of visual stimuli remains relatively constant over a remarkably wide range of visual conditions, our visual system can be in error, as shown by these standard examples. One should make sure that such illusions are minimized in visual displays.

A vase or two faces in profile may be seen, in accordance with whether the white is seen as figure or background.

Long lines are parallel

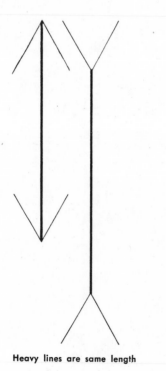

Heavy lines are same length

Horizontal and vertical lines are same length

after-images

It has been known for many years that visual activity continues after stimulation of the retina has ceased. In positive after-images, the black areas will appear as black and the white areas as white. In negative after-images, however, the colors will be reversed; in the case of other colors, negative after-images will produce colors which are complementary to those of the actual picture.

Focus your attention on the center of the sketch opposite for about two minutes; then replace the page with a sheet of white paper. The after-image will appear just as you see it here; or, if the stimulation has been long enough, the after-image will be reversed.

FACTORS THAT MAKE
SEEING EASIER

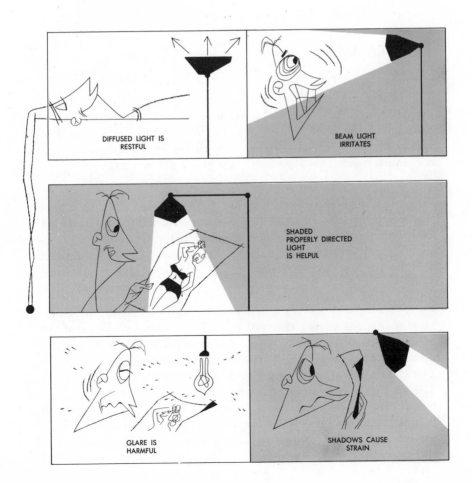

DIFFUSED LIGHT IS RESTFUL

BEAM LIGHT IRRITATES

SHADED PROPERLY DIRECTED LIGHT IS HELPUL

GLARE IS HARMFUL

SHADOWS CAUSE STRAIN

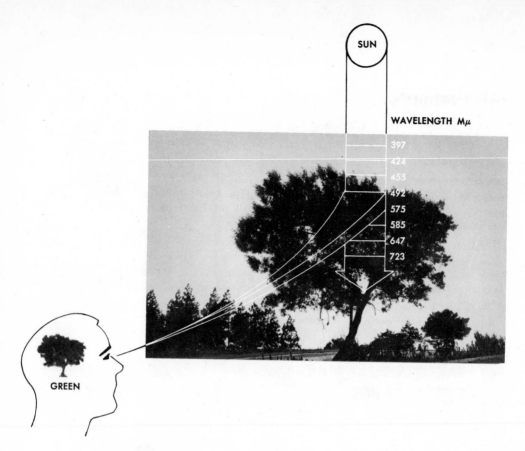

WAVELENGTH Mμ

397
424
455
492
575
585
647
723

GREEN

COLOR

Light can be defined as physical energy in the form of electromagnetic radiations. The eye is sensitive to only a relatively narrow band of these radiations — wavelengths from 400 to 720 millimicrons, approximately. The light travels through the lens and is focused on the retina, where it is absorbed in quantal units of energy.

The solar spectrum (radiation from the sun) contains all the visible wavelengths. Physical objects selectively absorb this radiation, so that the energy they transmit or reflect has a different energy distribution per wavelength than that of the original light. This difference provides the key to color vision.

The central nervous system of man is able to classify the distributions of light energy that fall upon his eyes; these classes of distribution are seen as colors. There are an infinite number of distributions of light energy which may be experienced as the same color. The eyes do not analyze out the separate wavelengths, as does a prism. The nervous system simply classifies impulses from groups of wavelengths and labels them colors from experience. Color is a psychological experience; it is not a property of the electromagnetic energy we see as light, but a perceptual response of the human being to that energy.

sensitivity zones

Not all zones of the retina are equally sensitive to color. Toward the periphery, objects can still be distinguished while their color cannot. Some colors are recognized at greater angles away from the fovea than others. The accompanying figure shows the limits of the retinal zones in which the various colors can, under normal illumination, be correctly recognized.

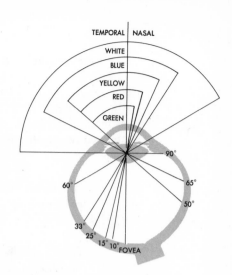

formation

Normal color vision is called trichromatism because any one of the 160 or more distinguishably different hues may for the most part be produced by variously mixing three independently adjustable primary colors, such as red, green, and blue. Mixing colors is often confused with mixing pigments. The former is an additive combination while the latter is subtractive.

When yellow and blue lights in proper proportion are thrown on a screen, the mixture appears white; the yellow and blue are said to be complementary colors.

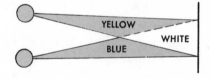

Color mixing may also be accomplished by using a "color wheel." The colors to be mixed occupy different sectors of the wheel, which when rotated at sufficient speed produces new colors in accordance with the rules of additive color mixture. This principle has been applied in experimental color-TV systems.

When artists mix yellow and blue pigments, however, a green results. This is done by double subtraction. The yellow pigment absorbs certain rays, while those remaining give it its yellow color. The same applies to the blue pigment. The light remaining after the yellow and blue pigments have both absorbed their respective wavelengths may be so balanced as to give a sensation of green.

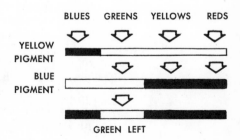

3-23

trichromatic system

Since color is a personal experience, it is necessary to arrive at a method by which we can compare and specify colors. The two fundamental reasons for a "trichromatic system" as is generally used today are:

A suitable mixture of three arbitrarily selected radiations can be combined to produce any given color.

Color specifications can be precisely quantized, making it possible to compare colors.

T	Tomato
L	Lemon
W	White (illuminant C)
E	Equal energy spectrum
PI	limit of colors obtainable from Printer's Inks

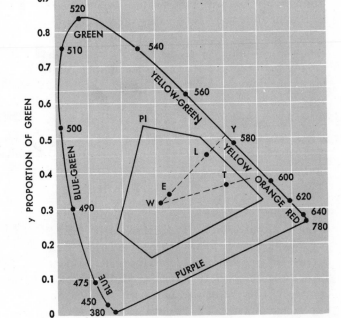

This is a chromaticity diagram[5] for plotting color in terms of the amount of a standard red, green, and blue that will match them. The position of each spectrum color is shown by the roughly triangular figure. The purest colors obtainable with printers' ink (PI) are also shown. This chart, standardized in 1931 by the International Commission on Illumination, uses red, green, and blue lights which are mathematically specified and arbitrarily designated as the three primaries.

Since the spectrum colors are the most saturated, they are located on the periphery of the curve and all other psychologically experienced colors fall inside this boundary. In general, white would be located in the center of the diagram and would be compounded of red, green, and blue, so chosen that equal amounts of each, when mixed additively, would produce white. The white defined as $1/3R + 1/3G + 1/3B$ is approximately the color of light from the northern summer noonday sun on a clear day and has been designated as "Illuminant C" by the ICI.

The numbers along the curves are wavelengths. If a color falls in the upper corner it looks "greenish"; if in the lower right corner, "reddish"; if in the lower left corner, "bluish." A dotted line drawn from W through L will give a wavelength of approximately 576 millimicrons, which means that the lemon would look yellow under Illuminant C. The saturation of any color is determined by its nearness either to W or to the spectral curve; for example, the closer to Y, the more saturated the lemon color appears.

The total amount of arbitrary red, blue, and green required to match a given color is always expressed as unity. Simply stated, this means that if the amount of any two of the standard colors is known, the other color can be determined by subtraction from unity. It is common practice to express the percentages of red and green on the abscissa and ordinate respectively and to subtract their sum from unity to determine the amount of blue.

aesthetics of color

Many persons believe that some correlation exists between color and non-visual sensations. Reds, oranges, and yellows are usually considered warm, advancing colors, and probably stimulating. Violets, blues, and greens, at the other end of the scale, are usually considered cool, receding colors, and are inclined to be restful. As a rule, a color is as cool as it is blue and as warm as it is red. However, pale colors tend to seem cooler than dark colors.

Although experimental evidence on the subject is controversial, it is generally agreed that color schemes in work areas do have an effect on performance. Some stenographers have found, for instance, that the colors on a shorthand pad can affect their work; dead-white paper with black ruled lines tired their eyes much more quickly than did dull, off-white paper with pale, gray-green lines. It would seem that a harmonious combination of colors in an area would promote efficiency and that a discordant color scheme would be conducive to restlessness and consequent loss of efficiency.

color abnormalities

The term "color blindness" is one frequently misused in connection with color abnormalities. In the absolute sense, color blindness should refer to a complete absence of psychological color experience. Because the so-called "color-blind" person usually does experience certain colors, it is suggested that the term "color deficient" be more applicable in most cases.

Trichromatism is usually considered normal color vision. (See facing chart.)[4] There are color-weak individuals, however, even among the trichromats; their impairment may be so slight that only very sensitive tests will reveal it. The largest proportion of color-deficient people have this type of color weakness, which is called "anomalous trichromatism." Though resembling normals in that they require three primaries to match spectrum colors, they may need them in abnormal amounts. Color deficiency is almost always hereditary in origin, present to some degree in about 8 per cent of the male population. Females, however, are seldom afflicted.

The next most common form of color deficiency is red-green dichromatism. Dichromats have been divided into two principal subgroups — protanopes (red blind) and deuteranopes (green blind). For all dichromatic observers, color is restricted to two basic color groups, yellows and blues, which are not confused with each other. Dichromats can usually match all spectral colors, as they see them, by suitable combinations of the two independently adjustable primaries.

There are several important differences between protanopes and deuteranopes. For protanopes, the red end of the spectrum, seen as yellow, is foreshortened, whereas deuteranopes are able to see hue (though again yellow) out to normal limits of the spectrum. In the diagram, the colors seen by a protanope are compared with those seen by a normal trichromat. The protanopes have a gray band centered around 493 millimicrons and cannot distinguish red or blue-green from gray; deuteranopes, on the other hand, have a neutral point around 500 millimicrons but cannot distinguish green or reddish-purple from gray. These differences are small but reliable and serve as one means of distinguishing between the two types of dichromats.

Monochromatic vision is extremely rare. Observers with this deficiency see only in terms of shades of gray. Acuity is poor in monochromats; their vision approximates black and white photography with poor definition.

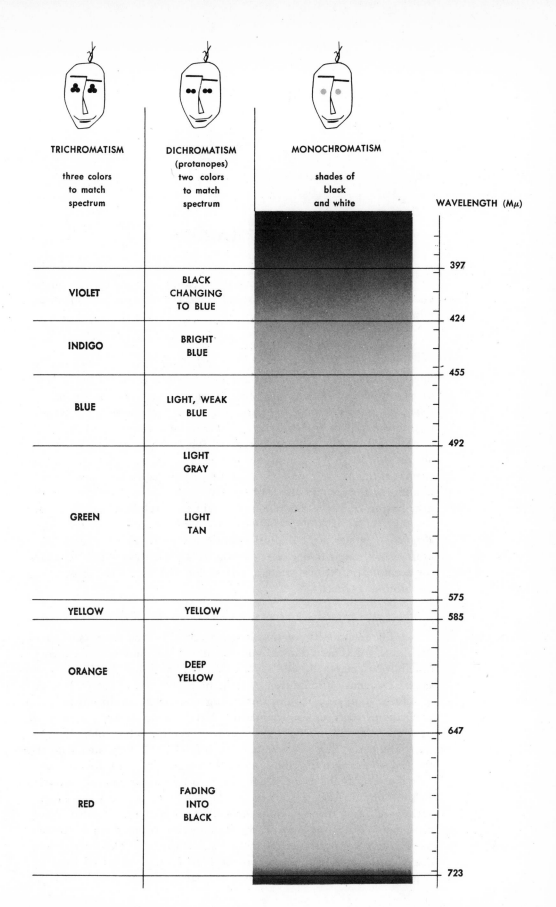

TRICHROMATISM	DICHROMATISM	MONOCHROMATISM	WAVELENGTH (Mμ)
three colors to match spectrum	(protanopes) two colors to match spectrum	shades of black and white	
			397
VIOLET	BLACK CHANGING TO BLUE		
			424
INDIGO	BRIGHT BLUE		
			455
BLUE	LIGHT, WEAK BLUE		
			492
	LIGHT GRAY		
GREEN	LIGHT TAN		
			575
YELLOW	YELLOW		585
ORANGE	DEEP YELLOW		
			647
RED	FADING INTO BLACK		
			723

3-27

PSYCHOPHYSICAL RELATIONS

Let us, in closing, point out the relation between certain physical, psychophysical, and psychological aspects of seeing which are often misunderstood.

The physical stimulus, light, is *radiant energy* (measured in physical units, such as the erg) usually distributed over a wide band of the spectrum. When this physical energy acts on the organism, *luminous energy* results. Its magnitude is not in one-to-one relationship to the radiant energy, but is a differential function of the spectral composition of that radiant energy. If, for example, radiant energy is all above 750 millimicrons, no luminous energy results. Luminous energy, then, is a psychophysical concept, measured in such units as the candle, the lumen, and the lambert. Given the spectral radiant energy distribution of light and the well established response curve of the "average" observer, it is possible to convert radiant to luminous energy. *Brightness* is the psychological counterpart of luminous energy but, again, is not in one-to-one relation to it. It is a sensation which depends, for example, on the eye's state of adaptation and on the background of the luminous object.

The relationship of wavelength to color is even less precise than the above. It has been pointed out that an infinite number of frequency distributions may yield the same color. On the other hand, any particular frequency distribution of light may give rise to the perception of a large number of colors, depending upon field conditions as well as on the person's set and adaptation. A distinction between sources of light and reflecting surfaces is helpful in deciding what colors will be seen. The perception of a source color is fairly well correlated with its spectral wavelength distribution. Reflecting surfaces will, for the most part, be seen as the color which they would appear under "normal" (white) illumination, regardless of the character of the light illuminating and being reflected from them. This phenomenon is called "color constancy." When the color of the illumination is unknown to the observer, this color constancy breaks down, and the color of a surface then does depend to a large extent on the kind of light reflected from it; that is, the surface is now seen as if it were a source.

references

The author wishes to acknowledge his gratitude to the publishers mentioned below for permission to use material based on the following articles and books.

1. Bartley, S. H. "Some Factors in Brightness Discrimination" *Psychological Review* vol. 46, no. 4, July 1939, pp. 337-358.

2. Blackwell, H. R. "Contrast Thresholds of the Human Eye" *Optical Society of America, Journal* vol. 36, no. 11, November 1946, pp. 624-642.

3. Boring, E. G. *Sensation and Perception in the History of Experimental Psychology* Appleton-Century-Crofts, Inc., 1942, p. 228.

4. Chapanis, A. "Color Blindness" *Scientific American* vol. 184, no. 3, March 1951, pp. 48-49.

5. Chapanis, A., et al. *Applied Experimental Psychology* John Wiley and Sons, Inc., 1949, p. 72. (Adapted by permission of authors and publisher.)

6. Coermann, R. *Investigation Regarding the Effect of Vibration on the Human Organism* Air Force, Air Materiel Command Translation No. 349, 19 May 1941.

7. Dodge, R., and Cline, T. S. "The Angle Velocity of Eye Movement" *Psychological Review* vol. 8, 1901, pp. 145-157.

8. Ferree, C. E., and Rand, G. "Visibility of Objects as Affected by Color and Composition of Light, Part II, With Lights Equalized in Both Brightness and Saturation" *Personnel Journal* vol. 10, 1931, pp. 108-124.

9. Graham, C. H. and Margaria, R. "Area and the Intensity-Time Relation in the Peripheral Retina" *American Journal of Physiology* vol. 113, no. 2, October 1935, pp. 299-305.

10. Hecht, S., adapted by Luckiesh, M., and Moss, F. K. *The Science of Seeing* D. Van Nostrand Co., 1943, p. 73.

11. Hecht, S., and Hsia, Y. "Dark Adaptation Following Light Adaptation to Red and White Lights" *Optical Society of America, Journal* vol. 35, no. 4, April 1945, pp. 261-267.

12. Hecht, S., and Williams, R. E. "The Visibility of Monochromatic Radiation and the Absorption Spectrum of Visual Purple" *Journal of General Physiology* vol. 5, 1922, pp. 1-34.

13. Kuntz, J. E., and Sleight, R. B. "Effect of Target Brightness on 'Normal' and 'Subnormal' Visual Acuity" *Journal of Applied Psychology* vol. 33, no. 1, February 1949, pp. 83, 91.

14. Luckiesh, M., and Moss, F. K. *The Science of Seeing* D. Van Nostrand Co., 1943, p. 125.

15. Ludvigh, E. "The Visibility of Moving Objects" *Science* vol. 108, 16 July 1948, pp. 63-64.

16. Osterberg, G. "Topography of the Layer of Rods and Cones in the Human Retina" *Acta Ophthalmologica* (Copenhagen) vol. 13, Suppl. 6, 1935, p. 103.

17. Sloan, L. L. "Rate of Dark Adaptation and Regional Threshold Gradient of the Dark-Adapted Eye: Physiologic and Clinical Studies" *American Journal of Ophthalmology* vol. 30, 1947, pp. 705-720.

18. Wertheim, R. "Uber die indirekts Sehscharfe" *Zeitschrift fur psychologie und Physiologie der sinnesorgane* vol. 7, 1894, pp. 172-187.

19. Williams, S. B., and Hanes, R. M. "Visibility on Cathode-Ray Tube Screens: Intensity and Color of Ambient Illumination" *Journal of Psychology* vol. 27, 1949, pp. 231-244.

chapter

4

audition

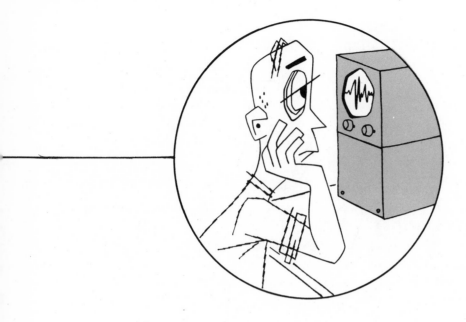

audition

Hearing is our second most important sense, in terms of information gathering. Hearing depends on (1) the ear and its associated neurology, (2) the sound source, a vibrating body, and (3) the transmission medium which transmits the pressure vibrations from this source. The first is termed the *auditory system;* the second and third combine to become the *sound system.* We are concerned primarily with the auditory system as it is affected by the products of a sound system. Our concern stems from the fact that we are unable to alter the auditory system; we can, however, build a sound system conforming to the requirements of this auditory system.

Until fairly recent years, construction of an effective sound system depended largely upon trial and error. Today, an efficient system can be designed, because we now have new knowledge concerning the response characteristics of the ear to sound impinging on it, the properties of the sound originally emitted, and the effects of the state of the carrying medium on that sound.

We present in this chapter background information fundamental to the development and application of principles upon which the recommendations of Chapter 2 were based.

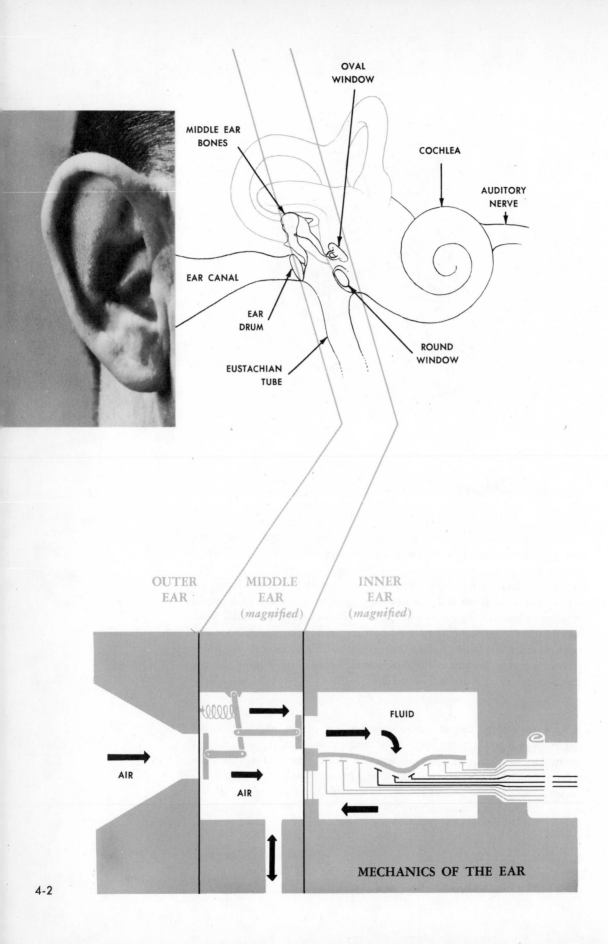

OVAL WINDOW

MIDDLE EAR BONES

COCHLEA

AUDITORY NERVE

EAR CANAL

EAR DRUM

EUSTACHIAN TUBE

ROUND WINDOW

OUTER EAR

MIDDLE EAR (*magnified*)

INNER EAR (*magnified*)

AIR

AIR

FLUID

MECHANICS OF THE EAR

4-2

THE EAR

The structure of the ear is adapted to receive and transmit to the brain the vibrations which constitute the hearing stimulus. The human ear responds over great ranges in both frequency and intensity.

In man, the outer ear lacks efficiency in collecting sounds but assists somewhat in the localization of sounds, especially the high-frequency sounds. The ear canal directs sound to the eardrum, which is a thin, tough, slightly conical membrane between the outer and middle ears. Being thin and flexible, it vibrates with the fluctuations of sound pressure and transmits these vibrations to the bony mechanism of the middle ear.

The focusing of pressures at the apex of the ear drum, plus leverage gained through the middle-ear bones, results in a mechanical advantage estimated at about 30 to 1. As a consequence, almost infinitely small fluctuating pressures at the eardrum produce piston-like vibrations at the oval window of the inner ear. These vibrations initiate a motion in the cochlea which is sufficiently large to elicit the hearing response. Very intense vibrations are damped by means of two muscles attached to the middle ear bones. The Eustachian tube connects the middle-ear cavity with the oral cavity and keeps the over-all air pressure approximately equalized on both sides of the eardrum.

The cochlea contains a spiral canal which is partitioned into three channels; each is filled with a fluid by means of which impulses travel from the oval window through the cochlea. These impulses cause a bulging of the flexible partitions of the canal. The partition called the basilar membrane is displaced so that each frequency creates maximum resonance at its particular place. Rows of tiny hair cells along the basilar membrane constitute the primary receptors for hearing. Nerve impulses are carried from these receptors by way of the auditory nerve to the auditory centers of the brain.

The functions of the outer and middle ears can be bypassed by bone conduction, when the head is in direct contact with the vibrating body. The inner ear is still essential, however; the cochlear action is identical for both ear-canal-conducted and bone-conducted vibrations.

HIGH PRESSURE

LOW PRESSURE

SOUND
SOURCE

SOUND AND HEARING

In common usage, the word *sound* is used in reference to both physical sound which enters the ear and our response to that sound. In this chapter, however, *sound* is used only for the physical aspects of sound as the physicist defines and can measure them. The subjective aspect — response of the auditory system to the sound — will here be termed *hearing*.

The use of two distinct systems — one physical, one subjective — is required because what we hear as sound does not bear linear relationship to the physical sound that enters the ear. Hearing experience may exist for which there is no physical basis; on the other hand, measurable physical sound may be present but not elicit a hearing response on the part of the normal listener.

In this section we define briefly the elements of sound and of hearing and then consider the important relationships existing between elements of the two systems.

elements of sound

Physical sound is the result of vibrations of a source — air, metal, string, wire — which emits pressure fluctuations in all directions from it, at a speed depending on the medium in which the vibrations travel. The form of the vibrations is cyclic — a compression and rarefaction completing one cycle. The sound produced by a series of such cycles has three physical dimensions — *frequency, intensity* or sound pressure level, and *duration* — which can be measured with instruments and controlled.

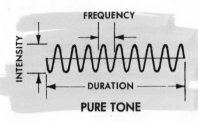

PURE TONE

Frequency indicates the number of pressure-gradient cycles occurring in a specified period of time and is usually measured in cycles per second. A range of frequency may be indicated by the octave, the interval between any two sounds having a frequency ratio of 2 to 1. The octave is divided into twelve equal logarithmic intervals called semitones, having a ratio of 1.0595 to 1; and the semitones into 100 equal log intervals called cents. A frequency series commonly used in acoustical measurements and analyses includes the frequencies 128, 256, 512, 1024, 2048, and 4096 cycles per second. The frequency 256 cycles per second corresponds approximately to middle C on the piano.

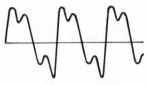

PERIODIC SOUND

Vibration patterns can be classified into simple sounds and complex sounds. Fluctuations occurring with a regular period and having only a single frequency are termed simple, or "pure," tones and are rarely found outside laboratory conditions. All remaining sounds are considered complex; these in turn may be divided into periodic and non-periodic sounds. The periodic sounds include frequencies which are integral multiples, or harmonics, of the fundamental frequency. The non-periodic sounds have irregular wave patterns and possess no dominant harmonic relationships — such irregular fluctuations are defined as noise. White noise is sound containing all audible frequencies.

NON-PERIODIC SOUND

WHITE NOISE

Any periodic sound, no matter how complex, can be analyzed into pure sine-wave components, as Fourier, the French mathematician, demonstrated in 1822. Such analysis of periodic vibrations into a number of simple components is important in any study of sound.

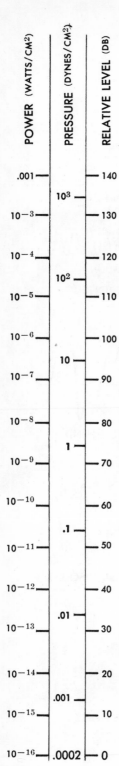

POWER (WATTS/CM²)

PRESSURE (DYNES/CM²)

RELATIVE LEVEL (DB)

The magnitude of a sound may be measured in units of sound pressure (dynes per square centimeter) or sound energy (watts per square centimeter). By sound pressure is meant the root-mean-square of the pressure between the high and low points of the pressure cycles. The energy which flows through a medium in the transmission of sound is proportional to the square of the pressure.

In addition, it is usually more important to know the ratio of intensities of two sounds than to determine the absolute value of either, because the range of ear response is so broad — the loudest sound the ear perceives, short of the threshold of pain, is several billion times more intense than the faintest sound, at the threshold of hearing. To handle this wide range of intensities, we use a unit called the *bel.* The difference in intensity level between two sounds is given by the common logarithm of the ratio of these two intensities expressed in bels. It is usually further divided into ten units, *decibels,* which are more convenient. The decibel (db) is defined as 10 times the common logarithm of the ratio of the two intensities (E) or 20 times the ratio of the two pressures (P).

Although it is possible to express any sound as being so many decibels more or less intense than another sound, it is useful to accept a common intensity level for a reference. In audition it is convenient to use a reference level near the normal threshold of hearing. The American Standards Association has established this level to be 10^{-16} watt per square centimeter, in power unit, and 0.0002 dyne per square centimeter, in pressure unit. Unless otherwise stated, use of the decibel scale in this chapter will be in reference to this intensity level.

The intensity of a sound diminishes according to the inverse square of the distance, assuming, of course, that the sound transmission is not interefered with by reflections (such as echoes or standing waves) or refracting factors (such as wind or temperature gradients). Under ideal conditions, doubling the distance results in a loss of 6 decibels.

Duration, measured in seconds or fractions thereof, is an important consideration in sound-system design, since very short sounds (0.1 second or less) appear different to the hearer from longer-duration sounds.

elements of hearing

Any discussion of the subjective aspects of sound must be based on evaluation of a listener's response to sounds of accurately controlled physical dimensions. The dimensions which define physical sound are not satisfactory for describing hearing elements, since the relationship between the two fields is not linear. It has been necessary, therefore, to devise other terms to describe the hearing response — *pitch, loudness,* and *duration* are the subjective counterparts of the physical dimensions frequency, intensity, and duration, respectively. Although these subjective dimensions cannot be measured as accurately as the physical ones, they are valuable in illustrating the lack of linearity between sound and hearing.

Pitch is the experienced sensation of highness or lowness of a sound. Although primarily dependent upon the frequency components of the sound, pitch varies unevenly along the frequency scale and may also vary in relation to intensity and duration (see page 4-14). Most sounds have pitch; some do not. Any sound which has frequency components capable of localizing a predominant excitation on the basilar membrane will appear to have pitch. Sounds with random, irregular, or a broad band of frequency components do not have pitch.

The octave and its subunit, the semitone, have been used as a measure of pitch as well as of frequency. However, since equal units should logically represent equal distances along a scale, and the semitones and octaves do not — octaves located near the upper and lower frequency limits appear much shorter than do octaves near the middle frequencies — the octave does not prove to be a satisfactory unit for pitch.

Another unit has been suggested for which equal units do represent equal distances along the pitch scale — this unit is called the *mel*. It is defined as a unit of equal pitch, as judged by an average listener. A pure tone of 1000 cycles per second and 40 decibels above threshold (as defined on page 3-6) has been arbitrarily chosen as having a pitch of 1000 mels. Other tones may be measured with reference to this pitch. A tone judged twice as high in pitch as the reference tone would have a pitch of 2000 mels; one half as high, 500 mels. This unit is useful where it is desired to separate sounds along a subjective scale rather than along a frequency scale; it also, when compared with the frequency scale, gives clues as to the frequency location of sounds that are most distinct and easily discriminated by listeners.

Loudness is the hearing response most closely associated with intensity. Though loudness is the first-order effect of intensity, the relationship is not linear, and it is somewhat less dependent on intensity than is pitch on frequency. The ability to detect variations in loudness is largely dependent on the unique characteristics of the ear; the magnitude is relative to the total nerve energy produced by the sound in the ear. Magnitude of loudness increases slowly in the low loudness levels, as compared with decibel increases of intensity from near-threshold level, but it increases more rapidly with higher intensities.

Three scales are used in dealing with the element of loudness — the *phon* scale of equal loudness-level, the *sone* scale of subjective loudness, and the *sensation level,* the level in decibels above the auditory threshold.

The phon scale of equal-loudness-level uses a 1000-cycle reference tone. The loudness, in phons, of any sound is the numerical value of the intensity, in decibels, of the reference tone when it is adjusted to sound equally loud. Thus, a sound which equals in loudness a 1000-cycle, 60-decibel-intensity tone is a 60-phon sound. Rarely will the intensities of the two sounds be equal, however.

When it is necessary to know whether a sound is twice as loud as another sound — one-half as loud, ten times as loud — the sone scale is most useful. The reference level of one sone is defined as being the loudness of a 1000-cycle tone 40 decibels above threshold; one milli-sone corresponds to the hearing threshold. A sound judged twice as loud as a sound of one-sone loudness is at two on the sone scale.

It is often important to know the magnitude of a sound above the threshold. This *sensation level* is measured in decibels above the intensity of the just-audible sound. The thresholds of sounds of different frequencies vary greatly in intensity. Individuals' thresholds also vary widely. For the prediction of many auditory responses it is necessary to know these thresholds. The sensation level is, as a consequence, a useful measure.

Numerous other elements have been named as subjective characteristics of sound, in addition to the more-or-less direct counterparts of the physical elements. Among these are brightness, roughness, vocality, fullness. A number of these make up what is commonly known as quality or timbre. Although some of these attributes may be dependent on both the frequency and intensity of a pure tone, the majority depend on sound complexity.

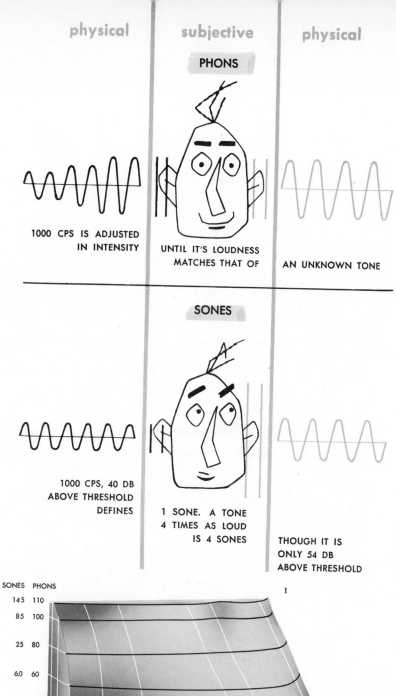

PHONS

1000 CPS IS ADJUSTED IN INTENSITY   UNTIL IT'S LOUDNESS MATCHES THAT OF   AN UNKNOWN TONE

SONES

1000 CPS, 40 DB ABOVE THRESHOLD DEFINES   1 SONE. A TONE 4 TIMES AS LOUD IS 4 SONES   THOUGH IT IS ONLY 54 DB ABOVE THRESHOLD

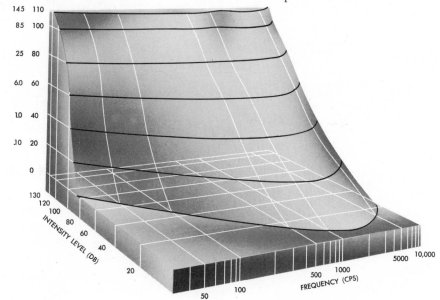

thresholds of hearing

The human ear is limited in its ability to respond to sound. Just as the eye is responsive to only a part of the light spectrum, so the ear is responsive to only a part of the sonic spectrum. Numerous sounds surround us undetected because of these limitations — some sounds are too low in frequency to be heard; many are too high. Frequencies near the upper and lower limits require great intensities before they reach the threshold and for this reason are usually not heard. Other sounds are so intense as to cause feeling, pain, or even physical injury in the ear. These latter sounds we avoid. Although the extent of useful sound appears generous, this area of listening response is, nevertheless, only a small part of physical sound as a whole.

The human auditory response to frequency is commonly accepted as falling between the frequencies of 20 and 20,000 cycles per second, as shown. It is important to understand, however, that no clear generalizations can be made concerning the frequency limitations of hearing since intensity is an essential element, especially near the extremes.

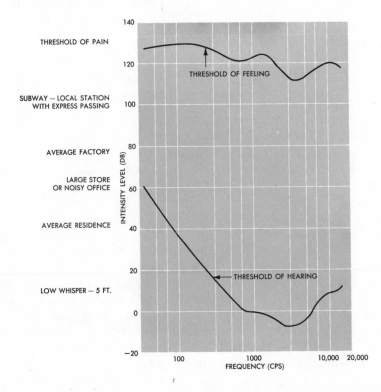

Individuals' thresholds vary greatly at the higher frequencies. Indeed, a person's threshold may vary from time to time. The ear is so constructed that with advancing age it declines in its ability to respond to high frequencies. This relation is brought out in greater detail in a later section. (See also p. 4-31.)

When the intensity of sound is increased to very high levels, frequency components normally considered below or above the thresholds can be made to elicit a hearing response. These intensity levels are near the feeling threshold and, even though the tones can be heard, there is no true perception of pitch. The hearing elicited by these very intense sounds is probably brought about through distortion within the ear which breaks up a portion of the sound energy into components, some of which fall within the range of hearing. Hearing has thus been reported of sounds up to 100,000 and as low as 5 cycles per second.

The intensity limits of hearing extend from the minimum intensities at which a sound can be heard to intensities at which feeling and discomfort begin. This range of useful intensities varies greatly within the frequency limits. The greatest differences occur at the minimum thresholds. The sound-pressure level of discomfort is fairly constant throughout the audible frequencies.

The minimum intensity to which the ear responds varies as much as 80 decibels or more, as can be seen by comparing the areas of least and greatest sensitivity in the facing graph. Throughout the area of greatest sensitivity (2000 to 3000 cycles per second) the ability of the acute ear to respond to pressure is amazing — even the normal ear responds to sound-pressure levels as small as one three-millionth of a gram. Sound pressures near the threshold of pain may be several billion times the minimum threshold pressures.

Within the range of normal hearing, individual differences of minimum thresholds vary 20 decibels or more. One person's threshold may vary 5 decibels within a short period of time. This makes the establishment of a minimum audibility curve a somewhat arbitrary matter. A reference curve has been adopted by the American Standards Association, however, to represent the minimum audible pressure existing in the field surrounding the listener's head. The intensity represented by the curve at a frequency of 1000 cycles per second is selected as zero decibel. This is 0.0002 dyne per square centimeter, or 73.8 decibels below one dyne per square centimeter.

Unlike the minimum threshold, the threshold of discomfort remains at about the same intensity throughout the audible frequencies. As sound reaches a level of about 120 decibels, it becomes uncomfortable to hear; at 130 decibels, sound begins to elicit a feeling sensation; at about 140 decibels, the sensation becomes painful.

just noticeable differences

Most aural communication is based upon detection of changes in the signal. The magnitude of frequency and intensity changes required at the source to produce just-noticeable changes is thus of interest to the designer of signal equipment.

The frequency difference required to produce a just-noticeable change in pitch varies essentially according to frequency — at low frequencies, smaller differences in frequency are detected than at high frequencies. This just-noticeable difference of pitch is not wholly dependent on frequency, however — the sensation level is a contributing factor. Below a sensation level of 20 decibels, the ear rapidly loses its ability to detect frequency changes; above this level, the ear will fairly consistently detect a change of 3 cycles per second in a tone of 1000 cycles or less; beyond that frequency, the just-noticeable difference remains fairly constant at 0.3 of one per cent of the tone's frequency.

Detectability of loudness changes is likewise dependent on both intensity and frequency. At sensation levels of 20 decibels or less the intensity increment that is just noticeable as a loudness change is comparatively large — on the order of 2 to 6 decibels, depending on the frequency. Above a sensation level of about 20 decibels an intensity increment of about ½ to 1 decibel is detectable, except at the frequency extremes, where the increment is somewhat larger. Within the frequency limits of about 500 to 10,000 cycles per second, just-noticeable differences of intensity are smallest.

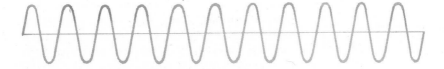

characteristics of pure tones

Studies to determine the relationships existing between the elements of sound and of hearing have been made using pure tones primarily, because numerous subjective attributes associated with complex sounds tend to confuse a listener's judgment. It should not be assumed, however, that the relationships found apply only to pure tones. In some cases the relationships are found to be similar for pure and complex sounds; in other cases they are different. The section titled Characteristics of Complex Sounds deals briefly with the dissimilarities which exist with complex sounds. (See also p. 4-16.)

In studying the influence of the physical dimensions of sound on pitch, it is found that under some conditions each of the dimensions has an effect. Frequency is the major variable although both intensity and duration have some influence.

In a plot of pitch versus frequency, the function is a negatively accelerated curve, when frequency is on a linear scale. When advancing upward from the lower frequency threshold, each unit of pitch requires an increasingly large frequency interval, indicating that a unit of pitch could best be compared with a logarithmic frequency interval. However, as pointed out earlier, a scale of semitones, which are log intervals, does not maintain a constant relation with pitch. If, in our plot of pitch versus frequency, we use a log scale for frequency, the function is an S-shaped curve. In log intervals, pitch advances slowly at lower frequencies, more rapidly throughout the 1000- to 10,000-cycle middle range, and more slowly again as the frequencies approach upper limits of audibility. This relationship can be seen in the example of the mel keyboard,[2] a piano keyboard (based on logarithmic intervals) distorted so that equal distance along the keyboard represents equal pitch.

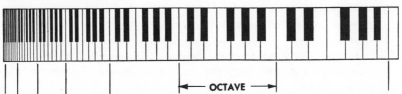

WHEN INCREASED
IN INTENSITY
LOW TONES

SOUND LOWER

HIGH TONES

SOUND HIGHER

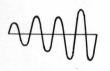

4000 CPS
OR HIGHER

Pitch, probably more than any other phase of hearing, maintains stability under varying sound conditions. However, at certain frequencies the intensity becomes an important variable influencing the pitch of a pure tone. At both low and high frequencies intensity changes can affect pitch changes — with an increase in intensity, low tones (below about 500 cycles per second) appear lower and high tones (above about 4000 cycles per second) appear higher. In the middle frequencies, where the ear is most acute, intensity changes have little, if any, effect on pitch. Tones located between about 500 and 4000 cycles per second maintain almost constant pitch even when varied over wide intervals of intensity.

When the duration of a tone is very short the pitch is affected. There is, in fact, a duration at which the tone will be clearly heard but no pitch will be perceived — the tone will appear as an atonal click when the interval is about 0.01 second or less, although this critical duration is somewhat dependent upon frequency. Above a tone duration of 0.01 second the click gradually begins to take on pitch qualities, but the pitch will normally appear lower than that of another tone of the same frequency but longer duration. An increase of tone duration up to about 0.1 second will result in improved pitch qualities. At that interval the pitch is judged as accurately as any longer tone of the same frequency.

In examining loudness and its relation with the elements of sound, we find that although intensity is the principle factor, frequency and duration also contribute to loudness changes. As in the case of pitch, however, there is no simple relationship between loudness and the physical dimensions.

Since any discussion of the effect of intensity upon loudness is inconclusive unless the remaining variables are held constant, we will assume a 1000-cycle reference tone of more than 0.1-second duration. This is a convenient reference since a 1000-cycle tone is also specified for the loudness measure (sone), loudness-level (phon), and the pitch measure (mel).

In comparing the loudness measure in sones with the intensity measure in decibels, we find that loudness advances slowly at low intensities, then more rapidly as intensity is advanced. As a 1000-cycle tone is advanced from 20 to 40 decibels above threshold, the loudness advances from about 0.1 to 1 sone; as intensity is increased from 40 to 60 decibels, loudness advances from 1 to 6 sones; from 60 to 80 decibels, loudness increases from 6 to 30 sones. Between intensity levels of about 40 to 100 decibels, intensity and loudness approach a straight-line function, but at both lower and higher intensities large deviations occur.

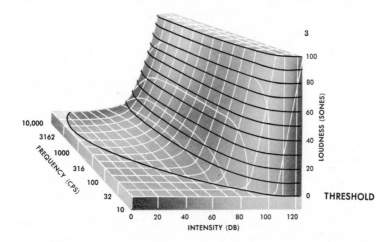

When we consider the influence of frequency on loudness, we find that between the frequencies of about 700 and 4000 cycles per second loudness is maximal and the loudness function is almost identical with that of a 1000-cycle tone. Above and below these frequencies loudness diminishes more and more rapidly with respect to intensity as frequency approaches audible limits. At these frequency extremes, however, loudness increases more rapidly with a similar decibel gain. For example, as the intensity of a 50-cycle tone is increased from 20 to 40 decibels above threshold, its loudness is increased about 50 times — from 1 to 50 sones. A similar increase for a 1000-cycle tone results in a loudness gain of about 10 times — from 0.1 sone to 1 sone. Near the upper frequency limits a similar phenomenon occurs, though less pronounced.

Duration also affects loudness. Maximum loudness is attained at about 0.5 second; beyond this interval there may be a slight decline in loudness as the ear adapts to the sound. For tones of very short duration the loss of loudness is pronounced. This critical duration, below which a tone sharply loses loudness, is about 0.15 to 0.2 second, although it is somewhat dependent on frequency — low-frequency tones lose more loudness than do higher-frequency tones of comparable duration. To maintain equal loudness for tones shorter than this critical duration, the intensity required is inversely proportional to the duration.

characteristics of complex sounds

Although it is important for our understanding of hearing to know of the ear's response to pure tones, it nevertheless remains a fact that rarely are pure tones experienced except under laboratory conditions. This is due partly to the sound-generating source and partly to the characteristics of the ear itself. Few sound sources when caused to vibrate will produce a pure sine-wave tone. A piano string when struck will vibrate not only with a fundamental frequency through its entire length, but it will vibrate in segments at frequencies standing in harmonic relation to the fundamental. Other tone-producing instruments likewise propagate tones with varying harmonic frequencies and intensities.

The pitch of complex sounds depends on the presence of dominant frequency components. Most sounds, even some we classify as noises, have predominant frequency components, hence pitch. The pitch of a number of random frequencies, if limited to a small band, will be centered midway. Thus a segment of white noise, containing all frequency components from 1000 to 1100 cycles per second, would match in pitch a tone of about 1050 cycles. An outstanding characteristic of the complex tone is its pitch stability. The tones produced by musical instruments can be varied over wide ranges of intensity without an appreciable change in pitch because the stabilizing effect of the harmonics located within the middle frequencies tends to keep the pitch from changing. This is not generally true for pure tones.

A number of interesting observations are made in relation to loudness of complex sounds. The mechanism of the ear is so arranged that when tones are sufficiently separated in frequency as to stimulate separate areas of the basilar membrane their loudnesses are additive. For example, if five tones sufficiently separated in frequencies, each of 1-sone loudness, were sounded together in one ear, the over-all loudness would be 5 sones. When the areas of excitation overlap, however, the sounds mask each other and the loudnesses do not summate. This relationship does not hold for separate tones in each ear. The loudnesses of widely separated tones in each ear are not additive. As the tones are brought close enough together to stimulate similar areas on the basilar membranes, the loudnesses begin to summate. Tones identical in frequency and phase in either or both ears are additive in loudness.

The varying harmonic components and intensities which are combined in a complex tone account for a number of subjective attributes of sounds, quality or timbre being one of the most important.

other characteristics

When tones are combined a number of new hearing sensations come into existence which do not occur for single tones. When two tones of the same frequency are played in phase they will appear to be a single tone, but the loudness will be a summation of the two. By altering the phase of one, we hear the same pitch but less loudness. Identical tones exactly opposite in phase cancel out completely and cannot be heard.

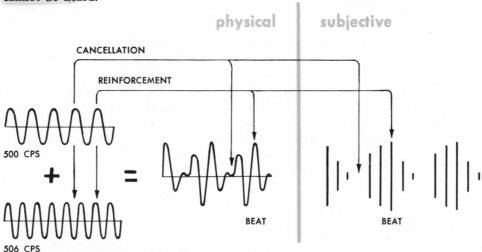

Two tones only slightly different in frequency will be in phase part of the time and out part of the time, causing the loudness to build and fade; these tones are said to *beat*. Beating occurs at a frequency equal to the difference between the two tones. The pitches of the two tones merge and are heard as one tone, called the *intertone*, whose pitch is halfway between the pitches of the two component tones. As the tones are varied as to their separation, beats appear to pass through three distinct stages:

At close frequencies, up to about six beats per second, the beats are most distinct, appearing as smooth variations in loudness; in this stage only the intertone is heard.

When the frequency interval between the tones is increased, the beats are faster and the intertone appears to be throbbing or pulsating. The primary tones can be resolved with the intertone. This change begins at about eight beats per second.

When the tone separation gives rise to more than about 20 beats per second, the intertone becomes faint and appears to "buzz" rather than throb. The two original tones become more predominant over the intertone as the frequency differential becomes greater.

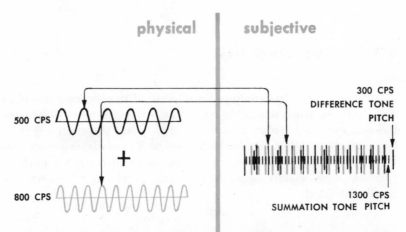

Two tones, so separated in frequency that they excite separate areas on the basilar membrane, appear as two distinct tones and there is no beat. When two such tones are loud, however, there will be heard two supplementary tones. The more distinct will be a *difference tone*, based on the frequency difference between the two tones; somewhat less loud will be a *summation tone*, based on the sum of the original frequencies. When two loud tones are sounded together, the listener will hear four tones, at pitches as shown.

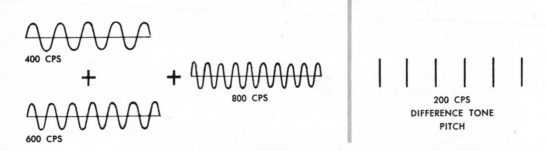

A strange phenomenon of complex tones occurs when several tones are separated by a common frequency interval of 100 cycles or more — the tones will then take on an additional pitch based on the common difference. Thus a pitch is perceived for which no tone exists. This explains how we are often able to hear deep, bass tones from a sound system that is physically incapable of emitting them.

A pure sound wave may be heard as a complex sound, because of aural characteristics which generate harmonics within the ear itself. Known as *aural harmonics*, or *subjective overtones*, these have been measured in complexity up to eight or nine in very loud tones. Aural harmonics appear somewhat sooner and are more pronounced in low- than in higher-frequency tones, occurring by the time most tones are 50 decibels above threshold. As intensity is increased beyond the level at which aural harmonics appear, additional overtones farther removed occur; each successive harmonic appears at a lower loudness.

MASKING

Almost every auditory communications system contains unwanted sounds which raise the hearing threshold and decrease the intelligibility of the desired sound or signal. The amount of masking at any frequency is the number of decibels the quiet threshold of a pure tone is raised because of the masking sound.

effects on a pure tone

When one pure tone masks another pure tone, the intensity and frequency relationships of the tones determine the extent of the masking.

A pure tone is more effective in masking a tone higher than itself than it is one lower. Masking is greatest when the masking frequency is close to the signal frequency and less as the two are more and more separated in frequency.

The masking effect increases as the intensity level of the masking tone rises. The graph[4] shows masking at frequencies from 200 to 4000 cycles per second produced by a tone of 1200 cycles per second. The top curve is for an intensity level of 80 decibels, the lower for one of 40 decibels.

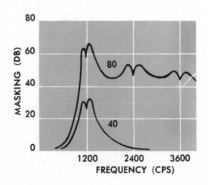

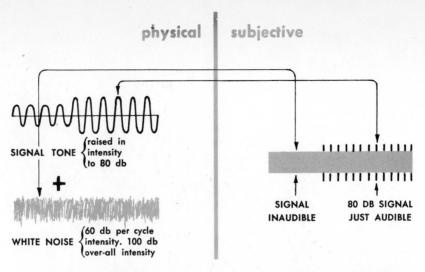

SIGNAL TONE {raised in intensity to 80 db

+

WHITE NOISE {60 db per cycle intensity. 100 db over-all intensity

SIGNAL INAUDIBLE

80 DB SIGNAL JUST AUDIBLE

A white noise has been found to mask a pure-tone signal most effectively. It is possible, however, for the ear to distinguish a pure tone whose intensity level is below that of surrounding white noise, since a large part of the over-all noise intensity is made up of components so far removed in frequency from the signal frequency that they are not effective in the masking of that signal. Only a critical band of the white noise centered on the signal frequency is responsible for any of the masking. The width of this critical band varies over the frequency spectrum, being narrower in the low-frequency end and wider in the high-frequency end. In general, the width of the critical band is approximately 20 times the just noticeable difference of a particular signal frequency. When the total energy in the critical band is just equal to the energy of the signal tone we have complete masking.

Although valuable information is obtained from studies of pure-tone and white-noise masking, rarely is the designer of an acoustical system faced with either. His problem is everyday masking noise, which possesses an irregular spectrum with a few strong components. The most common masking is average room noise. Seacord found that: The average home (50 per cent) has an over-all noise level of 43 decibels, without a radio; with a radio, the level goes up to 50 decibels. The average business establishment has a noise level of 57 decibels. The average factory noise level is 77 decibels.

The spectral composition of these average noises includes mostly low-frequency components (below 3000 cycles per second). The masking effect of average room noise at 43 decibels is shown in the accompanying graph.

The pitch of a pure tone heard above a white noise still sounds about the same as the pitch of a tone heard when no masking exists. When the tone is only slightly above its masked threshold, however, a pitch rise of as much as 10 per cent may occur. The apparent loudness of a pure tone is lowered by white-noise masking.

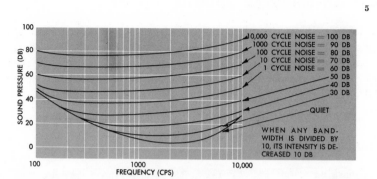

5

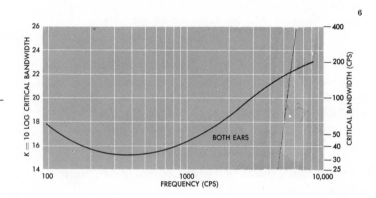

6

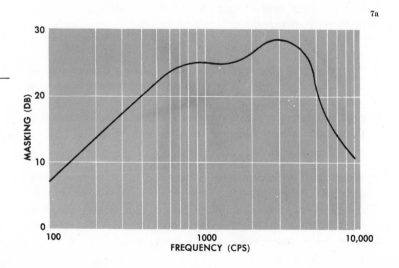

7a

effects on complex sounds

The principles governing masking of pure tones may in general be applied to the masking of complex sounds. The effects differ, however, in that they are complicated by the random character of the complex sound being masked. The section on Speech includes more material on masking effects.

residual masking

A masking sound not only raises the threshold of a simultaneous signal sound but may also affect the threshold of subsequent signal sounds. This phenomenon of masking by preceding sounds is termed *residual masking* or *auditory fatigue*.

Although residual masking varies widely among subjects, the following generalizations can be made about it:

The frequency range of residual masking is similar to that of simultaneous masking and, like it, varies with frequency. It is less for low tones than for high tones, but the extent of fatigue range to frequencies other than that of the fatiguing tone is more pronounced for low tones than for high tones.

The maximum amount of fatigue occurs at or near the fatiguing frequency.

The duration of residual masking is partly determined by the frequency of the masking sound. The ear recovers its original sensitivity sooner after stimulation by low-frequency tones than after high tones.

The intensity of the masking sound influences the duration of fatigue. For low-intensity sounds (30 decibels or so above threshold), the fatigue lasts only a fraction of a second; for high-intensity sounds (110 decibels or above), recovery may require from several minutes to a number of days.

Auditory fatigue increases with duration of exposure. While the ear may recover within several hours from a few minutes' exposure to very intense sounds (130 to 140 decibels), recovery time is much longer following a long period of exposure, even at lower intensities.

SPEECH AND
SPEECH INTELLIGIBILITY

spectrum characteristics

The speech spectrum of the normal voice lies almost entirely within the frequency range of 100 to 8000 cycles per second; the average distribution of components is shown in the graph.[2] Spectral analysis of speech over a period of time has indicated that over half the speech energy is expended in frequencies below 1000 cycles per second. The singing voice covers somewhat greater range but has similar spectral composition.

Speech is a constantly changing pattern of sound with respect to both frequency and intensity. Some speech sounds are characteristically of higher intensity than others; some are of higher frequency. For example, the average power in the word "snowball" is greater than that in the word "velvet"; the frequency components in the word "cool" are lower than those in the word "see." Ordinarily, the vowel and diphthong sounds carry the most speech power, the consonants carry the least. The intensity range from the loudest vowel to the weakest consonant is about 30 to 40 decibels.

Despite their characteristic low intensity, the consonant sounds contribute more to speech intelligibility. This is important when considering the perception of speech under masked or distorted conditions.

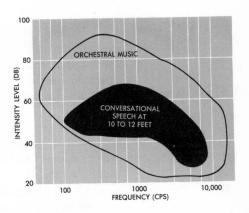

At high frequencies the voice is more directional.

RMS peaks are about 12 db above and the weakest syllables are about 18 db below the average level.

CHANGES IN SOUND PRESSURE LEVEL OF VOICE VS CONDITION

	NORMAL	RAISED VOICE	LOUD VOICE	SHOUTING
Shift in db level	−6	0	+ 6	+ 12

intelligibility

Several terms — discrimination, perception, articulation, and intelligibility — have been used to express the effectiveness of speech. The speech may be presented in a quiet background or may be subjected to masking, distortion, or intensity changes. Articulation improves as the number of sounds per word is increased.

QUIET BACKGROUND

Under ideal conditions of undistorted speech in a quiet background, intensity is the only variable of consequence. The fundamental frequency of the natural voice appears to have no significant effect on intelligibility — a high- or low-pitched voice can be understood equally well.

At an intensity level of approximately 10 decibels, some of the speech sounds can be detected but the pattern cannot be perceived as words. As the level approaches 15 decibels, a small percentage of the words becomes intelligible. Above this level, however, a small increase in intensity makes an increasingly large per cent of the words intelligible, so that when the speech intensity has reached a level of about 40 decibels almost maximum intelligibility has been attained. Above about 100 decibels, speech intelligibility decreases slightly.

NOISE BACKGROUND

Of basic importance to speech intelligibility is the ratio of speech energy to noise energy, expressed as S/N and represented by a decibel value. The over-all sound level of the speech and noise is comparatively unimportant; as long as the intensities of both speech and noise are changed equally, intelligibility varies only slightly. Only by changing the ratio of speech to noise is intelligibility grossly affected. The per cent of word intelligibility for various S/N ratios is shown.[9] It can also be seen that each S/N ratio has an optimal over-all intensity level. As the level is increased beyond this point, intelligibility decreases even though the S/N ratio remains the same.

Voice messages are more intelligible than printed messages to subjects simultaneously engaged in a competing task, when that task is complex.

When speech intelligibility remains above 60 per cent, it is considered satisfactory. If it gets below 30 per cent, it is probably unsatisfactory.

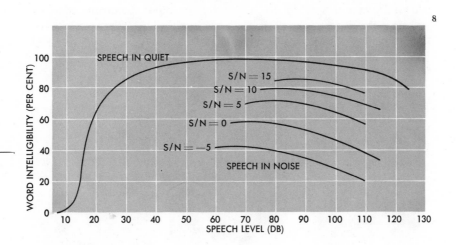

Some speech sounds can be detected as much as 18 decibels below the level of a masking white noise (S/N = −18 decibels) although the threshold of intelligibility is several decibels higher. Such sounds represent only the high-intensity vowels and contribute little to intelligibility. Only after some of the lower-intensity consonant sounds become audible above the masking noise does the speech become intelligible. For satisfactory communication of most voice messages in noise, the speech level should exceed the noise level by at least 6 decibels. This S/N ratio is not optimal, since only about 75 per cent of the words are intelligible. For most messages this percentage is acceptable, since the rest can usually be filled in by the listener. Rarely is it necessary to have perfect intelligibility of a spoken message, because we usually impart more information than is actually needed to get the idea across.

From previous statements we can conclude that maximal masking results when the masking noise is near or below the signal frequency. Since much of the voice energy is in lower frequency components (below 1000 cycles per second), it is expected that high-pitched noises are not as effective in disrupting speech as are low-pitched noises. Of single-frequency components used to mask speech, an intense sine wave of about 300 cycles per second produces the most masking; as the intensity of the tone is lowered, however, the most effective frequency moves upward to about 500 cycles per second.

When the intensity of over-all speech and noise is in excess of about 80 decibels, distortion within the ear itself is a factor in lowering speech intelligibility. Ear plugs have been found to improve speech intelligibility under these conditions. They do not change the S/N ratio but do bring the intensity level of both the speech and noise down by as much as 20 decibels, reducing aural distortion and permitting the speech sounds to become intelligible. Three satisfactory ear plugs are shown, and a table is included to indicate effectiveness through the intensity range.

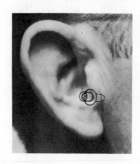 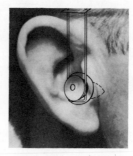 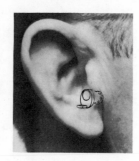

PERCENT IMPROVEMENT IN SPEECH INTELLIGIBILITY WITH EAR PLUGS

LEVEL ABOVE THRESHOLD (DB)	SPEECH TO NOISE RATIO			
	−5 DB	0 DB	5 DB	10 DB
60	−4	−5	−6*	−6*
70	0	−2	−5	−4
80	5	3	0	−1
90	7	6	5	3
100	9	7	7	6
110	11*	9	9*	8

extrapolated

The masking effect of other voices is about as effective as white noise in masking speech. The ear is able to discriminate between two and possibly three voices, but when as many as four or more are combined a single voice cannot be discriminated above the babble.

DISTORTION

As we have seen, speech retains a remarkable degree of intelligibility even when varied over wide ranges of intensity and frequency, or when subjected to masking. But how is intelligibility affected when the speech components are distorted or even when some are eliminated?

There are several methods of distorting speech — the rate at which the speech is presented may be altered; the speech signal may be interrupted; certain components of the signal may be clipped out; or filters may be used to pass only certain frequencies of the signal.

When the speed of presentation is changed (by recording and then replaying at varying rates) all frequency components as well as the rate of speaking are multiplied by a constant factor. Speech may be speeded up by a factor of 1.1 or slowed down to 0.9 of the original rate without adversely affecting its intelligibility. When speeded up by a factor of 1.6 or slowed down by a factor of 0.7, the intelligibility drops to 50 per cent.

The effect of turning speech on and off at periodic intervals is quite pronounced. Generally speaking, if the rate of interruption is sufficiently high (on the order of several thousands per second) speech intelligibility is good, even when the speech is on but about 15 per cent of the time. Speech that is on one-half and off one-half the time has word intelligibility of 40 per cent when interrupted once each second, 85 per cent when interrupted ten times per second, and a slightly lower amount when interrupted 100 times per second; but the figure rises to 95 per cent when interruptions are up to about 2000 times per second. Speech that is on as much as 75 per cent of the time is affected only slightly by interruptions at any rate.

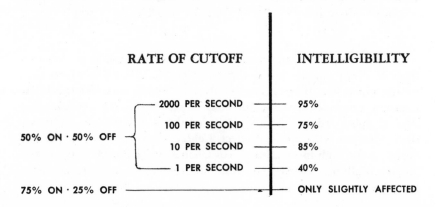

	RATE OF CUTOFF	INTELLIGIBILITY
	2000 PER SECOND	95%
	100 PER SECOND	75%
50% ON · 50% OFF	10 PER SECOND	85%
	1 PER SECOND	40%
75% ON · 25% OFF		ONLY SLIGHTLY AFFECTED

4-27

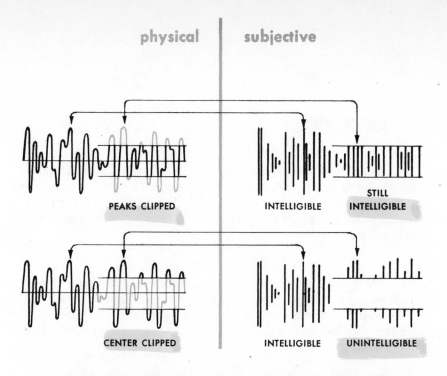

PEAKS CLIPPED   INTELLIGIBLE   STILL INTELLIGIBLE

CENTER CLIPPED   INTELLIGIBLE   UNINTELLIGIBLE

Amplitude clipping is a distortion of speech accomplished by electronic circuits designed to pass only certain amplitude portions of the sound, cutting off, or out, amplitude levels not passed.

Peak clipping cuts off the extremes of sound energy. When the remaining sound energy is sufficiently amplified, the chief effect of peak clipping is a change of speech quality rather than of intelligibility. Peak clipping can be varied as to the extent to which it limits the high-amplitude components. Peak clipping of 6 decibels is hardly perceptible; when clipped 24 decibels most speech is readily intelligible, although it possesses little expression. Even "infinite" clipping, which extends down to the lowest-intensity components, does not completely destroy the speech — in fact, its intelligibility score is still about 70 per cent.

Very little center clipping, on the other hand, is required to make speech completely incomprehensible. As little as 6 decibels of center clipping leaves no intelligible speech at all, while even 2 decibels is comparable to infinite peak clipping in its effect on perception.

The reason for the great differences in the effects of the two types of distortion lies in the fact that the vowel sounds, which contribute much less to intelligibility than do consonants, are the high-intensity components, while the consonants are mostly low-intensity. Peak clipping reduces the amplitude of the vowel sounds but passes the consonants with minimal effect. Center clipping does just the opposite — the high-intelligibility consonants are reduced, leaving the low-intelligibility vowels; the resultant resembles static much more than speech.

"Talkers" tend to speak more intelligibly when the side tone is attenuated above 600 cps.

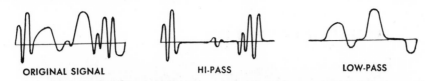

ORIGINAL SIGNAL   HI-PASS   LOW-PASS

Few electronic systems are capable of passing all frequency components with equal fidelity. Some, called filters, have been designed specifically to pass only components above or below a certain frequency, or within certain frequency limits. How much can the speech spectrum be altered by these systems and still retain sufficient intelligibility?

Consider first the effect of high-pass filters that eliminate all frequencies below a selected point. When all frequencies above 600 or 700 cycles per second are passed, almost maximal intelligibility is maintained. As the cutoff point is raised above this frequency, intelligibility suffers; at a cutoff of 1500 cycles, intelligibility drops to about 75 per cent; at 2300 cycles, to 50 per cent; and at 3700 cycles, to 25 per cent.

When the low-pass system is used, passing speech components below 7000 cycles per second, intelligibility is not impaired, although some quality may be lacking. A cutoff at 2000 cycles yields an intelligibility score of 75 per cent; at 1500 a score of 50 per cent; speech components below 1000 cycles are only 25 per cent intelligible.

The midpoint in the effective speech spectrum is about 1900 cycles per second, at which frequency both the low- and high-pass speech-perception scores are equal. The fact that these equal scores are not 50 per cent, however, but 68 per cent, leads to the assumption that when no speech components are cut off more are present than are necessary for maximum intelligibility.

To study a limited band of frequencies, both a high- and a low-pass cutoff are used. A common technique is to center the band at a frequency and vary its width symmetrically above and below this center. Various bands within the voice spectrum can be examined in this manner and the contribution of each to speech intelligibility determined. Intensity is a factor in determining the intelligibility of a limited band of frequencies; in general, as a band is narrowed its intensity must be raised to maintain its intelligibility. At optimal intensity level, a band of 400-cycle width, centered at 1500 cycles, will give an intelligibility score of only 10 per cent; a band of 1000-cycle width will yield about 40 per cent; a band between 250 and 3500 cycles gives intelligibility almost equal to the total voice spectrum but lacks the quality of the full spectrum.

SOUND LOCALIZATION

Our ability to locate sounds is dependent primarily upon binaural cues, which resolve into differences in loudness, in time of arrival, and in sound composition. For some sounds there may be differences in phase which assist in localization. Probably the maximum usefulness of these cues is obtained by moving the head so that the sound strikes the ears in a number of different ways. From experience, we expect the sounds to change in proportion as the head is moved and the relationships are changed.

SOUND
SOURCE

SHADOW
ZONE

A difference in the intensity level of a sound at the two ears shifts the apparent direction of the sound toward the ear having the higher level. This effect can be aided or counteracted by superimposing a time difference operating in the same or opposite direction respectively.

When a click in one ear leads that in the other by about 0.03 millisecond, the sound just begins to shift toward the first side; when there is a time difference of 0.65 millisecond or more, the sound appears completely localized on the side of first arrival, this localization remaining until the time difference becomes so great (3 milliseconds or more) that fusion is lost and the sound is heard separately in the two ears. Sounds of equal level arriving at the two ears at the same instant are localized in the median plane (directly ahead, behind, or overhead). Sounds at either side are rarely mislocated as being on the opposite side; however, large errors are made in locating sounds as up or down, ahead or behind.

Pure tones are not as accurately localized as are complex sounds, probably because complex sounds give additional cues which the ear compares. Of the pure tones, we are best able to locate those between the frequencies 500 and 700 cycles per second. Low- and high-frequency tones are easier to locate than middle-frequency tones. The largest errors seem to occur around 2000 cycles per second.

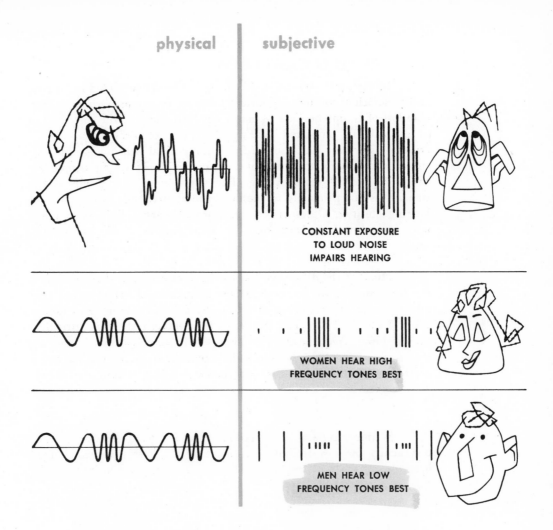

CONSTANT EXPOSURE
TO LOUD NOISE
IMPAIRS HEARING

WOMEN HEAR HIGH
FREQUENCY TONES BEST

MEN HEAR LOW
FREQUENCY TONES BEST

HEARING
WITHIN THE POPULATION

Hearing acuity varies greatly within the population. The differences can be explained as being due chiefly to normal individual variations, age factors, sex, and noisy environment background. These do not include the small percentage of the population having unusual hearing ability or loss due to anomalies or diseases.

"Normal" hearing covers a considerable range of ability. The auditory thresholds even within a homogeneous age and background group will vary widely. This is due to individual differences within the normal hearing group which may vary 20 decibels or more, as well as differences within the individual, which commonly cause the threshold to vary as much as 5 decibels or more within a relatively short period of time.

In a general way, normal hearing has been considered as hearing ability sufficient to carry on normal listening functions without noticeable loss of comprehension. A more vigorous study of the distribution of normal and impaired hearing, however, requires more specific criteria. The most common yardstick for normal hearing is based on the central hearing tendency of a large sample of young people between 20 and 29 years of age. The selection of this group as the standard is due primarily to the detrimental effect age has upon most hearing abilities. Other criteria of normal hearing have been based upon the central tendency of an over-all sample of the population.

Much of the difference in hearing acuity within the population can be accounted for in terms of age differences. Advancing age usually results in the lowering of sensitivity for the higher tones (above about 1500 to 2000 cycles per second), although there is little loss in the lower frequencies. The changes in sensitivity with age are shown, for men, with the zero point obtained from the median value of the total sample of male and female subjects within the decade 20 to 29 years.

Within comparable age groups, men and women differ in auditory acuity. At low frequencies, below 1760 cycles per second, men hear better than women; at higher frequencies women hear better than men.

Some hearing loss is directly related to past exposure to loud noises. Although individual losses vary widely, exposure to high-intensity noises (generally considered in excess of 85 db) over long periods of time almost inevitably results in permanent hearing impairment. As in the case of residual masking, occupational hearing losses occur principally at the frequencies of the noise, but prolonged exposure results in loss in all parts of the scale.

The important consequence of hearing loss is, of course, the impairment of verbal communication. The relationship of such impairment with hearing loss measured in decibels was studied in a survey conducted by the U.S. Public Health Service. The persons tested classified their hearing abilities in one of the five categories indicated on the graph[7b] and their actual hearing loss in the speech-frequency range was measured to give the curve corresponding to the appropriate group. From data collected during the 1939-1940 World's Fairs in San Francisco and New York, another graph[7c] was compiled, showing hearing loss with respect to frequency.

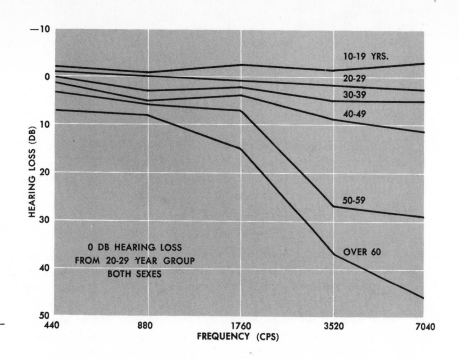

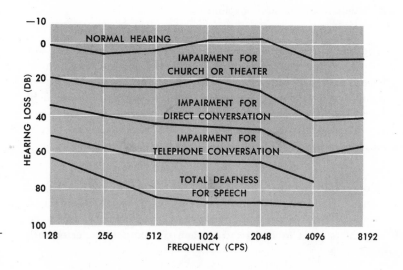

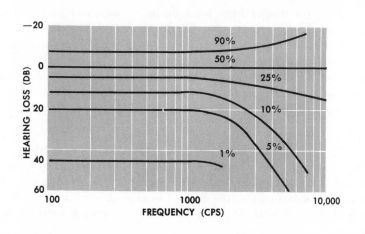

SOUND AND PERFORMANCE

Sound, extending in reaction beyond the auditory system, may influence the performance of a task other than hearing and may contribute to such feelings as boredom, fatigue, or relaxation. In terms of performance, some sounds may be inhibitive, some have no appreciable effect, and some may be facilitative.

Any increase in noise level above threshold tends to increase muscular tension and consequently increase expenditure of energy. For muscular performance tasks not requiring fine coordination and precision, noise apparently has little adverse effect, even at such levels as 120-130 decibels for short periods of time, and may, in fact, slightly improve performance for a brief time. Fine muscular tasks requiring a high degree of coordination and precision, however, are adversely affected by noise. Prolonged exposure to the noise will gradually result in a degree of accommodation.

The effect of noise on mental performance varies as the task changes in complexity. Simple repetitive tasks are not affected, although more energy is required to maintain the level of performance. Any mental activity demanding intense concentration is hindered by noise. Some adaptation to continued noise is possible in mental performance. There is no apparent effect of noise upon visual accommodation, perspective, dark adaptation, or distance judgment.

Workers in a noisy background are more quickly fatigued, more nervous and irritable than workers in a quiet background. High-frequency noise is more annoying than low-frequency, and irregularly variable sounds more irritating than continuous or periodically changing sounds.

Extensive studies have been made in industrial plants of the effect of music of various types (classic, popular, slow, fast, etc.) on work. The results are somewhat inconclusive because of the number of uncontrolled factors, but it is agreed that music does facilitate performance of simple repetitive tasks and, in some instances, has tended to decrease accidents. On tasks requiring mental concentration, music is frequently distracting.

The outstanding effects of music are upon the morale of the worker — it will relieve boredom and fatigue, aid relaxation, promote a feeling of well-being, and improve employee interrelationships. Results of polls indicated that the manual worker almost unanimously approves of music at work and feels that it improves working conditions.

references

The author wishes to acknowledge his gratitude to the publishers mentioned below for permission to use material based on the following articles and books:

1. Stevens, S. S., and H. Davis, *Hearing, Its Psychology and Physiology*, Wiley, 1938, p. 124.

2. Boring, E. G., *et al*, *Foundations of Psychology*, Wiley, 1948, p. 323.

3. Stevens, S. S. (editor), *Handbook of Experimental Psychology*, Wiley, 1951, p. 1002.

4. Fletcher, H., *Speech and Hearing*, van Nostrand, 1943, p. 169.

5. Hawkins, J. E., and S. S. Stevens, *Masking of Signals by Noise*, Harvard University, Psycho-Acoustic Laboratory, Report no. MHR-125 (also listed as OSRD 5387), 1 October 1945, p. 9.

6. French, N. R., and J. C. Steinberg, "Factors Governing the Intelligibility of Speech Sounds," *Acoustical Society of America, Journal*, vol. 19, January 1947, p. 97.

7. Knudsen, V. O., and C. M. Harris, *Acoustical Designing in Architecture*, Wiley, 1950. a., p. 30. b., p. 24. c., p. 25.

8. Chapanis, A., *et al*, *Lectures on Men and Machines — An Introduction to Human Engineering*, Systems Research Laboratory (Special Devices Center, Office of Naval Research), Johns Hopkins University, Report no. 166-I-19 (RESTRICTED), 1947, pp. 127, 129.

body measurement

The data presented in this chapter are intended primarily for use in the design of equipment and layout of workspace. Measurement of the human body, however, has been performed for many different purposes, including the classification of body types according to race, geographical location, age, and sex.

Anthropometric data (human body measurements) are normally taken with the human subject placed in a rigid, static position. It does not represent the dynamic, pliable human body which stretches, bends, twists, or relaxes. It is also important to note that anthropometric data represent statistics and therefore the several dimensions cannot be combined to "create" a single human body. In other words, it is possible to find a person with the height of the tallest man and yet find that his arm reach is not necessarily that of the man with the longest arm reach.

In using the data on the following pages, consider dimensions from a functional point of view: i.e., short or lesser dimensions should be used for defining reach limits, and long or greater dimensions should be used for defining clearances.

The ideal approach would be to create a special set of dimensions based on the exact population of users for the equipment being designed. For example, if one were designing the cockpit of a military aircraft for U.S. Air Force, it would be logical to collect anthropometric data on Air Force pilots. Even here, it is possible to find that fighter pilots differ from bomber pilots.

In measuring a given population, it is generally desirable to identify the distribution of measurements. Most of the persons measured will fall somewhere in the middle of the distribution while a small number will appear at each end of the distribution. It is seldom practical from the cost standpoint to design for the entire population; rather, one selects a reasonable cut out of the middle. For example, it is common practice to design for all those people between the 5th and 95th percentiles — there are so few people below the 5th and above the 95th percentiles that it is not practical to increase the cost and difficulty of design by including them.

TYPICAL ANTHROPOMETRIC NOMENCLATURE

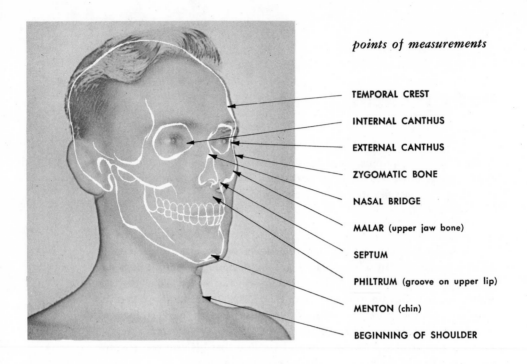

points of measurements

TEMPORAL CREST

INTERNAL CANTHUS

EXTERNAL CANTHUS

ZYGOMATIC BONE

NASAL BRIDGE

MALAR (upper jaw bone)

SEPTUM

PHILTRUM (groove on upper lip)

MENTON (chin)

BEGINNING OF SHOULDER

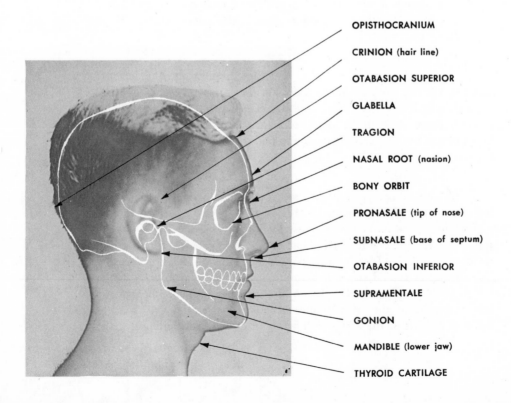

OPISTHOCRANIUM

CRINION (hair line)

OTABASION SUPERIOR

GLABELLA

TRAGION

NASAL ROOT (nasion)

BONY ORBIT

PRONASALE (tip of nose)

SUBNASALE (base of septum)

OTABASION INFERIOR

SUPRAMENTALE

GONION

MANDIBLE (lower jaw)

THYROID CARTILAGE

HEAD MEASUREMENTS

There are a number of identifying characteristics of different head types which may be measured and correlated. The description of the measurements and the accompanying illustrations, showing points of measurements, are based on studies made by the Army Air Corps during World War II.[2] The spreading and sliding calipers are used for most of these measurements.

BIOCULAR DIAMETER   distance between external canthi

INTEROCULAR DIAMETER   distance between internal canthi

BITRAGION DIAMETER   contact distance between the two tragia

BIZYGOMATIC DIAMETER   greatest breadth across zygomatic bones, points marked with skin pencil

BIGONIAL DIAMETER   distance between gonia, measured with firm contact

NASAL ROOT BREADTH   distance between junctures of cheek bone and nasal bone, just inside internal canthi

NASAL BRIDGE BREADTH   width between juncture of nasal skeleton end and cheek bone

NASAL BASE BREADTH   distance across alae (wings) of nose, when in natural rest position

NASAL ROOT SALIENT   distance between internal canthus and nasion

NASAL BRIDGE SALIENT   distance from tip of bony bridge in midline of nose to juncture of bony sidewall with cheek

NASAL TIP SALIENT   distance from nasal wing to pronasale

MANDIBLE HEIGHT   distance between lower edge of center of menton and upper tip of gum between two central lower teeth

TRAGION-NASAL ROOT   distance between tragion and deepest concavity of nasal root

TRAGION-SUBNASALE

TRAGION-OTOBASION INFERIOR

TRAGION-GONION

MENTON-PHILTRUM   distance between midpoint of lower edge of chin and midpoint of philtrum

PHILTRUM-OTOBASION INFERIOR   distance between midpoint of philtrum and otobasion inferior

SUPRAMENTALE-OTOBASION INFERIOR

SUBNASALE-EXTERNAL CANTHUS

EAR IMPLANTATION LENGTH   distance between otobasion superior and otobasion inferior

CHIN PROJECTION   distance between gonion and most forward point on vertical midline of menton

CHIN-NECK PROJECTION   distance between tip of thyroid cartilage and midpoint of menton

MINIMUM FRONTAL DIAMETER   smallest distance between temporal crests, with moderate pressure

UPPER FACE HEIGHT   distance between nasion and lower tip of gum between two central upper teeth

HEAD HEIGHT   average perpendicular distance between tragion point and midlongitudinal line on top of head, measured on both sides, when head is in a position such that the line between the tragion point and the bottom of the bony orbit is horizontal

HEAD CIRCUMFERENCE   maximum of three measurements above eyebrows

HEAD BREADTH   greatest horizontal breadth of head above ear openings, wherever found, with moderate pressure on caliper points

INTERPUPILLARY DIAMETER   distance between centers of pupils, when subject is looking straight forward

BIMALAR DIAMETER   distance across malars, measured to midpoints of malars perpendicularly below external canthi when head is in horizontal eye-ear position

MOUTH BREADTH   distance between two corners of mouth in natural position, to edge of line of lip juncture, with contact only

CHIN BREADTH   maximum width of chin, measured by contact only, between points of intersection of mandible and menton

NECK BREADTH   diameter of neck halfway between otobasion inferior and shoulder, with contact only

FACE HEIGHT

CRINION-MENTON distance between hair line in middle of forehead and midpoint of lower edge of chin

NASION-MENTON distance between nasion and midpoint of lower edge of chin

NOSE HEIGHT distance between nasion and subnasale

NOSE LENGTH distance between nasion and pronasale

NASAL TIP HEIGHT distance between subnasale and pronasale

MENTON-SUPRAMENTALE distance between midpoint of lower edge of chin and supramentale (angle between chin and lower lip)

HEAD LENGTH distance between glabella and opisthocranion, with moderate pressure

EAR LENGTH maximum distance along axis of ear

NECK DEPTH diameter between tip of thyroid cartilage and back of neck, taken perpendicular to axis of neck, with contact only

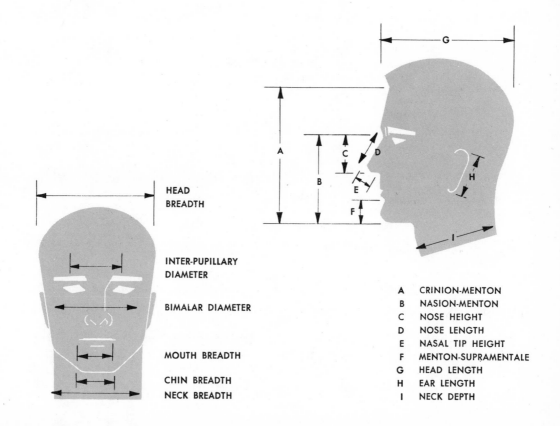

HEAD BREADTH

INTER-PUPILLARY DIAMETER

BIMALAR DIAMETER

MOUTH BREADTH

CHIN BREADTH

NECK BREADTH

A   CRINION-MENTON
B   NASION-MENTON
C   NOSE HEIGHT
D   NOSE LENGTH
E   NASAL TIP HEIGHT
F   MENTON-SUPRAMENTALE
G   HEAD LENGTH
H   EAR LENGTH
I   NECK DEPTH

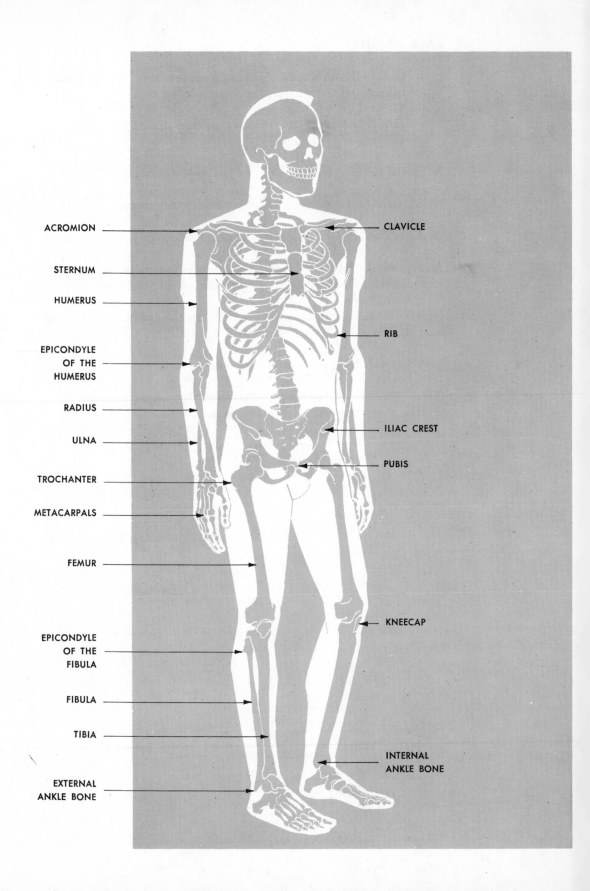

ACROMION

CLAVICLE

STERNUM

HUMERUS

RIB

EPICONDYLE
OF THE
HUMERUS

RADIUS

ULNA

ILIAC CREST

PUBIS

TROCHANTER

METACARPALS

FEMUR

KNEECAP

EPICONDYLE
OF THE
FIBULA

FIBULA

TIBIA

INTERNAL
ANKLE BONE

EXTERNAL
ANKLE BONE

TRUNK-LIMB MEASUREMENTS

The proper design of equipment which will facilitate most efficient use by the human operator requires, among other factors, information concerning dimensions of all parts of the body, in various positions. The measurements given here are adapted from a list[2] developed by the Army Air Corps during World War II, primarily for aircraft personnel records. They are applicable, however, to innumerable other fields of operation.

BIACROMIAL   distance between acromial points — external border of shoulder blade (clavicle)

CHEST DEPTH   dimension through chest (front to back) between sternum and spinal groove

BI-ILIAC BREADTH   maximum distance across brim of hip bones, when subject is standing with heels together

BIEPICONDYLAR (elbow)   distance between outer elbow projections when subject is seated with hands on sides of thighs, upper arm vertical and pressed against trunk

BITROCHANTERIC   maximum lateral distance measured across buttocks when subject is seated with trunk erect and knees together

STERNUM HEIGHT   vertical distance from lower tip of sternum to floor when subject is standing

LOWER RIB HEIGHT   vertical distance from lower edge of last front-attached rib to floor when subject is standing

NAVEL HEIGHT   vertical distance from center of navel to floor, when subject is standing

ILIAC CREST HEIGHT   vertical distance from top of iliac crest to floor when subject is standing

PUBIC HEIGHT   vertical distance from pubis to floor when subject is standing

STANDING KNEE HEIGHT   vertical distance from top of kneecap to floor when subject is standing

BIEPICONDYLAR (knee)   horizontal distance between lateral projections of knees when subject is seated with knees and feet together

EXTERNAL ANKLE HEIGHT   vertical distance from lower end of fibula to floor

INTERNAL ANKLE HEIGHT   vertical distance from lower end of tibia to floor

ANKLE BREADTH   distance between projections at lower ends of tibia and fibula

ANKLE THICKNESS   distance measured transverse to breadth

WEIGHT

STATURE   distance from floor to vertex of head, measured from either front or back when subject is standing with heels together, back straight, and head in eye-ear horizontal plane

BIDELTOID   maximum contact dimension across deltoid muscles when subject has arms at sides, palms forward

CHEST BREADTH   dimension across chest at nipple level

ABDOMINAL DEPTH   maximum horizontal contact dimension, front to back

CROTCH HEIGHT   vertical distance from crotch to floor, when subject is standing

FOOT LENGTH   distance between heel and longest toe of left foot when subject is standing with weight even on both feet

FOOT BREADTH   maximum distance across left foot, when subject is standing with weight even on both feet

_____

CHEST CIRCUMFERENCE   horizontal circumference just above nipples, measurement taken during quiet breathing

UPPER ARM CIRCUMFERENCE   horizontal circumference at the maximum of the biceps muscle

FOREARM CIRCUMFERENCE   circumference taken halfway between elbow and wrist

THIGH CIRCUMFERENCE   distance around thigh of left leg halfway between crotch and knee when subject is standing

CALF CIRCUMFERENCE   average of three measurements at maximum horizontal distance around left calf when subject is standing with weight even on both feet

ELBOW-SEAT distance between level of seat and elbow tip when subject is sitting erect with upper arm vertical, forearm horizontal

SITTING HEIGHT vertical distance (measured along back) from table top to crest of head when subject is seated erectly on table with backs of knees against table edge, lower legs dangling freely, and head in eye-ear horizontal plane

TRUNK HEIGHT vertical distance (measured in front) from table top to upper edge of sternum, when subject is seated as in sitting-height measurement

BUTTOCK-KNEE horizontal distance between buttock and skin over right kneecap when subject is seated as in sitting-height measurement

KNEECAP HEIGHT vertical distance from floor (at base of heel) to top of muscle mass near end of thigh bone when subject is seated with feet on floor

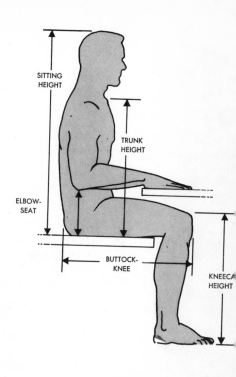

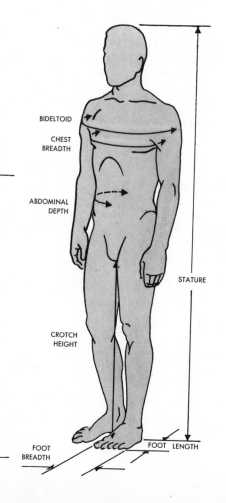

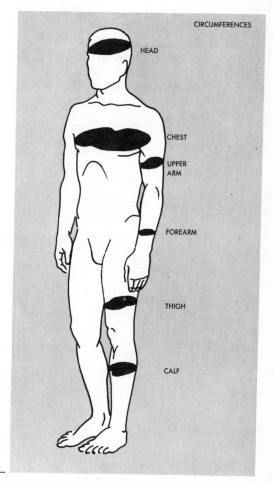

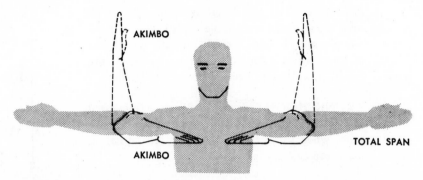

SPAN

TOTAL   distance between tips of middle fingers at maximum arm stretch without straining

AKIMBO   distance between elbow points when subject stands with arms flexed in horizontal plane, wrists straight, palms down, fingers straight and together, and thumbs touching chest; or, measurement may be taken with upper arms horizontal, forearms vertical

ANTERIOR ARM REACH   distance from wall to tip of right middle finger when subject attains maximum forward reach with both arms on standing with heels, buttocks, middle of back (in lateral sense) and occiput against the wall

ARM LENGTH   length of arm from top of clavicle to tip of middle finger with arm down by the side of the body

SHOULDER-ELBOW   distance from top of acromion to tip of elbow, measured when subject is sitting erect, with upper arm vertical, forearm horiontal

FOREARM LENGTH   distance from elbow tip to tip of middle finger with arm flexed at the elbow

WRIST BREADTH   distance between outside projection of distal end of ulna and that of radius at wrist joint

WRIST THICKNESS   the dimension transverse to wrist breadth

HAND LENGTH   distance from end of small wrist bone at base of thumb to tip of middle finger of right hand, palm up, with fingers extended and together

HAND BREADTH   distance between outside projections of distal ends of second and fifth metacarpals of the right hand, fingers extended and together

SOMATOTYPING

Somatotyping is a means of numerical classification for various body types. A somatotype is designated by three numerals, one for each component. These three numerals indicate the degree to which a subject exhibits each of the three components — the numeral "1" stands for the lowest observed amount of the component; the numeral "7" stands for the most extreme dominance of the component.

The actual measuring is done from photographs, as opposed to direct body measure. A grid consisting of 2-inch squares is usually set up as a background for the picture, chiefly for defining the horizontal. Seven diameters are measured in five regions of the body. All material on somatotyping is based on Sheldon's work.[16]

The three component dominances and their characteristics are:

ENDOMORPHY   soft, round form with loose, flabby tissue, small bones, and spherical head; body of relatively low density, which floats in water; physically weak; mean stature, 66.3 inches; mean weight, 179 pounds. Numerically, the extreme is 711.

MESOMORPHY   massive, solid form with cubical head, heavy muscles; physically awkward — hard and muscular, but muscle-bound; mean stature, 68.4 inches; mean weight, 141 pounds. Numerically, the extreme is 171.

ECTOMORPHY   slender limbs and body, with slight head, small face, fragile features; physically spry, great walker; mean stature, 69.8 inches; mean weight, 141 pounds. Numerically, the extreme is 117.

FIRST REGION
head · face · neck

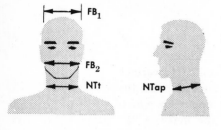

FB₁ (Facial Breadth One) Distance across head taken at the upper juncture of ear and head (frontal picture)

FB₂ (Facial Breadth Two) Distance across head taken at the lower juncture of ear and head (frontal picture)

NTap (Neck Thickness, anteroposterior) Shortest diameter of the neck (lateral picture)

NTt (Neck Thickness, transverse) Shortest diameter of the neck (frontal picture)

SECOND REGION
thoric trunk

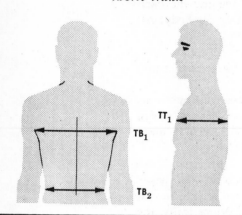

TB₁ (Trunk Breadth One) Distance between the uppermost visible points on the lines formed by the folds between arms and body (dorsal picture)

TT₁ (Trunk Thickness One) Horizontal diameter of the trunk at a point midway between the level of the center of the nipple and the angle between the neck and the chest (lateral picture)

TB₂ (Trunk Breadth Two) Minimum diameter at the narrowest level of the waist (dorsal picture)

THIRD REGION
arms · shoulders · hands

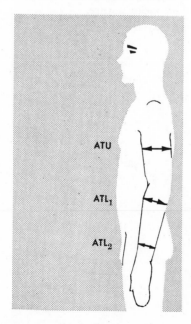

ATU (Arm Thickness Upper) Arm diameter, in a plane perpendicular to the axis of the arm, at a level midway between the forward depression of the elbow and the top of the shoulder (lateral picture)

ATL₁ (Arm Thickness Lower One) Forearm diameter, in a plane perpendicular to the axis of the forearm, at the level of greatest thickness below the elbow (lateral picture)

ATL₂ (Arm Thickness Lower Two) Diameter, in a plane perpendicular to the axis of the forearm, at a level two inches above the angle formed by the juncture of arm and thumb. (The 2-inch measurement is laid off on the arm by adjusting dividers to the width of one of the 2-inch background squares.) The back of the hand must lie in a plane approximately at right angles to the axis of the camera (lateral picture)

TT₂ (Trunk Thickness Two) Minimum horizontal diameter at the level of the waistline (lateral picture)

TB₃ (Trunk Breadth Three) Maximum horizontal diameter at the widest level of the hips* (dorsal picture)

TT₃ (Trunk Thickness Three) Horizontal diameter at the level defined photographically as the vertex of the angle formed by the skin line of the abdomen and the upper line of the pubic hair (lateral picture)

* The points are usually found over the trochanters; but in high endomorphy they are frequently above the iliac crests, and in high mesomorphy they are often well below the trochanters, as is much more frequently the case with women.

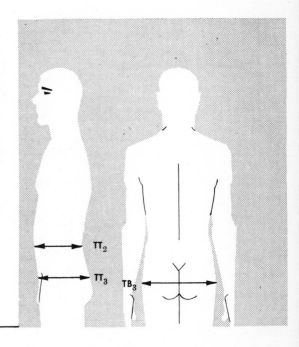

FIFTH REGION
legs · feet

LTU₁ (Leg Thickness Upper One) Horizontal diameter at the level of the center of the photographic angle formed by the buttock and leg (lateral picture)

LTU₂ (Leg Thickness Upper Two) Horizontal diameter at the level of the photographic center of the slight hollow immediately above the kneecap* (lateral picture)

LTL₁ (Leg Thickness Lower One) Maximum diameter at the level of the greatest thickness of the left calf, in a plane perpendicular to the axis of the leg (dorsal picture)

LTL₂ (Leg Thickness Lower Two) Minimum diameter at the narrowest point on the left ankle (dorsal picture)

* In rare cases (of extreme endomorphy) in which this hollow cannot be seen photographically, the measurement is taken at the upper margin of the kneecap.

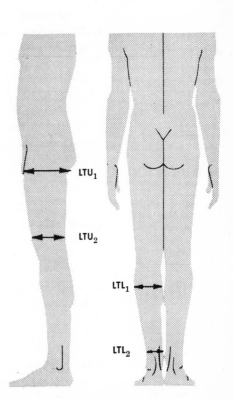

5-13

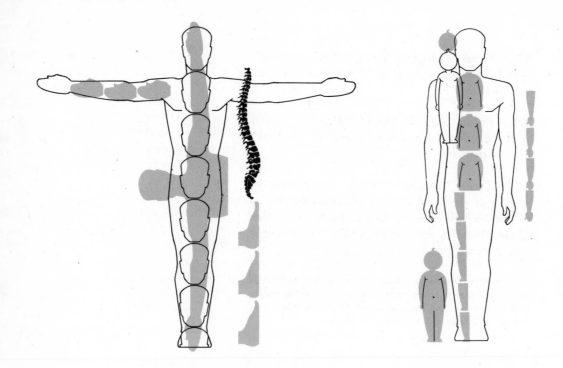

MEASUREMENT DATA

Ancient artists, as far back as the Greek or earlier, studied body-member relationships and developed a "rule of thumb" for ideal proportions of the adult figure. They also noticed the surprisingly different proportion relationships in the body of the average child as compared with those of the adult.

In this chapter, an attempt has been made to incorporate as many actual measurement data as possible to give a picture of the whole body as well as of the limbs and their relationship to the rest of the body.

When considering the size of limbs and the range of body and limb movements, we must take into account the fact that the problems that have risen in the past have been specific for the task concerned. As a consequence, work in this field is rather incomplete and there are, of course, certain discrepancies from one study to another. In these instances, the cross relationship of variable factors must be taken into account.

A table of component dimensions is presented on pages 5-17 and 5-19 of this chapter.

In general, the data contained in this book reflect the guide dimensions of a rather select population representing military personnel between the 5th and 95th percentiles. The reason is fairly simple — it would take an entire book to present all of the data which has been collected over the past 100 years for all types of human body dimensions. The data presented are useful only as a guide and should be considered as "ball-park figures," to be used in developing a first cut at the dimensional aspects of equipment design. The data will serve their best purpose if used, for instance, to establish dimensions for an early mock-up. Once such a mock-up is constructed, it should be evaluated by trying it out on a number of different sizes of people: i.e., tall-slender people, tall-heavy people, short-slender people, short-fat people, and so on. Find people with extra-short arms and legs to check out the location of controls or to see over an instrument panel, and people who are tall and long-legged to check out clearances.

When it is necessary to design special devices such as helmets, eyepieces, or other items which must be worn, it is advisable to get assistance from a specialist who understands the intricacies of body dimensions and their interaction with certain design factors.

In designing equipment for military personnel, the designer will find that the population of users is more limited than that of ordinary civilian populations. This makes the job easier, usually. Certain occupations also limit the size of their personnel — which makes the design job more definitive. For example, the selection of personnel for space operations is based on size and weight restrictions within the vehicle itself, and thus the population of users is much more limited. On the other hand, truck drivers for civilian vehicles may vary over an extremely wide range. Design with flexibility in mind wherever possible: i.e., provide a range of mechanical adjustment. Do not be caught in the trap of designing for the "average man." There is no average man, other than as a statistical artifact.

In this chapter we have tried to present, besides a compact tabulation of suggested human body dimensions, other information which will help the designer to understand more about human body measures. In addition, certain other information is provided to aid in understanding and reading other technical documents or reports which the designer may wish to consult — but which are written in language suited more to the anthropologist than to the designer.

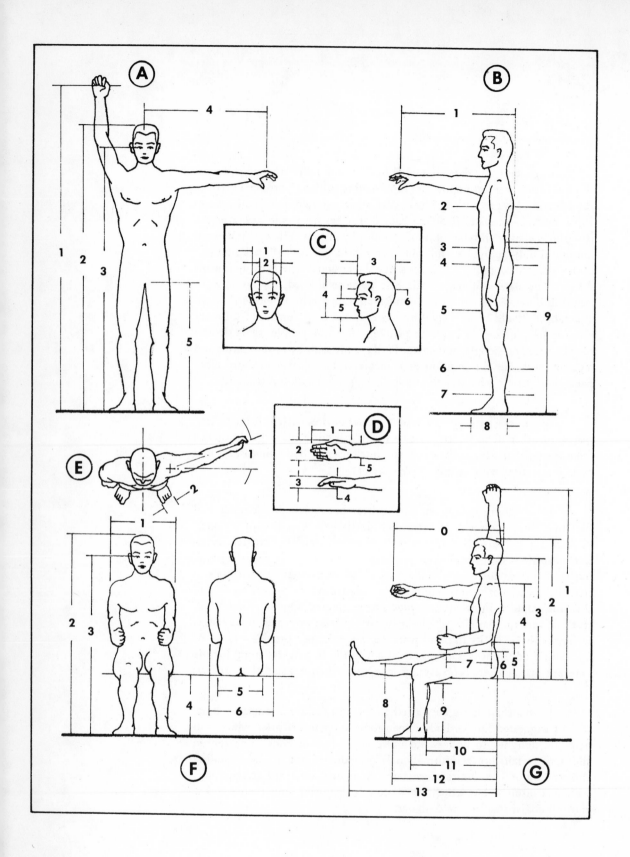

MALE HUMAN BODY DIMENSIONS

Selected dimensions of the human body (ages 18 to 45) suitable for initial design of crew space and equipment. Locations of dimensions correspond to illustrations on the page at the left.

	DIMENSIONAL ELEMENT	DIMENSION (in inches except where noted)	
		5th PERCENTILE	95th PERCENTILE
	Weight	132 LB	201 LB
A	1 Vertical reach	77.0	89.0
	2 Stature	65.0	73.0
	3 Eye to floor	61.0	69.0
	4 Side arm reach from CL of body	29.0	34.0
	5 Crotch to floor	30.0	36.0
B	1 Forward arm reach	28.0	33.0
	2 Chest circumference	35.0	43.0
	3 Waist circumference	28.0	38.0
	4 Hip circumference	34.0	42.0
	5 Thigh circumference	20.0	25.0
	6 Calf circumference	13.0	16.0
	7 Ankle circumference	8.0	10.0
	8 Foot length	9.8	11.3
	9 Elbow to floor	41.0	46.0
C	1 Head width	5.7	6.4
	2 Interpupillary distance	2.27	2.74
	3 Head length	7.3	8.2
	4 Head height	—	10.2
	5 Chin to eye	—	5.0
	6 Head circumference	21.5	23.5
D	1 Hand length	6.9	8.0
	2 Hand width	3.7	4.4
	3 Hand thickness	1.05	1.28
	4 Fist circumference	10.7	12.4
	5 Wrist circumference	6.3	7.5
E	1 Arm swing, aft	40 degrees	40 degrees
	2 Foot width	3.5	4.0
F	1 Shoulder width	17.0	19.0
	2 Sitting height to floor (std chair)	52.0	56.0
	3 Eye to floor (std chair)	47.4	51.5
	4 Standard chair	18.0	18.0
	5 Hip breadth	13.0	15.0
	6 Width between elbows	15.0	20.0
G	0 Arm reach (finger grasp)	30.0	35.0
	1 Vertical reach	45.0	53.0
	2 Head to seat	33.8	38.0
	3 Eye to seat	29.4	33.5
	4 Shoulder to seat	21.0	25.0
	5 Elbow rest	7.0	11.0
	6 Thigh clearance	4.8	6.5
	7 Forearm length	13.6	16.2
	8 Knee clearance to floor	20.0	23.0
	9 Lower leg height	15.7	18.2
	10 Seat length	17.0	21.5
	11 Buttock-knee length	21.0	26.5
	12 Buttock-toe clearance	32.0	37.0
	13 Buttock-foot length	39.0	46.0

NOTE: All except critical dimensions have been rounded off to the nearest inch. For more thorough analysis see Hertzberg et al.[3]

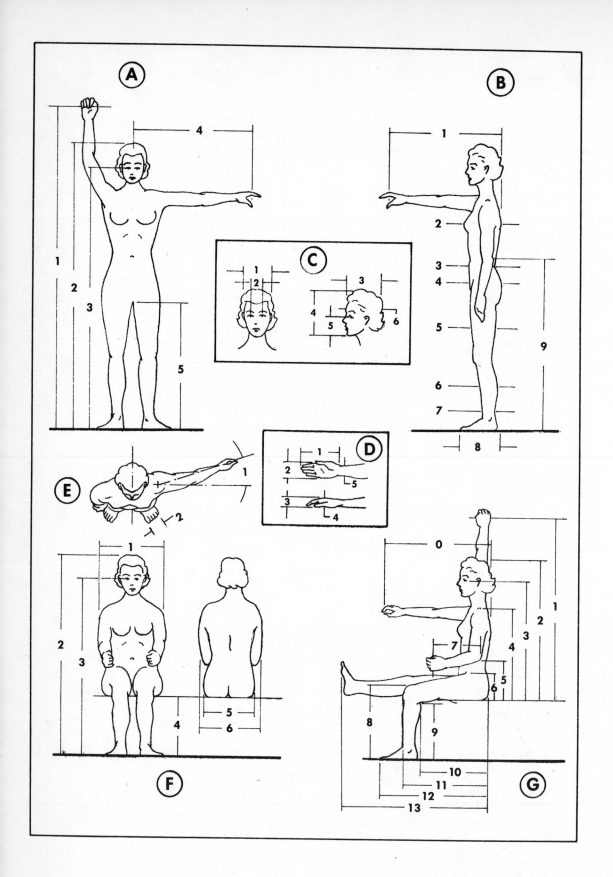

FEMALE HUMAN BODY DIMENSIONS

Selected dimensions of the human body (ages 18 to 45) suitable for initial design of work-place and equipment. Locations of dimensions correspond to illustrations on the page at the left.

	DIMENSIONAL ELEMENT	DIMENSION (in inches except where noted)	
		5th PERCENTILE	95th PERCENTILE
	Weight	102 LB	150 LB
A	1 Vertical reach	69.0	81.0
	2 Stature	60.0	69.0
	3 Eye to floor	56.0	64.0
	4 Side arm reach from CL of body	27.0	38.0
	5 Crotch to floor	24.0	30.0
B	1 Forward arm reach	24.0	35.0
	2 Chest circumference (bust)	30.0	37.0
	3 Waist circumference	23.6	28.7
	4 Hip circumference	33.0	40.0
	5 Thigh circumference	19.0	24.0
	6 Calf circumference	11.7	15.0
	7 Ankle circumference	7.8	9.3
	8 Foot length	8.7	10.2
	9 Elbow to floor	34.0	46.0
C	1 Head width	5.4	6.1
	2 Interpupillary distance	1.91	2.94
	3 Head length	6.4	7.3
	4 Head height	—	9.0
	5 Chin to eye	—	4.25
	6 Head circumference	20.4	22.7
D	1 Hand length	6.2	7.3
	2 Hand width	3.2	4.0
	3 Hand thickness	0.84	1.14
	4 Fist circumference	9.1	10.7
	5 Wrist circumference	5.5	6.9
E	1 Arm swing, aft	40 degrees	40 degrees
	2 Foot width	3.2	3.9
F	1 Shoulder width	13.0	19.0
	2 Sitting height to floor (std chair)	45.0	55.0
	3 Eye to floor (std chair)	41.0	51.0
	4 Standard chair	18.0	18.0
	5 Hip breadth	12.5	15.4
	6 Width between elbows	11.0	23.0
G	0 Arm reach (finger grasp)	22.0	33.0
	1 Vertical reach	39.0	50.0
	2 Head to seat	27.0	38.0
	3 Eye to seat	25.0	32.0
	4 Shoulder to seat	18.0	25.0
	5 Elbow rest	4.0	12.0
	6 Thigh clearance	3.5	6.0
	7 Forearm length	14.0	18.0
	8 Knee clearance to floor	17.0	22.0
	9 Lower leg height	13.5	18.8
	10 Seat length	16.5	21.0
	11 Buttock-knee length	19.0	25.9
	12 Buttock-toe clearance	27.0	37.0
	13 Buttock-foot length	34.0	49.0

NOTE: All except critical dimensions have been rounded off to the nearest inch. For more thorough analysis see Daniels et al.[4]

CLOTHING EFFECT ON DIMENSIONS

Various types of clothing will add not only weight to the body weights shown on the preceding pages, but also increased dimensions in most cases. These additions must be given due consideration in preliminary design, but should be checked out again in mock-up evaluations using the particular type of special clothing which is expected to be used in actual operation of the equipment. If a pressure suit is worn, it should be pressurized to evaluate not only the space dimensions, but also the restrictions to reach and movement.

The modifying dimensions which are presented on the page to the right represent only the particular types of clothing measured, and although these will be adequate for early design, they may not represent exactly the clothing which will be used in all new designs.

It will be noted that certain apparent inconsistencies occur in the table. For example, when a pressure suit is inflated, it sometimes reduces rather than increases certain dimensions. This is because of the peculiar characteristics of such garments, which tend to contract and shrink the occupant. Another dimension which may appear strange is the exceptionally small difference in foot length that a modern woman's pointed shoe makes. This is because most of the increase that would be expected is lost in the high angle produced by the high heels.

When considering the additional dimensions caused by certain types of clothing, it is important not to design to the limit: i.e., some additional clearance is required to account for gathering and bunching of the garment at bending points and for extra attachments often found on garments, such as belt loops and buckles — or personal equipment leads, in the case of high-altitude protective garments.

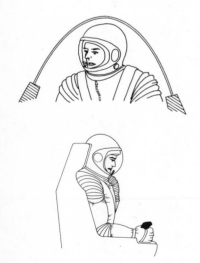

Attention is called to two particular problems with high-altitude garments. Helmets may be longer than they are wide — so space must be provided (for instance, under the canopy of the cockpit) so that the pilot can turn his head.

A pressurized suit adds considerable dimension to the length of the forearm and to the distance from elbow to elbow. A control mounted on the armrest must account for this added dimension. And the cockpit must be wider to account for the pressurized flight suit.

EFFECT OF VARIOUS TYPES OF CLOTHING ON HUMAN BODY DIMENSIONS

(All dimensions in parentheses are negative values)

DIMENSION	STREET CLOTHES		WINTER CLOTHES		HEAVY FLIGHT CLOTHING	PRESSURE SUITS[a]	
	MEN	WOMEN	MEN	WOMEN		UNPRES-SURIZED	PRES-SURIZED
Weight	5 lb	3½ lb	10 lb	7 lb	12–15 lb	21 lb	21 lb
Stature	1 in.	½–3¾ in.	1 in.	½–3¾ in.	3 in.	3½ in.	2½ in.
Vertical reach	1	½–3¾	1	½–3¾	i	(−2½)	(−16½)
Eye height, standing	1	½–3¾	1	½–3¾	1	(−3½)	2½
Crotch to floor	1	½–3¾	1	½–3¾	1	(−1)	(−1)
Foot length	1¼	½	1½	½–¾	1	1	1
Foot width	½–¾	¼–(−½)[b]	½–1	¼–½	¾	¾	¾
Head length	—	—	—[c]		4½	4½	4½
Head width	—	—	—[c]		4½	4½	4½
Hand length	—	—	¾	½	½	½	¼
Hand width	—	—	½	¼	½	½	1
Hand thickness	—	—	½	¼	½	¾	1¼
Fist circumference	—	—	1	¾	1	1¼	3
Shoulder width	½	¼	2–3	1	1½	1	½
Hip width	½	¼	2–3	1	1½	1	2¾
Elbow-to-elbow width	¾	¼	2–3½	1–1½	1	6	9
Thigh clearance	½	¼	1	¾	2	1¾	2
Forearm-to-fist length	½	¼	¾	½	1	1½	5½

[a] Certain pressurized garments are designed for seated position and therefore shorten certain dimensions. The helmet however, tends to rise under pressure.

[b] Women's dress shoes confine and shrink foot width.

[c] An Army steel helmet is approximately 12 by 10¼ inches.

Typical flight helmet dimensional characteristics:

	A	B	C	D
Lombard	1.25	1.00	2.60	1.55
MA-2	1.45	1.40	1.80	2.15
P-4	1.25	1.25	2.13	1.73

STATURE–WEIGHT–AGE AVERAGES, MEN

| HEIGHT | | AGE | | | | | | | | | | | | |
FT	IN	16	17	18	19	20	21	22	23	24	25-29	30-34	35-39	40-44
5	00	101	103	105	107	110	112	114	116	118	122	126	128	131
5	1	106	108	110	112	115	117	119	121	123	124	127	130	133
5	2	111	113	116	117	120	121	122	123	124	126	130	132	135
5	3	115	117	119	121	124	125	126	127	128	129	133	135	138
5	4	119	120	122	124	127	128	129	130	131	133	136	138	140
5	5	124	125	126	128	130	131	132	133	135	137	140	142	145
5	6	128	129	130	132	133	134	135	137	139	141	144	146	149
5	7	133	134	135	136	137	138	140	141	143	145	148	150	153
5	8	137	138	139	140	141	142	144	146	147	149	152	155	158
5	9	141	142	143	144	145	147	148	150	151	153	156	160	163
5	10	145	146	147	148	149	151	153	155	156	157	161	165	168
5	11	150	151	152	153	154	156	158	160	161	162	166	170	174
6	00	155	156	157	158	160	162	164	165	166	167	172	176	180

This table, representing average actual weights, is based on a table published by Florence L. Meredith.[6]

APPROXIMATE LOCATION OF CENTERS OF GRAVITY AND WEIGHTS OF BODY COMPONENTS[7]

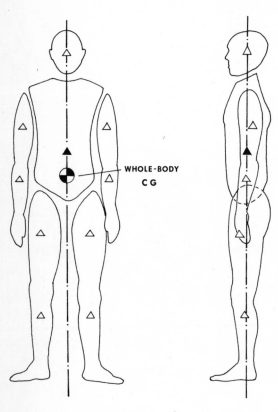

WHOLE-BODY
C G

The center of gravity is subject to variation because of body weight, stature, and build. In general, the CG tends to lower with shorter statures and rise with taller statures. It has been found that the whole-body CG is slightly above half of the height above the soles of the feet (standing) and that it is constant regardless of age.

Head	11.9 lb
Trunk	78.2 lb
Arms (hands)	21.3 lb
Legs (feet)	58.6 lb
Total weight	170.0 lb

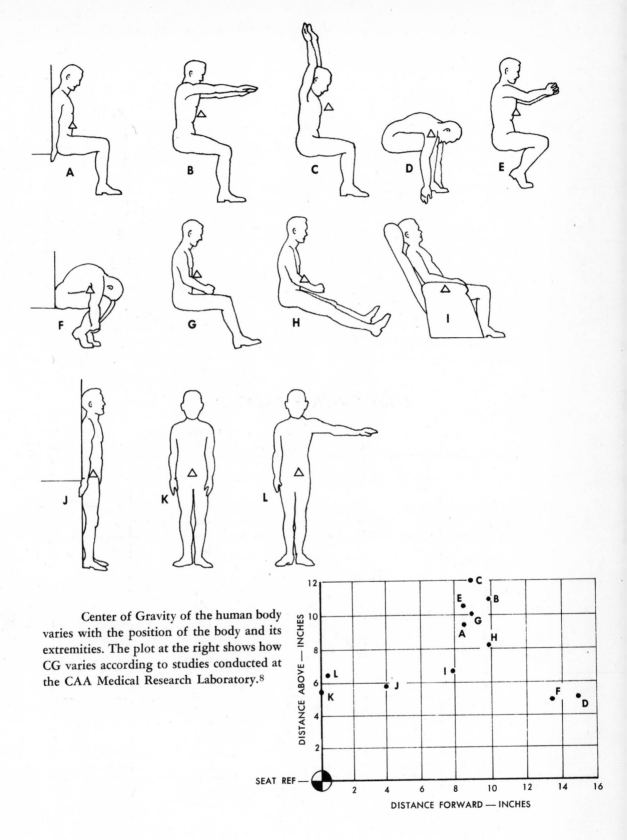

Center of Gravity of the human body varies with the position of the body and its extremities. The plot at the right shows how CG varies according to studies conducted at the CAA Medical Research Laboratory.[8]

BODY SURFACE AREA[9]

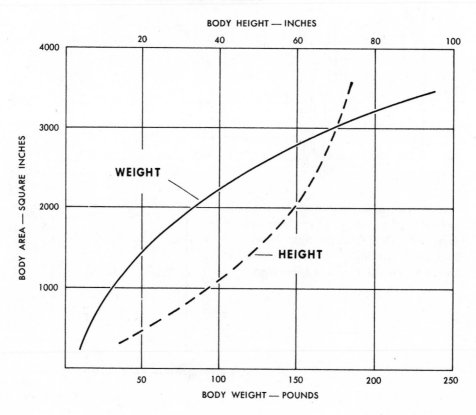

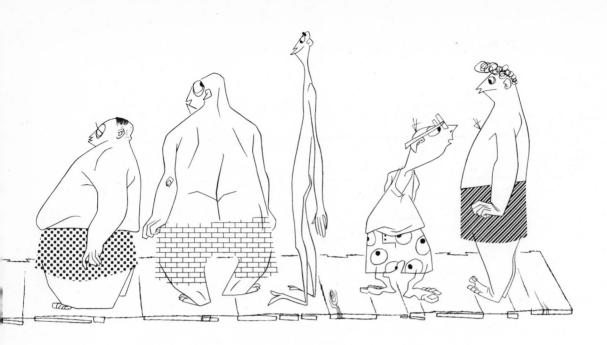

STATURE AND CHEST RELATIONSHIPS

Measurements were made on approximately 24,600 male Army separatees to determine interrelationships between 24 dependent and two independent body dimensions, stature and chest circumference. The subjects measured represented all parts of the United States, a dozen widely varying occupations, and more than a dozen background nationalities (not including Far Eastern, however). The ages varied from 15 to 41, with a sharp maximum between 19 and 21.

A nomograph[10] was constructed from the measurement data collected, from which can be read the average values of the 24 dimensions associated with any selected pair of stature and chest-circumference values. This nomograph, shown on the next page, should be of aid to designers of clothing and other equipment for service men.

A straight line passing through known values of stature and chest will also pass through average values for all other dimensions shown. Each average value thus indicated is midpoint of a range determined by adding to and subtracting from the midpoint the amount shown at the bottom of each vertical line. This range will include about 70 per cent of men with the original given values of stature and chest.

A table[10] showing the most reliable correlations and the per cent of accuracy of each is presented on page 5-27.

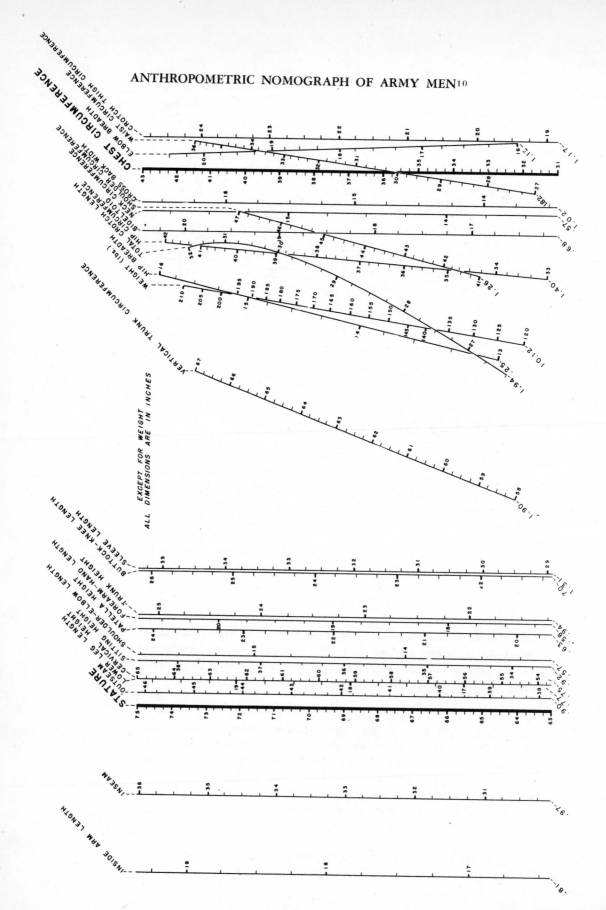

DIMENSION	CORRELATION WITH	
	STATURE	CHEST CIRCUMFERENCE
WEIGHT		.820
TORSO		
sitting height	.722	
trunk height	.587	
cervical height	.948	
waist circumference		.745
hip circumference		.744
bideltoid		.706
cross-back width		.486
hip breadth		.649
shoulder circumference		.806
neck circumference		.627
ARM		
inside arm length	.718	
sleeve length	.624	
inseam	.819	
forearm-hand length	.640	
shoulder-elbow length	.660	
elbow breadth		.677
wrist circumference		.556
LEG		
lower leg	.688	
patella height	.795	
buttock-knee height	.751	
outseam	.886	
total crotch length		.467
crotch-thigh circumference		.731

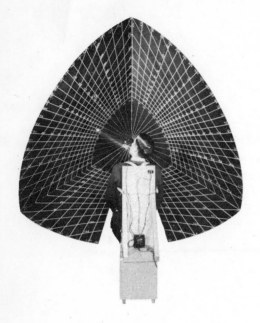

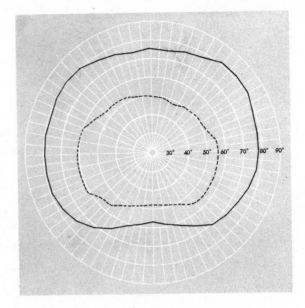

Subject being tested to determine limits of head movement.

Average limits of head movement of 40 subjects, in degrees of angular deflection.

MOTION OF BODY COMPONENTS

Motion of body components of course increases the body's usefulness in relation to the equipment with which it is associated. Head motion, for example, greatly enlarges the scope of the eyes. A plot of head movements has been worked out, using forty subjects tested as shown. As maximum points of rotary head movement are approached, the pivot points change, making accurate definition of the physical limits of head movement difficult.

The human torso, although of more importance in its capacity of housing the vital organs of the body, has some very important characteristics that should be considered whenever men must fit into a work-space and must serve not only as the connecting link between the limbs but also as the elastic link for extending some of the distances of these limbs.

The typical body movements which must be considered in designing equipment — clothing, seating and work space, instruments and groups of instruments — are listed and described. The degrees of movement indicated are based on studies by Frescoln,[11] Rosen,[12] Silver,[13] and the authors.

DEFINITIONS OF TYPICAL
BODY MOVEMENTS[11]

ABDUCTION	movement from the median line
ADDUCTION	movement toward the median line
CIRCUMDUCTION	continuous circular movement of a limb
CLOCKWISE	to the right
COUNTERCLOCKWISE	to the left
DEPRESSION	lowered from a normal position
ELEVATION	raised from a normal position
FLEXION	the process of bending
EXTENSION	the straightening of a flexed limb or part
EXTERNAL ROTATION	turning on the axis, outward
INTERNAL ROTATION	turning on the axis, inward
INSPIRATION	inhalation of air into the lungs
PRONATION	downward turning of the palm, or attitude of lying face down
SUPINATION	upward turning of the palm, or attitude of lying face up

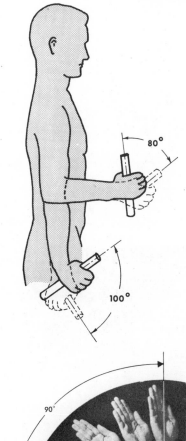

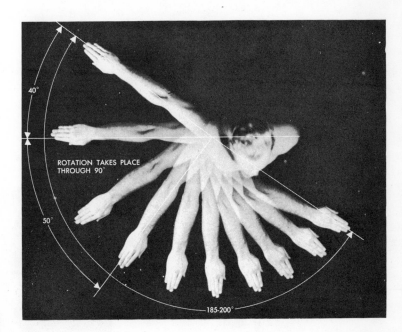

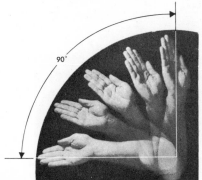

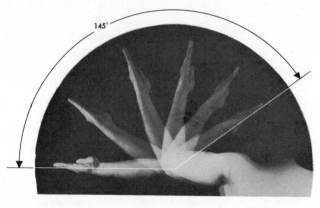

145°

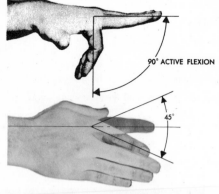

90° ACTIVE FLEXION

45°

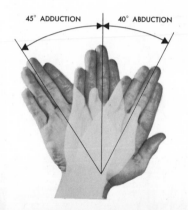

45° ADDUCTION   40° ABDUCTION

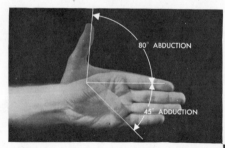

80° ABDUCTION

45° ADDUCTION

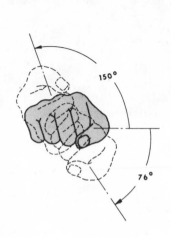

150°

76°

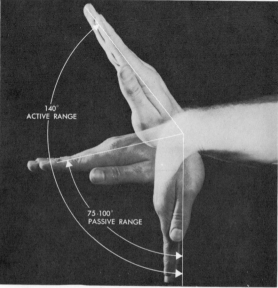

140°
ACTIVE RANGE

75-100°
PASSIVE RANGE

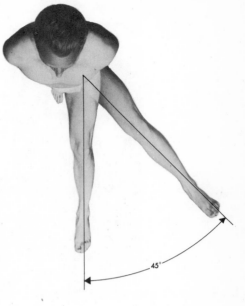

180°
130°

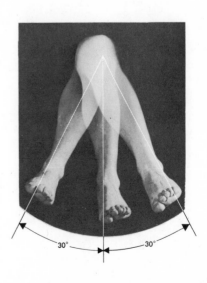

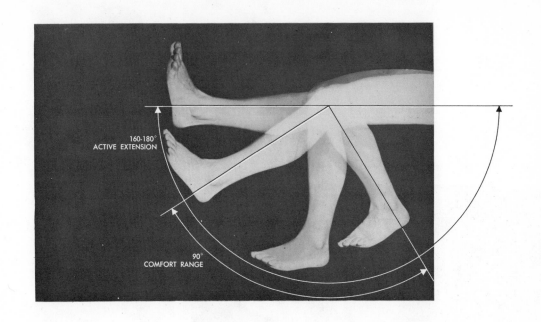

160-180°
ACTIVE EXTENSION

90°
COMFORT RANGE

45° ADDUCTION   50° ABDUCTION

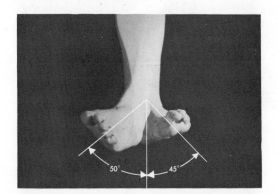

50°   45°

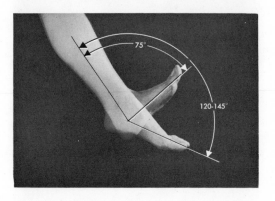

75°

120-145°

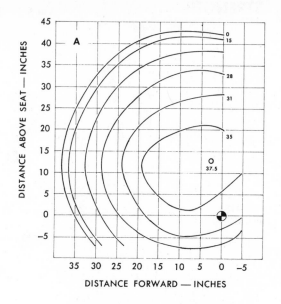

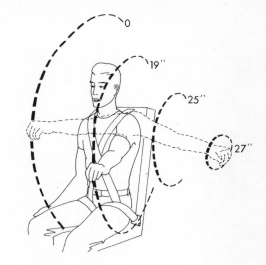

ARM REACH ENVELOPES

Useful limits for arm reach should be based on those of the small man. In the accompanying graphs selected data for a man with a 5th percentile arm reach are shown.[5] In the first plot the subject was in shirt sleeves and not restricted by shoulder harness. In the second, he was restricted by shoulder harness, and in the third the subject was in a Navy Mark IV pressure suit, pressurized at 3.5 psig.[14]

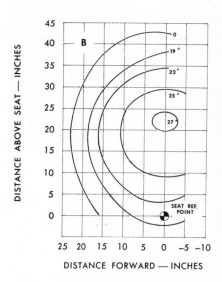

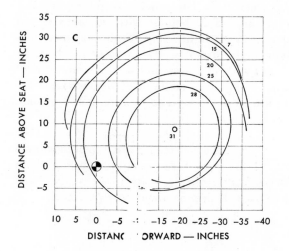

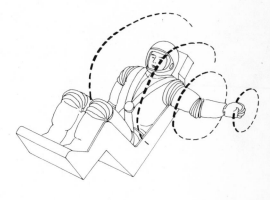

STRENGTH

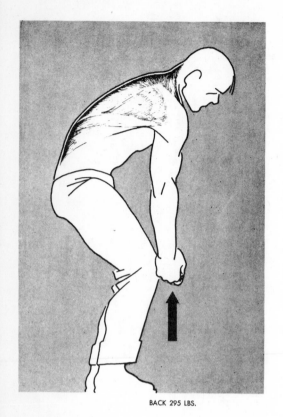

BACK 295 LBS.

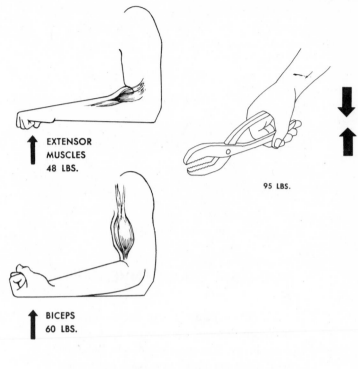

EXTENSOR
MUSCLES
48 LBS.

BICEPS
60 LBS.

95 LBS.

The lifting power of components is shown.

Leg strength is second only to postural strength. Force in stretching is greater than in bending. Maximum force with back rest is approximately 450 pounds for short periods. Throw-off (point at which leg ceases to function alone and other body components begin to operate) occurs around 40 pounds with no backrest and 60 pounds with backrest. With the knee at a right angle, strain begins to occur at about 28 pounds with a backrest and at 50 pounds without backrest. With an angle of 45 degrees from the vertical, thrusts may rise to around 155 pounds.

Leg and arm strength reach their maximum around the age of 25 years and decline about 50 per cent from 30 years to 65 years. Hand strength will decline about 16.5 per cent.

ARM STRENGTH WITH
ELBOW FLEXION (Right Arm)

The force which can be applied to a side-arm joystick controller varies with the position of the subject's arm as illustrated below (after Hunsicker[15]).

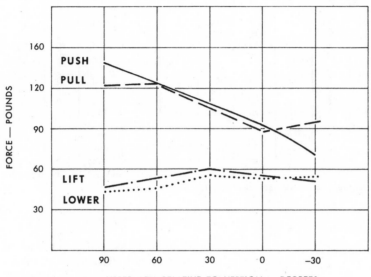

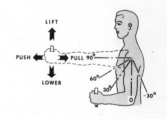

FOREARM-WRIST STRENGTH

The preferred neutral position for a side-arm controller is approximately 8° to the right, and 15° forward of the vertical.

The maximum right-roll torque which can be applied is approximately 57 inch–pounds for the preferred position, although about 12 inch–pounds is recommended for operational use. For left roll, 87 inch–pounds is maximum, with 13 inch–pounds recommended for operational use.

Maximum pitch-down force is approximately 133 inch–pounds, with 18 inch–pounds recommended — maximum pitch-up approximately 29 inch–pounds, with 12 inch–pounds recommended for operational use.[15]

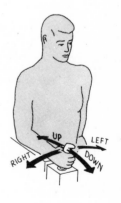

MANUAL FORCES IN A PRESSURIZED SUIT[14]

MEASUR- ING POINT	DISTANCE FROM SRP			STIRRUP Ⓑ		KNOB Ⓐ			
	Verti- cally	Later- ally	Longi- tudi- nally	Push	Pull	Clock- wise	Counter- clock- wise	Clock- wise	Counter- clock- wise
A-1	34	12	11	15	60	110	100	55	45
B-1	28	30	5	50	80	125	140	65	75
2	28	24	15	45	85	105	105	50	55
3	28	16	20	35	85	145	140	70	70
4	28	9	21	30	80	80	100	60	65
C-1	18	31	4	45	70	125	145	50	65
2	18	28	12	55	90	85	120	65	60
3	18	21	19	65	80	115	135	80	60
4	18	6	22	50	80	125	140	80	55
D-1	8	28	4	45	55	130	150	30	55
2	8	25	12	50	75	105	140	35	45
3	8	19	18	50	90	120	140	50	65
4	8	10	20	45	80	105	150	45	65
E-1	2	20	5	60	85	100	125	50	50
2	2	12	14	60	80	95	140	50	60

NOTE: Measuring points are in inches from the Seat Reference Point (SRP). Push and pull figures are given in pounds, rotating forces in inch pounds.

The subject used in gathering the data in the above table represents a 20th percentile man. Measurements were taken in a Goodrich Mark IV full pressure suit inflated to 3.5 psig. The subject was secured by a seat belt only.

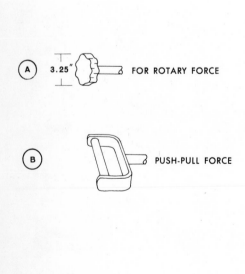

Ⓐ 3.25″ FOR ROTARY FORCE

Ⓑ PUSH-PULL FORCE

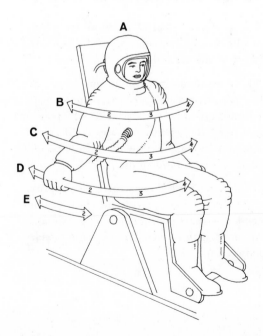

LEG REACH ENVELOPE[5]

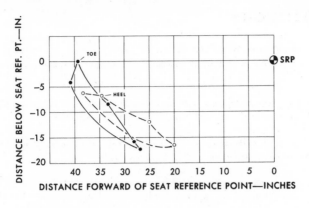

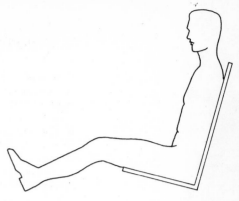

Optimum areas for location of toe-operated and heel-operated pedal controls are shown in the above graph.

LEG STRENGTH[5]

The following maximum forces can be applied to pedal controls by the average man assuming proper back support and optimum leg angle:

Up to 400 pounds of force can be applied by an average man in area A of the graph below, up to 600 pounds in area B. Line C represents a recommended optimum path of pedal travel where force application is considered a requirement.

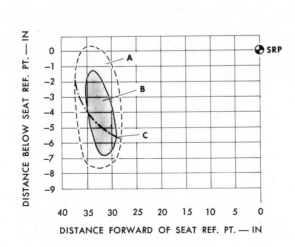

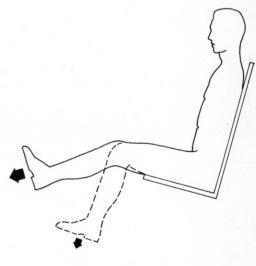

references

1. Randall, F. E., and Damon, A. *Official Surveys of Aviation Cadets and Other Flying Personnel* (Army Air Force. Air Force Systems Command, Memo Report No. EXP-M-49-695-4B) 31 August 1942.

2. Randall, F. E. et al. *Human Body Size in Military Aircraft and Personal Equipment* (Army Air Force. Air Materiel Command, Technical Report no. 5501) 10 June 1946.

3. Hertzberg, H. T. E. et al. *Anthropometry of Flying Personnel, 1950* (Air Force. Wright Air Development Center, Technical Report no. 52-321) September 1954.

4. Daniels, G. S. et al. *Anthropometry of WAF Basic Trainees* (Air Force. Wright Air Development Center, Technical Report no. 53-12) July 1953.

5. ———. *Human Engineering Investigations—Design Guides* (Convair Division of General Dynamics Corp. Report no. HFE 64-20) 6 March 1958.

6. Meredith, F. L. *Hygiene* Blakiston Co., Philadelphia, 1941.

7. Lay, W. E., and Fisher, L. C. "Riding Comfort and Cushions" *SAE Journal* vol. 47, 1940, p. 482.

8. Swearingen, J. J. *Determination of Centers of Gravity* (Department of Commerce, Civil Aeronautics A Medical Research Laboratory Project no. 53-203) May 1953.

9. Boyd, E. *The Growth of the Surface Area of the Human Body* University of Minnesota Press, 1935.

10. Randall, F. E. *Anthropometric Nomograph of Army Men* (Army Department. Quartermaster Climatic Research Laboratory, Environmental Protection Section Report no. 147) 10 January 1949.

11. Frescoln, L. D. "Range of Bodily Movements" *Medical Times* vol. 57, 1929, pp. 197-198.

12. Rosen, N. G. "A Simplified Method of Measuring Amplitude of Motion in Joints" *Journal of Bone and Joint Surgery* vol. 4, 1922, pp. 570-579.

13. Silver, D. "Measurement of the Range of Motion in Joints" *Journal of Bone and Joint Surgery* vol 5, 1923, pp. 569-579.

14. Pierce, B. F., and Murch, K. R. *Strength and Reach Envelopes of a Pilot Wearing a Full Pressure Suit in the Seated and Supine Positions* (Convair Division of General Dynamics Corp. Report ZR-659-034) 23 July 1959.

15. Hunsicker, P. A. *Arm Strength at Selected Degrees of Elbow Flexion* (Air Force. Wright Air Development Center, Technical Report no. 54-548) 1955.

16. Sheldon, W. H. et al. *The Varieties of Human Physique* Harper and Brothers, 1940, chap. 3.

other factors

In the first five chapters of this guide we have given the design engineer a set of practical recommendations plus an introduction to the two prime sensory capacities of the human element in a man-machine system. A discussion of body dimensions completed the set of major human factors to be considered as equipment-design parameters. There are, however, a number of other physiological and psychological functions that affect the human operator, many of which present problems of considerable magnitude in the operation of the man-machine system. It is well for the design engineer to be acquainted with them so that he will have some idea of their bearing upon the problems with which he may be confronted.

Treatment of any finite number of characteristics could not begin to exhaust the human's innumerable facets. We have, therefore, restricted ourselves in this chapter to three of the more important additional fundamental categories: (1) the sensory system, supplementing the vision and audition chapters with information on other senses — touch, taste, smell, kinesthesis, equilibrium; (2) the motor system, including some of its general characteristics as well as their application to specific motor tasks of operational importance; and (3) mechanisms whereby the human's orientation in his environment is maintained or disrupted.

It is hoped that the subjects discussed in this chapter, combined with the material presented in the first five chapters, will complete a core of information to provide the reader with a fuller insight into the capabilities and limitations of the human operator.

BODY SENSITIVITY

the skin senses

Much of our information about the body's immediate surroundings comes to us through the medium of the skin. In fact, much of our learning to see and hear, and to interpret visual and auditory stimuli, respectively, is intimately tied in with the skin senses.

The traditional sense of touch has been broken down into *four primary skin senses: pain, pressure, cold,* and *warmth.* There is, indeed, much experimental evidence pointing to the existence of specific neural receptors for each of these primary senses. Seven types of receptor nerve endings[1] are shown in the skin cross section below.

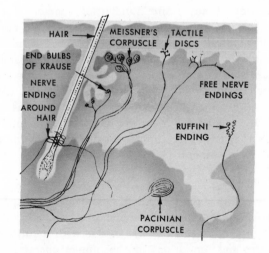

The specific-receptor hypothesis of skin sensitivity springs from the fact that there are on the skin "spots" of special maximum sensitivity — heat, cold, pain, and pressure spots — which are fairly stable and as a rule correlated with the degree of concentration of specific nerve endings. When one probes over the skin with a pointed instrument, he may find, with moderate stimulation intensity, discrete spots which give rise to the sensation of warmth, others which yield cold, others only pressure, and still others only pain. Because of the distribution of nerve endings in the skin, increasing the intensity of an applied stimulus will increase the spread of mechanical stimulation and may bring about the response of less sensitive elements, arousing other sensations besides the one first elicited at a particular spot. Further, any sufficiently strong stimulus applied at a spot sensitive to another stimulus may arouse that spot's usual response; for example, a sharp beam of heat applied to a pain spot will yield the sensation of pain, not heat. In general, pain, pressure, cold, and heat spots rank in that order with respect to average number of nerve endings per unit skin area.

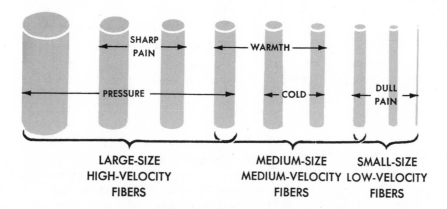

These sensations, regardless of the type or types of receptor that may be peculiar to them, are each delegated to a range of one of the three main cutaneous nerve fiber sizes in the body — large, medium, and small — with corresponding impulse-conduction velocities. Notice that the diagram shows some overlap; some pressure fibers, for example, are the size of some of the longer warmth fibers.

The skin senses can adapt to certain ranges of stimuli, under continuous non-changing stimulation. Under these conditions they cease to give their characteristic sensation.

THRESHOLDS
PAIN | PRESSURE
GRAMS/MM²

Location	PAIN	PRESSURE
CORNEA	0.2	
CONJUNCTIVA (inner surface of eyelid)	2	
TIP OF TONGUE		2
ABDOMEN	15	26
LOIN		48
BACK OF FOREARM	30	33
FRONT OF FOREARM	20	8
BACK OF HAND	100	12
FINGERTIP	300	3
CALF OF LEG	30	16
THICK PARTS OF SOLE	200	250

PAIN

Mechanical, chemical, thermal, and electrical stimulation may all arouse pain. This sensation is the one most generally aroused over the skin surfaces. One would expect this to be true, since the free nerve endings are generally conductors of pain experience, and this type of fiber is the most numerous in the skin.

Thresholds for pain induced by mechanical or electrical stimulation vary with the place stimulated. The degree of pain from chemical stimulation is proportional to the hydrogen ion concentration (acidity) in chemical solutions. Highly alkaline solutions also produce a pain sensation. Minimum thermal stimulation (by radiant heat focused on the skin, to eliminate effects of pressure) needed to produce pain has been found to be 0.21 gram-calorie per second per square centimeter.

PRESSURE

Bending or stretching of the skin, either inward or outward, is adequate stimulus for the sensation of pressure. Strong pressure affects "deep pressure" fibers thought to be the Pacinian corpuscle while light pressure stimulates only the hair bulbs and free nerve endings.

Thresholds for pressure vary with the area of the skin tested, depending upon the concentration of nerve fibers and thickness of the skin. Holway and Crozier believe that the just noticeable differences of pressure sensitivity are dependent upon the proportion of neurons available for firing at any given moment.

SENSITIVITY TO VIBRATION is not a separate sense; it is primarily dependent upon pressure sensitivity. Some of the effects of vibration have already been discussed in Chapter 2, pages 2-233–2-235, and Chapter 3, page 3-17.

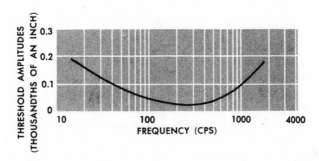

The curve of vibration amplitude threshold as a function of frequency of vibrations looks a good deal like the auditory threshold curve, but is displaced toward the lower frequencies. Discrimination between frequencies is fairly efficient. With practice, one can recognize 400 cps, for example, as different in frequency from 420 cps. Absolute and differential sensitivity to the degree present for vibratory stimuli make it conceivable for a person to be able to learn to "hear" through skin vibratory sensations, particularly if the different frequencies were delivered by the vibrating source to specific parts of the skin in a manner analogous to the frequency response of the ear. In that case, different frequencies stimulate different parts of the basilar membrane.

People can feel as little as 0.00004-inch double amplitude of vibration when the frequency is between 100 and 500 cycles per second. In the higher and lower frequencies (above 1000 and below 60 cycles per second) the amplitude must be increased to 0.00015 to be felt. Since vibration depends on pressure receptors, it is most sensitively perceived in regions most sensitive to pressure. (See drawing, page 6-4). Over most of the frequency range, the limit of tolerance to vibration amplitude is roughly 15 to 20 times the threshold amplitude. Sensibility to frequencies as low as 10 cycles per second and as high as 8000 cycles per second have been measured, when amplitude was sufficiently high. Since neurons fire at a maximum rate of 500 impulses per second, it has been proposed that groups of nerves must fire in synchronous successive volleys in order to yield accurate response to the high frequencies.

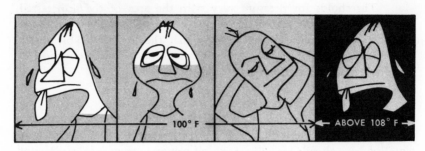

TEMPERATURE

Evidence regarding specific receptors for warmth and cold is as yet indecisive. Suggested for the former is the Ruffini cylinder, for the latter, the Kraus end bulb. (See diagram, page 6-2.) An alternate hypothesis is made by Nafe, who maintains that thermal stimulation is initiated mechanically, through constriction (for cold) and dilation (for heat) of the blood vessels. Still a third theory, by Jenkins, is that thermal sensitivity depends upon variable concentrations of thermally sensitive free nerve endings in the skin.

Skin temperatures constantly undergo small fluctuations, brought about reflexly by many internal and external influences. The skin, however, is a poor conductor, and that fact, coupled with stabilizing body processes, permits adaptation of the skin temperature, within limits, to external temperature changes.

When a specific region of the skin becomes adapted (insensible) to an external temperature, it is said to be at "physiological zero," which at the various regions on the skin can be attained for external temperatures between 64 and 108° F. There is a so-called "neutral zone," of 1.8 to 3.6° F range around the physiological zero point, in which no temperature is sensed. Although the various regions of the skin may all be at different temperatures, adaptation at all these regions is present simultaneously. The normal skin temperature — neutral zone under standard environmental conditions — is from 90.5 to 92.3° F.

Only partial adaptation takes place to temperatures outside the limits of complete adaptation; that is, even when one is best adapted to a temperature of, for example, 40° F, a temperature of 45° F will still feel cold. Temperatures below 32° F and above 125° F become painful. For typical skin temperatures, tolerances, and optimum temperatures in working environments, see Chapter 2, page 2-226.

OTHER SKIN SENSATIONS

There are, of course, skin sensations and perceptions other than the primary ones. Tickle, itch, prick, roughness, and moisture are a few. These sensations are variations or combinations of the primary senses. Tickle, for example, results when a number of nerve fibers are activated in succession. In order to discriminate rough from smooth, movement over the skin is necessary, with resulting vibration (mediated by pressure receptors) a major cue. The sensation of moistness is a combination of pressure and cold, or pressure and heat.[1]

LOCALIZATION AND THE TWO-POINT THRESHOLD

As in the case of the retina for vision, neural projections from the skin eventually proceed to the cerebral cortex where a point-to-point relationship with parts of the body is maintained. The different sensory qualities are, in large measure, in separate nerve tracts in the spinal cord, uniting in a portion of the thalamus, which is located near the base of the brain. One of the many important functions of the thalamus is to serve as a way station or distribution center for impulses to and from all parts of the body. The point-to-point relationship for cutaneous sensitivity first obtains in this organ. From here, the neural "map" of the body goes to the cutaneous centers of the cortex, preserving the orientation.

The foregoing is the means by which localization of and differentiation between skin stimuli at separate points is possible.

The *two-point threshold* is the name given to the shortest distance between two points which, when simultaneously stimulated, are recognized as separate. This threshold varies with different parts of the body and can be improved by practice.

6-7

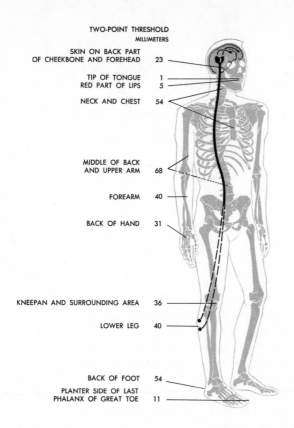

TWO-POINT THRESHOLD
MILLIMETERS

SKIN ON BACK PART
OF CHEEKBONE AND FOREHEAD   23

TIP OF TONGUE   1
RED PART OF LIPS   5

NECK AND CHEST   54

MIDDLE OF BACK
AND UPPER ARM   68

FOREARM   40

BACK OF HAND   31

KNEEPAN AND SURROUNDING AREA   36

LOWER LEG   40

BACK OF FOOT   54
PLANTER SIDE OF LAST
PHALANX OF GREAT TOE   11

This two-point threshold is, paradoxically, larger than the error of localization of a single point of skin stimulation. For example, the points in the diagram may not be recognized as separate on simultaneous stimulation of both, yet, if one is asked to locate each point when individually touched, his range of error is within the circles around the points. An explanation for this phenomenon is that stimulation from each of the two simultaneous contacts is diffuse and overlaps the other (neurologically and mechanically), resulting in a single impression, as if there were a continuous stimulus between the points, as shown, whereas the central point, or maximally stimulated area, of a single stimulus can be accurately judged despite the spread of actual stimulation from it. The two-points, to be recognized as separate, need to be far enough apart that overlap is not serious. Localization is best in mobile areas of the skin, such as the hands, feet, and mouth.

DISCRIMINATION OF FORM

An important practical aspect of discrimination via skin senses is the perception of form. Coding of knobs and handles depends upon this capacity. Examples of knob shapes found never to be confused with one another are shown on page 2-106.

kinesthesis · *the muscle sense*

Controlled action requires knowledge about the movement and position of body parts. Although vision and other senses contribute a great deal, our primary source of information about such movement and position is kinesthesis, or the muscle sense. We can, for example, close our eyes and still walk efficiently. Kinesthesis tells us where our limbs are, how far they have moved, the posture of the body as a whole; in short, it provides impulses by which coordination of all body parts involved in complex acts, such as walking, is possible.

NEURAL BASIS

The muscle sense is aptly named, since its stimulation arises from nerve endings located in muscles, tendons, and joints. Several special types of nerve endings, each terminating in a specific kind of end organ, are adapted to respond to one of three main types of stimulation — tension, stretch changes, or pressure. In the illustration[2] of sensory and motor innervation of a muscle, for example, are shown three different end organs innervated by special nerve endings. Discharge of the motor nerve fibers (A) ending on a muscle fiber causes the muscle fiber to contract. The sensory annulospiral nerve ending (B), terminating in an end organ called the *muscle spindle*, is adapted to register stretching of the muscle. The *Golgi tendon organ* (an end organ which is a specialized part of tendons and is located near muscle fiber-tendon junctions), and the free-branching club-shaped sensory nerve ending (C) shown innervating it, are adapted to record changes in muscle tension.

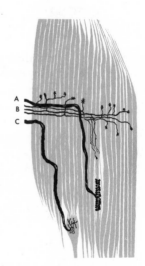

Neural centers and pathways for kinesthesis are very similar to those of the skin senses. However, greater complexity of termination in the cortex is involved here than was the case for the skin senses. In addition to nerve fibers projecting to the cortex, the kinesthetic system includes fibers from the cerebellum, a reflex center which contributes to muscular coordination. Conscious kinesthetic experience depends upon sensory impulses to the cortex; motor impulses from the cerebellum exert a steadying influence on voluntary muscles. Still other fibers do not reach the brain at all, but function in relatively simple sensory-motor reflex arcs through the spinal cord. (See drawing, page 6-19, for sensory-motor reflex arc.)

Kinesthetic fibers are, in general, of the larger variety, similar to the largest cutaneous fibers (diagram, page 6-3) and have high conduction velocities. Sensory neurons from voluntary muscles to the brain and motor neurons from the brain to the voluntary muscles have only one impulse-delaying inter-neuron gap (called the synapse) before reaching their destination, facilitating rapid reactions. Other nerve fibers usually have several delaying synapses.

SPECIAL CHARACTERISTICS OF KINESTHESIS

A unique feature of kinesthesis is the fact that stimulation comes from within the organism itself (proprioception) rather than from the external world, as it does for the other senses (equilibrium excepted). Also, kinesthetic stimuli are always present, usually below the level of clear awareness, limited in sensation qualities and relatively poorly localized. Sensitivity varies with different parts of the body. Data on performance in which kinesthesis is a major factor will be found in the section on Movement and Control, page 6-18.

equilibrium

Stimulation in the non-auditory labyrinth of the inner ear, shown at right, arises from position and movement of the head. The labyrinthine organs provide sensory data which, along with kinesthesis, contribute to the static and dynamic equilibrium of the body. Static equilibrium refers to maintenance of posture, dynamic to the smooth adjustments made to restore equilibrium under conditions which tend to upset it. The structures of the labyrinth function as described on pages 6-11 and 6-12.

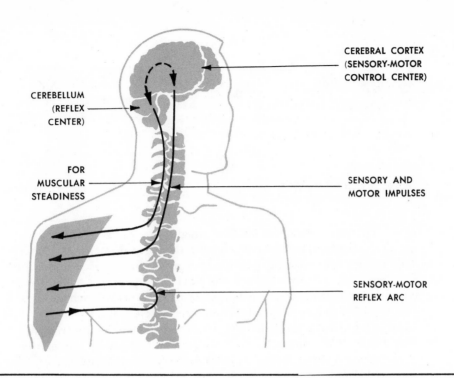

CEREBRAL CORTEX
(SENSORY-MOTOR
CONTROL CENTER)

CEREBELLUM
(REFLEX
CENTER)

FOR
MUSCULAR
STEADINESS

SENSORY AND
MOTOR IMPULSES

SENSORY-MOTOR
REFLEX ARC

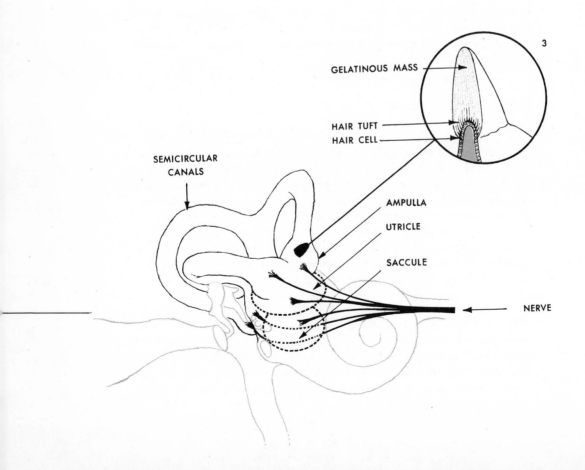

3

GELATINOUS MASS

HAIR TUFT

HAIR CELL

SEMICIRCULAR
CANALS

AMPULLA

UTRICLE

SACCULE

NERVE

6-11

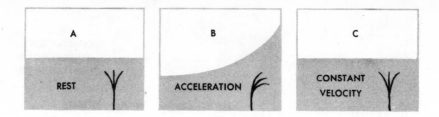

SEMICIRCULAR CANALS

The semicircular canals are roughly at right angles to one another, in approximate alignment with the three major space planes. This arrangement makes it possible to register angular acceleration in any direction, as follows: When the head moves, watery fluid in the canals flows, bending hair tufts located in a special part of each ampulla. (See circled diagram, p. 6-11.)[3] These hair tufts in turn activate nerve endings innervating the hair cells. Perceived motion results from this stimulation. The canals register positive and negative acceleration only. During maintenance of constant velocity (C), the intertial lag of the watery fluid (B) has been overcome, and no stimulation of the hair cell occurs. If the motion shown should suddenly stop, the fluid would, because of inertia, flow in the direction opposite to that shown in (B). Then erroneous perception of motion, to the right, in this case, would prevail. Certain ocular effects are intimately associated with labyrinthine responses. (See sections titled Nystagmus and Illusions Associated with Motion, pp. 6-45 and 6-46.)

UTRICLE AND SACCULE

While the semicircular canals register only angular motion, receptors in the utricle and saccule are responsive to linear motion and, continuously, to gravity. The response is initiated by the action of tiny calcium carbonate particles in a gelatinous mass into which hairs project. It is believed that these particles, acted on by gravity, place a stress on the hair cells. Inertia of the particles affects the hairs in the utricle and saccule during changes in linear velocity, in much the same manner as the inertia of the fluid affects the hairs in the semicircular canals during changes in angular velocity.

The section on Orientation, in this chapter, contains material on performance and effects dependent upon these labyrinthine mechanisms. They are of great importance in flying, not only for the correct cues which they sometimes provide, but also for the incorrect ones that it is often necessary to learn to ignore. Motion sickness is, at least in part, a function of labyrinthine stimulation.

taste · *gustation*

Gustatory neurons, ending in taste cells embedded in taste buds of the tongue, are the receptors for taste sensation. Solutions in the mouth must enter through a pore in the taste bud before reaching the taste cell to excite it by direct contact. The taste cell is thus a proximity receptor, in contrast to the remote receptor for smell (see next section).

There are four primary taste qualities: bitter, sweet, sour, and salt; other tastes are combinations of these. Sensitivity for these tastes is in the order given; quinine (bitter) can, for example, be detected in a 0.00005 per cent solution. Sensitivity varies in different parts of the tongue, the tip being most sensitive to sweet, the sides to sour, the tip and sides to salt, and the back most sensitive to bitter. Substances therefore vary in taste when stimulating different parts of the tongue. In addition, temperature and pressure stimulations influence taste. Hot coffee, for example, is distinctly different in taste from cold, even though both have identical ingredients. Taste sensitivity declines with age.

Bodily nutritional needs are sometimes manifested in taste preferences. For example, deficiencies of salt may induce a taste preference for it, so that the body consumes an increased amount to make up for the lack.

smell · *olfaction*

Olfactory neurons are located in a relatively inaccessible crevice high in each of the two nasal cavities. Therefore, only a small portion of a gas, vapor, or volatile material inhaled is able to reach and stimulate them. Olfactory receptors are extensions of the brain, as is the retina in the case of vision.

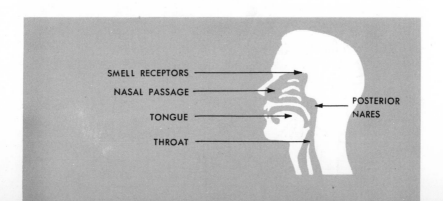

SMELL RECEPTORS

NASAL PASSAGE

TONGUE

THROAT

POSTERIOR NARES

Fundamental odor qualities are not well established, but experiments have suggested the following breakdown:

BASIC ODOR	TYPICAL STIMULUS SUBSTANCE
fragrant	violets
spicy	cloves
etherial (fruity)	oranges
resinous	balsam
burnt	tar
putrid	rotten eggs

Mechanical and chemical stimulation other than olfactory also are involved in the sense of smell. For example, the pungent odor of ammonia is partly due to excitation of pain receptors, as well as those of smell. In addition, smell stimuli are almost always mixtures of the salient ones listed above, thus adding more complexity to odor quality.

The olfactory sense is highly sensitive, despite its remote receptor location. Stimulus threshold varies with the odorous substance; for example, it is 0.2 of a milligram per liter of air for ethyl alcohol, and only one one-millionth of a milligram per liter for vanillin.

The phenomenon of adaptation — loss of characteristic sensation on continued stimulation — is very pronounced in the two chemical senses, taste and smell.

hunger

The physiological basis of hunger has not been definitely established. One theory is that chemical secretions in the relatively empty stomach are not sufficiently absorbed by food and thereby stimulate the stomach walls to contract. These contractions are associated with hunger pangs. They are greatest not when the body has been completely deprived of food over a long period, but rather when an inadequate amount of food has been consumed. Another theory is that blood deficiency products, such as CO_2, rather than the condition of the stomach *per se*, provide the stimulation for hunger sensations and resulting behavior. In corroboration of this theory, it has been shown, for example, that when well-fed animals are given blood transfusions from hungry ones, they exhibit "hunger" behavior.

Hunger results in increased overt, restless movements; and stomach contractions apparently facilitate many types of performance, such as increasing strength of grip or solving mechanical problems.

thirst

The chain of events leading to the thirst sensation is shown.

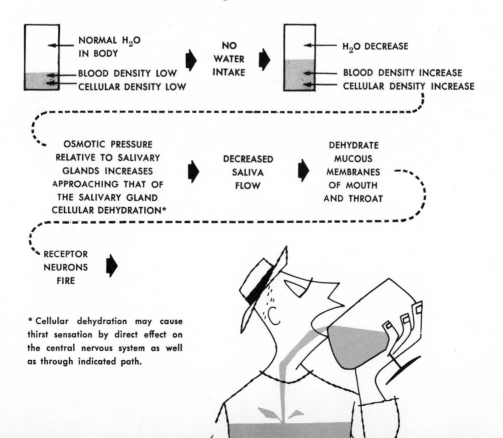

NORMAL H_2O IN BODY
BLOOD DENSITY LOW
CELLULAR DENSITY LOW

NO WATER INTAKE

H_2O DECREASE
BLOOD DENSITY INCREASE
CELLULAR DENSITY INCREASE

OSMOTIC PRESSURE RELATIVE TO SALIVARY GLANDS INCREASES APPROACHING THAT OF THE SALIVARY GLAND CELLULAR DEHYDRATION*

DECREASED SALIVA FLOW

DEHYDRATE MUCOUS MEMBRANES OF MOUTH AND THROAT

RECEPTOR NEURONS FIRE

* Cellular dehydration may cause thirst sensation by direct effect on the central nervous system as well as through indicated path.

6-15

FOOD — ENERGY

Although man may survive for approximately one month without food, or up to one week without water, it is necessary to provide these essentials if life is to continue beyond these periods. It is difficult to establish an "ideal diet," but it is equally important that any diet contain certain necessary elements. The Food and Nutrition Board of the National Research Council recommends the following daily dietary allowances:

AGE	HEIGHT	WEIGHT	CALORIES	PROTEIN	CALCIUM	IRON
25	67 in.	170 lb	3200	65 gm	0.8 gm	12 gm
45	67 in.	170 lb	2900	65 gm	0.8 gm	12 gm

VITAMIN A (I. U.)
5000
5000

THIAMINE	RIBOFLAVIN	NIACIN	ASCORBIC ACID
1.6 mg	1.6 mg	16 mg	75 mg
1.5 mg	1.6 mg	16 mg	75 mg

(NOTE: Allowances apply to normal, vigorous persons living in a temperate climate.)

The more active a person is, the more food he needs each day. Certain sedentary activities may require as little as 1800 calories each day, whereas extremely heavy work may require as much as 5000 calories.

WATER BALANCE FOR THE AVERAGE-SIZED MAN

SOURCE	GRAMS	EXCRETION	GRAMS
Fluids of diet	1200	Lungs	500
Food	1000	Skin	500
Oxidation within		Urine	1400
tissues	300	Feces	100
	2500		2500

ENERGY EXPENDITURE FOR VARIOUS ACTIVITIES

Sleep	245 to 285 Btu/hr
Light work (sitting)	400 to 450 Btu/hr
Flying	400 to 800 Btu/hr
Light but vigorous exercise	1400 to 2000 Btu/hr
Heavy, vigorous exercise	2000 to 3000 Btu/hr

The average energy expenditure of a crew member of a typical space vehicle has been estimated as follows:[4]

	K-CAL/HR	K-CAL/DAY	BTU/DAY
8 hours of sleep	65	520	2080
8 hours of light work	150	1200	4800
5 hours of rest, sitting	100	500	2000
1 hour of rest, lying down	80	80	320
1 hour of light exercise	200	200	800
1 hour of heavy exercise	500	500	2000
Total, 24 hours	2095	3000	12000

In order to maintain the average man in a good state of health, a certain metabolic balance is necessary. This is shown in the following table:[4]

METABOLIC MATERIAL BALANCE

MATERIALS	POUNDS PER MAN PER DAY
Water vapor generation	2.20
Oxygen consumption	2.0
Carbon dioxide generation	2.25
Metabolic water generation	0.41
Food (dry)	1.32
Urine production	3.0
Fecal output	0.58
Solid waste from food	0.08
Carbon in food converted by metabolism into CO_2	0.615
Hydrogen in food converted by metabolism into H_2O	0.046
H_2O, derived from food	0.99
Total H_2O output	5.45
Net water intake for drinking and food preparation	4.46

The following over-all balance is obtained (in lb per man per day):[4]

INPUT		OUTPUT	
Food (dry)	1.32 lb	CO_2	2.25 lb
Oxygen	2.00 lb	H_2O vapor	2.20 lb
Water	4.46 lb	Urine	3.00 lb
	7.78 lb		7.78 lb

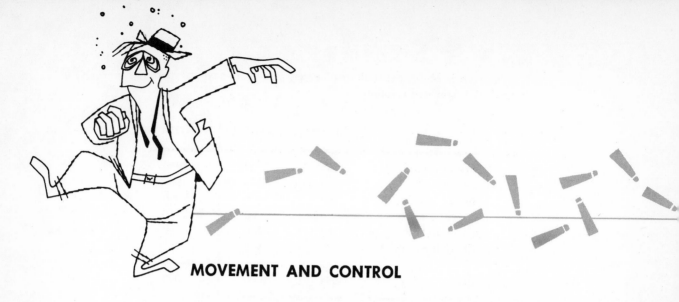

MOVEMENT AND CONTROL

While the sensory system provides the information which the human uses to adjust to his environment and to manipulate it to fit his needs and capabilities, it is the motor system that articulates directly with the physical world to accomplish these purposes.

A basic unit of all behavior, whether sensory or motor, is the neuron. Knowledge of its excitation characteristics helps in understanding human responses. The figure shows electrical potentials, as a function of time, induced in a neuron when it is adequately stimulated. The time scale is for a large fast fiber (type A). The cycle shown[5] may take from 300 to 1000 or more milliseconds for the slowest (type C) fibers. During the first millisecond after a stimulus (the spike potential period, exaggerated in the diagram for clarity), further stimulation, no matter how intense, can not re-excite the neuron. This period, called the refractory phase, therefore limits the frequency with which a neuron may respond. During the next few milliseconds, only stimuli above those normally effective in exciting the neuron can set it off again. On the other hand, subnormal stimulus intensity, applied during the latter portion of the cycle, can excite the fiber.

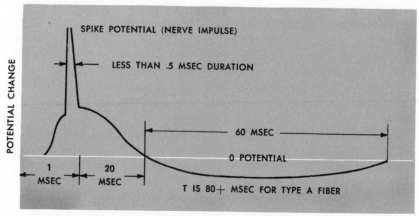

reflex activity

Reflexes are responses in a sensori-motor loop in which the higher neural centers are only remotely involved. Such involuntary activity is extremely important for the integration and control of life processes. The simplest schematic reflex, involving only one level of the spinal cord, is illustrated. Even in the case of reflexes, however, responses are dependent upon the body's general state. For example, an increased state of bodily tension increases the amplitude of the knee-jerk reflex. Motor responses learned so well that they become almost automatic are not reflexes.

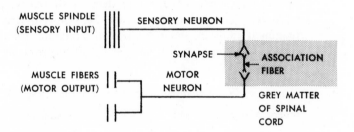

reaction time

The speed with which we may react to a stimulus is, among other things, dependent upon:

The sense to which it is presented — auditory reaction time (RT) is faster than visual RT (see graph on the next page).

Stimulus intensity — greater stimulus intensities, up to a definite limit above threshold, decrease RT; above the limiting intensity, no reduction in RT may be expected.

Practice — simple RT may be reduced as much as 10 per cent by practice.

Preparedness — "ready" signals reduce RT.

Motor unit responding — right hand and foot are faster than left, for right-handed people.

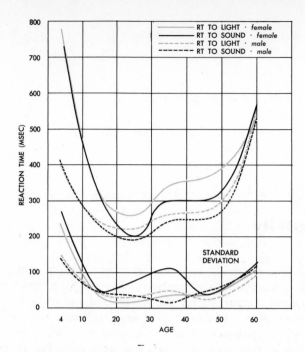

Age and sex.

Complexity — reaction time may be simple, as when a key is pressed in response to a light, or complex, as when a key is pressed only when a red, rather than an alternative green light, is flashed. The latter is complex, because a discrimination or judgment must be made before the reaction. An estimate for simple and complex RT can be obtained from the following formula:

$$RT \text{ (in milliseconds)} = 270 \log_e (n + 1)$$

where *n* represents the number of discriminations required before reacting.

RT's to discrete, isolated stimuli have considerable variability. The minimum RT variability one may expect can be expressed in these terms: 50 per cent of the RT's in a set of responses will fall within a ±15-millisecond range around the average RT of the set. Mean simple RT's do not often go below 150 milliseconds, even under the most favorable conditions. When responses are made at regular intervals to an external "pacing" stimulus or to one's own previous action (as in tapping), however, variability can be tremendously reduced and RT's can be as low as or lower than 100 milliseconds.

Speed of Perception-to-Action:

Brain perception of what eye sees	0.1	sec
Brain recognition	0.4	sec
Decision	4–5.0	sec
Motor Response	0.5	sec
Vehicle Reaction	2 +	sec
	7–8.0	sec Total

general motor characteristics

VOLUNTARY MOVEMENTS

Although few movements are exclusively one or the other, voluntary motion may be classified into two main general categories: (1) TENSION MOVEMENT — slow, tense movement, brought about by contraction of antagonistic muscles operating against one another with unequal tension; (2) BALLISTIC MOVEMENT — free movement, generally rapid, and least wasteful of energy; simultaneous operation of antagonistic muscle forces is minimum. Movement of body parts is the resultant of interaction between muscular and gravitational forces.

INVOLUNTARY MOVEMENTS, as distinguished from voluntary, are not under cortical control. Their purpose is to maintain basic life processes of the organism. Reflexes are included in the involuntary class of movements.

FEEDBACK

Voluntary movements, of the two general classes given (tension and ballistic) and intermediate stages between them, are part of a perceptual- or conceptual-motor process. Proprioceptive and perceptive impulses provide the cortex with the data which it uses to initiate and guide these movements. The perceptual-motor system, in its dynamic aspect, may be considered as a complex feedback system. For most tasks, there are at least three major loops, involving visual, tactile, and muscular feedback, as in the diagram. Movements of the arm can be perceived when the limb is moved 0.5° or more.

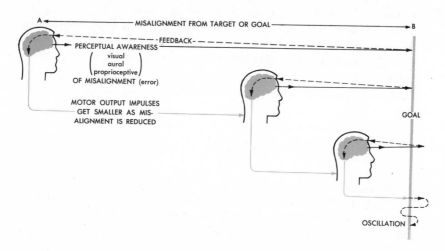

The human component in this system exhibits many parallels with mechanical and electrical servos. Such concepts as oscillation, inertia, damping, reverberation, and lag may all be used to describe neuro-muscular events in the human component. Its characteristics at a given time are partially determined by previous instructions and training. When functioning in a tracking system, the human component introduces "noise" (extraneous oscillations) with at least one strong frequency near 1 cycle per second, plus higher-frequency "tremors" which tend to decrease in amplitude with practice. In general, the human component is non-linear, but becomes more linear as the target path is "predictable" from past experience.

EFFICIENCY OF MUSCLE

Muscle efficiency is, on the average, low. Approximately three-quarters of muscle energy is liberated in the form of heat, one quarter in useful work. Very high and very low repetitive rates of movement are least efficient from the energy use standpoint.

Aside from steadiness, motor coordination ability is not generalized from task to task. For example, gross motor coordination is of doubtful correlation with fine motor precision. Also, an individual who turns a crank efficiently may be poor at operating a joy stick, etc.

motor performance on specific tasks

For practical convenience, control movements have been further divided into several functional categories, each of which has its own special characteristics, in addition to any of the general motor features discussed.

TREMOR

Tremor is the oscillation concomitant with effort to maintain a fixed position or direction. It is most obvious in the tension type of movement. The degree of tremor is measured by the distance or number of departures from the fixed path or position in a given time.

Tremor decreases when:

work is against friction;

member is supported; and

body is well supported while member performs activity.

Tremor increases when:

effort is made not to tremble; and

fatigue is present.

It is greatest in vertical motion, less in front-to-back motion, and least in side-to-side motion.

Steadiness is a generalized characteristic, applicable to the same degree in a given individual over a wide variety of tasks.

Tremor may be measured in the line of motion and at right angles to it. If motion in the horizontal plane is made at various angles with respect to the midline of the body, the amplitude of tremor at right angles to the line of motion varies in proportion to the sine of the angle of the line of motion. This relationship was revealed in a study by Corrigan and Brogden, in which the task was to keep from touching the sides of a narrow 35-centimeter slot with a stylus moved at 3 centimeters per second. Starting points and directions of the slot were varied over 360 degrees.

In the illustration below, zero degrees represents motion directly away from the midline of the body. Note that certain motions, as shown by the direction lines, give more precision than others.

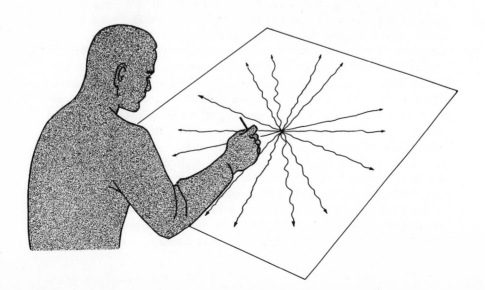

DISCRETE ADJUSTIVE MOVEMENTS

RESTRICTED BLIND POSITIONING. Errors exhibit a central-tendency effect, depending upon the range of movement under test. That is, within a particular range of distances to be moved, there is a central point below which movements tend to overshoot the mark and above which they tend to undershoot. When motion is against gravity, however, underestimation prevails at all distances. In the range shown, the central-tendency effect occurs with reference to a required movement of 4 inches. Movement toward the body has somewhat different error characteristics than movement away from the body. The absolute error, particularly for movements toward the body, increases with the distance moved. Per cent error, however, decreases up to 4 inches, remains constant for distances greater. Accuracy is unaffected by distance from body at which motion is executed or by the time allowed for the movement to be made. Accuracy for blind positioning is wholly determined by the initial motion; secondary adjustment, lacking all sensory information but proprioceptive internal feedback, contributes nothing.

FREE BLIND POSITIONING. The following is based on a study[6] in which practiced subjects had to reach blindly for targets placed around and above them at distances within 28 inches from each shoulder point. The subjects, blindfolded after first observing the situation, were to touch the bull's eyes of the targets. The magnitude of the average error made in reaching for each position is proportional to the diameter of the circle or long diameter of the ellipse enclosing the bull's eye at that point. The numerical value of this error is indicated next to the circles and ellipses. Arrows show the predominant direction and magnitude of errors in positioning to targets in their respective rows. As shown, errors are smallest for centrally located targets. Most accurate judgments are for targets directly forward. Targets above the shoulder are generally less accurately located than those below. Closer target positions (not shown) are judged more accurately than those illustrated. The position from which motion is initiated varies the results; however, most accuracy still obtains for targets directly ahead. Central tendencies show up again — that is, movements to points above the shoulder tend to be underestimated (arrowhead down), to points below the shoulder also underestimated (arrowhead up). Errors for unpracticed subjects are one and one-half to two times as large as those shown. These data have application to situations where controls must be reached under conditions of blackout, or when other tasks, such as scope viewing, must be attended to at the same time.

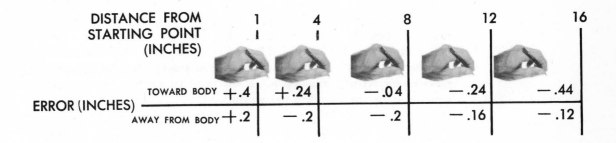

	1	4	8	12	16
ERROR (INCHES) TOWARD BODY	+.4	+.24	—.04	—.24	—.44
AWAY FROM BODY	+.2	—.2	—.2	—.16	—.12

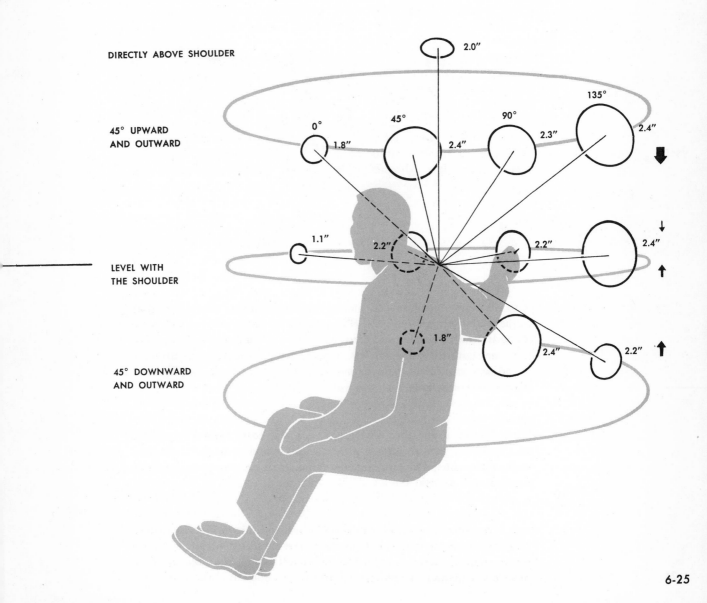

DIRECTLY ABOVE SHOULDER

45° UPWARD
AND OUTWARD

LEVEL WITH
THE SHOULDER

45° DOWNWARD
AND OUTWARD

VISUAL POSITIONING. In these reactions, free or restricted, time functions and motor patterns rather than accuracy are the most important factors. In this type of movement, small corrective secondary adjustments, as well as the initial gross movement, contribute materially to correct performance. RT is the third component involved in total time for the complete movement.

When sufficient time for the response is given, a high degree of accuracy is insured. Accuracy increases with increasing allowance of time per movement up to 1.5 seconds. Greater time allowances do not enhance visual positioning accuracies.

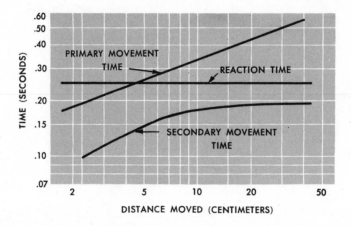

The figure[7(a)] shows times for visual positioning broken down into its three components, initial gross-movement time, secondary adjustive-movement time, and RT. Average RT is constant at 250 milliseconds for all distances and directions moved. Primary movement time increases with distance, but less than in direct proportion to distance. Secondary movement time remains relatively constant for distances above 10 centimeters.

Barnes found that movement back and forth between stops up to 15 inches apart consumed almost equal amounts of time. A good deal of the time, 100 milliseconds, is taken up in changing direction for this type of task.

A general conclusion relative to time required for visual position movements is that long distances are traversed about as fast as short ones. The longer the distance through which the hand must be moved, the greater the average velocity.

REPETITIVE MOVEMENTS

Discrete movements, repeated at regular intervals, such as tapping, are termed repetitive movements. Tapping is one of the simpler motor tasks, of limited practical use. Theoretically, however, tapping is of considerable interest, since the average time per tap, 100 milliseconds, shows up as a basic temporal behavior unit (page 6-39, "Serial Movement").

CRANKING AND WINDING operations serve mainly to accomplish positioning and/or tracking tasks, but there are principles which apply specifically to them in their own right.

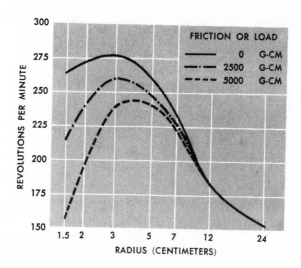

As shown in the graph,[7(b)] maximum turn rate decreases with increasing load for radii to 12 centimeters. Turn rate is maximum at radii between 3 and 5 centimeters (1.2 to 2 inches). In the study above, the maximum rate attained for zero load, 275 revolutions per minute, was reached using 3-centimeter radius (1.2 inches); at higher loads, radii giving highest speeds are slightly longer.

Errors, in terms of distance ahead of or behind a target, are (1) smallest for maximum rotation speeds; (2) decreased by inertia (heavy wheels or controls) especially for speeds below 50 rpm — inertia favors smoother performance; and (3) increased by friction or drag. This last effect is most pronounced at the slow speeds. However, friction aids in the discrimination of small load changes. See Chapter 2, page 115, for data on optimum diameters of cranks and wheels under various conditions.

CONTINUOUS CORRECTION MOVEMENT — TRACKING

Motion made in response to constantly changing stimuli, or to constantly changing stimuli-response position relationships is called tracking. Rate tracking involves smooth continuous motion to remain close to a target's correct position and rate. Position tracking requires quick adjustive movements of relatively large magnitude in order to correct for large errors.

The two types of tracking response, *rate tracking* and *position tracking* are observed during every tracking task. The task's difficulty determines in large measure the proportion of the tracking time taken up by each type. Experimentally determined criteria show sharp differences between the two. On the basis of these differences, the tracking going on at any moment may be placed in either the rate- or position-tracking categories.

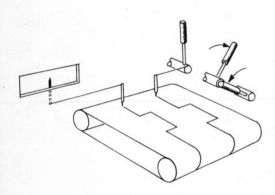 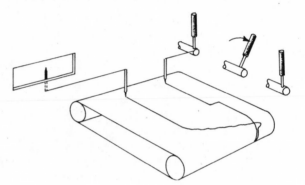

POSITION TRACKING

Adjustments are rapid.

Amplitude is large.

Error is large.

Ratio of variability of time for a complete movement to length of the movement is small; it remains constant for all amplitudes of position-tracking movement.

Time per movement is constant for all target speeds.

Number of position-tracking movements remains fairly constant at all speeds.

RATE TRACKING

Adjustments to the correct course or target position are slow; that is, complete movements consume a relatively long time, since they need not often be modified while one is "on track."

Amplitude of the adjustive movement is small.

Error is small.

Variability of movement time relative to movement length is large; it decreases with increasing movement lengths up to the length at which position-tracking starts.

Time per movement decreases as target speed increases.

Number of rate-tracking movements decreases with increasing target speed.

The total number of corrective movements of any sort therefore decreases with increasing target speed, and amplitude of both movement and error increase proportionately with target speed for both types of tracking.

Human tracking responses may be approximated by a relatively simple and familiar type of equation. These responses contain random elements, but not in such degree as to destroy the approximation. The equation is similar to ones applicable to physical systems with mass, friction, and resiliency, or to electrical systems with capacitance, resistance, and inductance. In tracking, the present position of the subject's hand as a function of time may be expressed as $H = a(dA/dt) + bA + c\int A dt,$ [8(a)] where H is present position, A represents the stimulus or target position at a time one RT length prior to the present moment, and $a,$ $b,$ and c are proportionality constants. Accurate response to $dA/dt,$ or target rate, is more difficult to develop than to the latter two terms, position and displacement. Although all three responses operate in the tracking task, target rate contributes least and so has the smallest proportionality constant, $a,$ in the equation. Hick[13] has found that thresholds for *recognizing* sudden accelerations (d^2A/dt^2) of a moving spot on a scope are approximately 12 per cent of the initial or comparison velocity. In general, however, *control* relative to the second or higher derivatives of target motion is practically negligible.

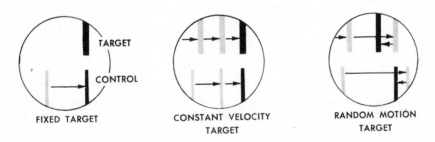

FIXED TARGET   CONSTANT VELOCITY TARGET   RANDOM MOTION TARGET

Responses which make use of anticipation of target position (based on dA/dt) lend additional effectiveness to the tracking performance; the dA/dt behavior of the target is then a cue contributing more to the tracking task than it would ordinarily. In the equation describing that tracking response, the constant a would have a greater value relative to the other constant terms. Accuracy will increase in direct proportion to the degree to which the operator can *predict* the target behavior on the basis of his past experience with it or with similar stimuli. For example, fixed targets are best "tracked," ones of constant velocity next, ones with random motion poorest, since, in the latter case, motion is unpredictable. Once a motion based upon visual and proprioceptive information is triggered off, it may momentarily continue correctly in the absence of vision, that is, the visual control which initiated it.

An element which greatly decreases the accuracy of motor control systems is *lag* between control movement or force and the time of display of the resultant of that control force or movement. Even a few milliseconds lag is enough to cause serious disruption.

COMPENSATORY TRACKING. The operator's task is to keep the target spot centered in the display by moving a control which compensates for the spot's motion away from the center. His performance generally is poor, since his only information is *error*, or the additional compensatory distance the spot must be moved to get on track (the center of the scope). The observer cannot judge how much of the error is due to his control motion and/or how much is due to the motion of the target.

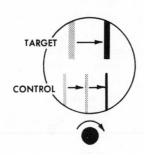

TARGET

CONTROL

FOLLOWING OR PURSUIT TRACKING. The upper trace (T) in this display moves, showing target motion; the controlled trace (C) is moved by the operator's control. His task is to align the two. Now, the operator, having more information about his performance and that of the target, as well as the difference between the two (error), can track much more accurately. Pursuit tracking, under almost all circumstances, is by far the more efficient of the two primary methods.

AIDED TRACKING. Means have been devised to improve an operator's ability to track. In an *aided tracking* system the controlled element, which can usually be seen with the target in a visual display, is given an output composed of two simultaneously operating factors: (1) a displacement in proportion to that of a handwheel controlling the element and (2) a change in velocity proportional to the displacement of the controlled element. Thus, for example, if an operator falls behind a target he is tracking, his turning the wheel will displace the element he controls in the direction of the target, and at the same time increase the element's velocity up to that of the target. Optimal *aided-tracking ratios* (K, in seconds) to incorporate into a tracking control can be determined on the basis of the fact, checked experimentally, that the tracker operates mainly on the basis of the magnitude of his error rather than its rate of change. Optimum values of K of from 2 to 3 seconds have been found, depending on conditions of operation. The better the operator, the smaller the optimal K will be. Also, the greater the ratio used, the greater will be the mean square error from the correct tracking path.

THE HUMAN TRANSFER FUNCTION

THE HUMAN TRANSFER FUNCTION. Beginning about fifteen years ago, a number of papers were published in this country (Elkind,[9] Ragazzini,[10] Searle and Taylor[11]) and in England (Craik,[12] Hick,[13] Tustin[14]) which utilized servo-mechanism theory in describing the role of the human in tracking. Until very recently, investigators have attempted to fit a linear input-output relationship to the operator, since a human "transfer function" describable in simple linear differential equations would make possible the application of servo-theory and linear-control-system synthesis techniques to human motor-performance in the tracking situation. To date, a direct transform from electro-mechanics to human motor behavior in tracking has not been possible, although some excellent and experimentally verified approximations have been developed (Senders[15]). However, most of the work in this field offers little of a generally applicable and detailed nature suitable for handbook-type utilization. Even for such a seemingly simple task as human tracking in one dimension, the construction of an adequate model of the human operator presents a formidable mathematical and engineering effort, since experience shows that man's performance appears to contain both nonlinear and nonstationary elements (Diamantides[16]).

The dynamics of the machine portion of a human-controlled system can generally be described by servo-type linear differential equations called system transfer functions. All of the various operator models appearing in recent literature surveys (Senders,[15] Bekey[17]) are attempts to provide human tracking behavior with a rigorous mathematical description. The models most commonly used to represent the human operator in a system similar to the one shown in the diagram below for a particular class of inputs may be termed continuous and linear in that they consist of linear differential equations whose coefficients depend upon the bandwidth of the input signal and on the dynamics of the particular controlled element.

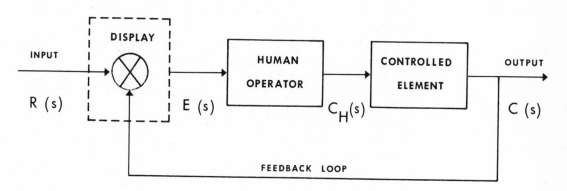

GENERAL SCHEMATIC OF A CLOSED-LOOP MAN-MACHINE SYSTEM

$R(s)$ = the system input or reference variable

$E(s)$ = human input or error variable

$C_H(s)$ = human output or human-controlled variable

$C(s)$ = system output or system-controlled variable

The operator's task in the diagram is commonly called a "compensatory tracking function" wherein the display represents a subtraction element and the operator is instructed to reduce the error signal to zero. Both blocks in the diagram can be represented by transfer functions — the controlled element is considered to be a ratio of polynomials in the complex frequency variable (s). For subsequent example calculations, the controlled-element transfer function used will be a simple variation of the relationship given by equation 1:

$$\frac{C(s)}{C_H(s)} = \frac{\sum_{i=0}^{m} a_i s^i}{\sum_{j=0}^{n} b_j s^j} \tag{1}$$

where the parameters a_i and b_j can assume a wide range of values depending upon the controlled-element dynamics.

In general, the results of the referenced studies indicate that the transfer function of the human operator is of the following form:

$$\frac{C_H(s)}{E(s)} = \frac{Ke^{-ts}(T_L s + 1)}{(T_I s + 1) T_N s + 1} = G_H(s) \tag{2}$$

The human transfer-function, $G_H(s)$, can be broken down into three or more parts for purposes of description. First, the operator's reaction time is contained in the pure time-delay term, e^{-ts}. Generally, the latter term is fairly constant for simple tasks having more or less random inputs. The first-order lag term, $T_N + 1$, portrays the neuro-muscular system, although it should be characterized as a damped second-order system since mass is involved. For practical purposes, however, very little error arises due to the approximation. The remaining terms in equation 2 represent an adaptive process utilized by the operator to adjust his responses to a given set of conditions and a given controlled element. In this latter respect, the performance of the human operator is similar to that of an electro-mechanical adaptive control system utilized in some of the most recent high-performance jet aircraft. The terms T, K, T_L, T_N, and T_I vary over a fairly wide range of values. However, for a specific task and a specific controlled element these terms remain relatively constant once the operator has become fairly proficient in the task. An upper limit for T_I is about 10 seconds; for T_L a practical upper limit is about 1 second; and 0.1 second is about the practical lower limit for T_N. Reaction time, T, may generally be assumed as about 0.2 seconds for most tasks, although under certain conditions the value may well halve or double this number.

In equation 2 the symbolism employed is that of Laplace transforms as commonly applied to linear systems, and this means that the principle of superposition does not apply in the ordinary sense, and often the term superposition applies to the human transfer-function, $G_H(s)$. However, "quasi-linear" relationship is used instead, on the assumption that the following properties (Bekey[17]) apply to the human input-output relationship: (a) the system is describable by a linear differential equation with coefficients which are dependent upon controlled-element dynamics and the input signal bandwidth, but remain constant for a specific system, and (b) the system's output is determined only in part by the linear transfer function — the remaining portion (remnant) contains the random or uncorrelated output. However, the remnant can be neglected in determining the best control-element dynamics unless the average linear correlation between input and output is relatively low.

An analogue model of the linear portion of the human transfer-function is, however, a useful aid in the preliminary design of a system to be controlled by a human operator. Once the controlled element has been established, the transfer function can be inserted in the control loop and standard analysis techniques can be used to evaluate total-system stability. There is no set rule that can be called upon to prove that a human can perform the required task. In general, however, if the transfer function control of the system exhibits marginal stability, then the controlled element dynamics, and/or system order, should be altered or system control effected by automatic systems, for it is doubtful that operator non-linearities — the adaptive process — are sufficiently flexible to provide satisfactory control in response to the likely range of forcing functions which might be imposed upon the system.

As an elementary example, consider the control of a simple third-order system where the controlled element has no appreciable dynamics:

$$\theta = K_i \theta_i; \text{ where } K_i \text{ is a gain,}$$
$$\theta_i \text{ is a control input, and}$$
$$\theta_o \text{ is the controlled variable}$$

In block diagram form:

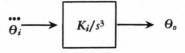

It has been demonstrated by previous experiments that such a system is uncontrollable by the ordinary human operator.

Actual operator performance is compared — in the figure below — with the performance of a simulated linear model of the human operator transfer function controlling the simple third-order system, in response to a step-function input. The control task is simple; a meter having two pointers is the display and the operator's task is to make one pointer follow the other. Note here that neither the operator nor the simulated linear operator transfer function is able to control the system. The system is highly divergent despite the control exercised by either the actual operator or the simulated transfer function model of the linear portion of operator tracking behavior.

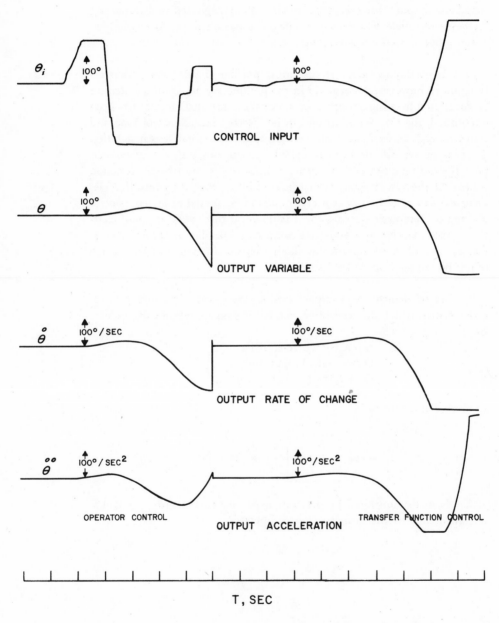

RESPONSE TO A SIMPLE THIRD-ORDER SYSTEM

This same system can be made controllable, however, by the utilization of a simple technique — a "quickened display" wherein rate and acceleration terms are added to the display and the operator's control task remains precisely the same as it was before "quickening" was employed. This is, of course, a common compensatory technique utilized in systems design. The figure below shows the results of adding a rate gain of 1.85 degrees per second per degree and 0.90 degrees per second squared per degree to the display. The resulting system is stable regardless of whether the actual human operator or a simulated linear portion of his transfer function closes the system loop. Note that the transfer function model provides somewhat smoother control than the actual operator does; however, the operator has little difficulty in making the appropriate control inputs.

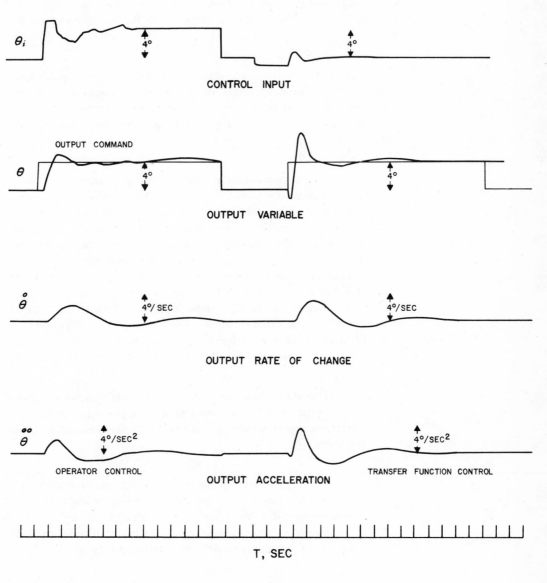

CONTROL INPUT

OUTPUT VARIABLE

OUTPUT RATE OF CHANGE

OUTPUT ACCELERATION

T, SEC

RESPONSE TO A "QUICKENED" THIRD-ORDER SYSTEM

In somewhat less precise terms than in the preceding discussion, the human operator has many — apparently, an infinite number of — transfer functions, since he exhibits non-linearities of several types as well as the capability of predicting subsequent tracking behavior within a task sequence. For example, when tracking simple sine-waves up to about 1.5 cycles per second, the human operator is capable of learning the characteristics of the signals and predicting their future course well enough to track with closed eyes. McRuer and Krendel[18] have described this behavior as "precognative tracking." Earlier, Westheimer and Conover[19] demonstrated this phenomenon by showing that untrained subjects could produce smooth eye movements in the absence of an external moving visual stimulus. No clear distinction is yet made in the literature between "smooth" eye motions and pursuit-type movements; nevertheless, it becomes apparent that experimental input to the operator must be random. According to Bekey, the evidence for superposition of response to simple input is clearly not applicable in the development of human-operator tracking theory.

In practice, however, for a particular class of input signals and a particular task, a linear representation of human tracking behavior is quite acceptable under most conditions. The following constraints and/or observed operator charactertistics apply to all but the most trivial operator tracking tasks:

Linear continuous models of human operators are often obtained by measurements of cross-correlation functions so designed that the resulting relationship best approximates the human in a statistical sense. The uncorrelated component of the output has often been dubbed "noise" generated within the operator; however, it may as well represent an as yet undetermined real component of normal operator behavior. Anyway, the difference between the actual human output and the model output is called the remnant, which includes in itself all those aspects of the tracking behavior which are not specified by the linear component (Tustin[14]). By definition among servo theorists, the combination of linear transfer function plus remnant is called a "describing function" (Elkind[9]).

For the trained operator, there is little change in transfer characteristics noted over a wide range of input signal amplitudes. Therefore, within certain constraints, the human acts best as a linear amplifier.

Generally, tracking behavior tends to improve with practice. This characteristic may be called learning or adaptation. The human seems to be able to sense certain changes in environmental and controlled-system parameters and to make adjustments in his behavior corresponding to or compensating for these changes.

There is a growing body of evidence which indicates that the human operator behaves as a sampling system in certain tracking situations; i.e., he accepts inputs on an intermittent basis even though his output (motor behavior) appears to be continuous (Bekey,[17] Noble et al.[20]). This ability of the operator to extrapolate and to sample is important in tracking, since it means that with predictable inputs, such as a single-frequency sinusoid, this behavior is somehow different from what it is with random-appearing signals. In this same context the operator exhibits an ability to equalize or to change his transfer function by introducing one or more compensatory factors as required by the stability characteristics or performance requirements of the element he is controlling.

Comparison of the input-output behavior of the operator by visual means as well as by analytic methods shows that the human tends to act as a low-pass filter. This statement tends to conflict with the assumption of linearity; however, within the "useful" range of the filter, the tendency of the operator to attenuate high frequencies is not so pronounced.

All human behavior in response to an external stimulus is characterized by a delay which is inherent in the neuro-muscular system. In operator tracking behavior this delay is often called "transport lag" and may vary from about 0.15 seconds for a highly trained operator on a simple task up to 1 or more seconds, depending upon the complexity of the tracking task and the nature of the control-display relationship.

The extent to which an operator is aware of the effects of his input on system output is demonstratively related to the goodness of his performance. Though obviously related to some extent to the "knowledge of results" requirement for learning, in the "practical sense," motivation plays a more significant role in human tracking behavior.

The nature of the control-display relationship itself has been subject to extensive experimental study and is demonstratively and dramatically related to the goodness of operator tracking performance within a given controlled-element configuration.

CONTROL-DISPLAY RELATIONSHIPS. Pursuit tracking will be superior to compensatory in those cases where target velocity and acceleration information is required by the operator, but pursuit tracking will lose its pronounced advantage when this information is not needed by the operator. Inclusion of information which is uncorrelated with tracking behavior required of the operator will be detrimental to his performance. The pursuit mode is superior to the compensatory for all conditions except for velocity and rate-aided systems at the lowest input speed — where compensatory performance is superior.

Chernikoff *et al.*[21] and Taylor and Birmingham[23] account for this superior compensatory performance by noting that the presence of an integral transformation in the control loop (rate and rate-aided systems) unburdens the operator, whereby a condition of "stimulus-response integrity" is achieved. Nevertheless, under most conditions pursuit tracking is preferable to the compensatory mode. If it is known that all inputs to the system will be in the ultra-low frequency range, i.e., from dc to approximately six cycles per second, the compensatory display may be superior to the pursuit type.

If it is necessary for the operator to utilize higher derivatives of the input signal in determining his motor output, a pursuit-type display is best, since it most clearly provides the necessary information. However, in those systems requiring the operator to respond only to the magnitude of the input signal with unity gain, a compensatory display may be best (according to Briggs[22]).

CONTROL RATIOS. Ratio of control movement to indicator movement has more effect on the time required to make settings within a given degree of tolerance than have such factors as inertia, friction, and size of controls. Primary adjustment times decrease with increasing distance moved by a controlled marker for each revolution of its control. Secondary adjustment times, however, increase with greater marker movement per control revolution. The figure[8(b)] below illustrates these two functions. Over-all time is minimum for gear ratios (pointer movement, in inches, per control revolution) between 1 and 2.

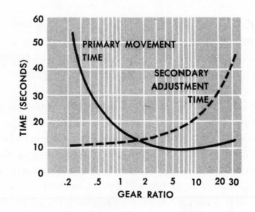

This ratio is optimum if fine tolerances are required. If accuracy of final adjustment is not too critical, however, it is advantageous to have higher ratios, so as to arrive more rapidly at a point within the coarser tolerance. In this latter case, ratios of about 6 to 1 are optimum. When levers are used in a right-left direction to control settings of a pointer on a linear scale, the optimum control ratio has been found to be between 1 to 4 and 1 to 3 (pointer movement distance with respect to lever-tip movement distance).

For joystick controls, the optimum condition for tolerances of 1/10 inch is two-and-one-half units of stick movement to one unit of indicator movement on a scope face.

SERIAL MOVEMENT

The force pattern or primary movement elicited by an initial stimulus may not, for a period of at least 100 milliseconds, be altered by the presentation of a second stimulus. It has even been shown that the time sequence of stimuli occurring within about 100 milliseconds of each other is undifferentiable. Movement elements at a maximum rate of 10 per second may therefore be considered units, since that rate is the limiting one at which motion is modifiable. In fact, when one stimulus follows another by as much as ½ second, the first sometimes delays RT to the second.

It might appear from the above that only one movement can be made during the 100-millisecond period, but this is not so. A sequence of two or more movements may be released as a functional unit within this short period. Solidification of sequential movements into a hierarchy of motions able to be triggered off as a functional motor unit is a major achievement in motor learning. An example of this is typing performance in which a sequence of letters is typed as a single motor pattern consisting of several integrated movements rather than as a separate motion in response to each individual character. Discrete sequential movements are involved as well.

ABSOLUTE ERROR
GREATEST
E/S RATIO CONSTANT
AND SMALL

MIDDLE RANGES
E/S RATIO CONSTANT
AND SMALL

RELATIVE ERROR
LARGE FOR VALUES
NEAR THRESHOLD

CONTROL FORCES

The forces which should be considered here are those exerted by the operator on the control and the opposing force of the control itself. Both aspects are necessary in control systems and provide a substantial part of the store of proprioceptive information (internal feedback) used by an operator of a control device. The degree to which such forces are discriminable over a wide range of movement is therefore an important limiting factor, along with such others as strength, speed, and fatigue, to the efficiency of operation of any control. Proprioceptive feedback is also an important contributor to the later stages of learning of visuo-motor tasks.

The sensitivity curve for discriminations of applied forces is like that of most sensory judgments and has characteristics which, if taken into consideration in control design, may enhance efficiency considerably. The pressure discrimination function may be described thus: error in discriminating or reproducing forces relative to a standard is large for values near threshold pressures; in the middle and higher ranges above threshold, the error/standard (e/s) ratio becomes constant and small; absolute error is therefore greatest for discriminations relative to high forces or pressures. For the airplane stick, the force at and above which the ratio of the error and the force to be reproduced becomes constant and small has been found to be 10 lbs.

One may compensate for this differential discriminability of forces by adjusting controls so that (1) when they are operating in regions of poor sensitivity, relatively large increments of force are required to accomplish a given movement, and (2) when operating in regions of better discrimination, correspondingly smaller increments of force are required for that same movement.

The following generalized principles may be stated regarding human application of force:

Several statements can be made about control forces on the basis of separate studies made by Jenkins, Fisher and Birren, and Clark.

Force application is equally accurate for hands and feet.

Controls centered in front of the observer permit maximum force application.

Control force greater than 30 to 40 pounds applied by hand and greater than 60 pounds by foot is fatiguing.

Use of fingers alone, rather than the whole arm or any part of it, requires least energy per given amount of control force applied. Maximum forces exertable, however, increase with use of whole arm and shoulder.

Maximum hand grip for a 25-year-old man is about 125 pounds, of a 60-year-old man, approximately 103 pounds. The right hand can exert an average of 10 pounds greater force than the left. Controls should not demand the maximum effort (see page 5-36).

The position of the body and of the members applying the force, the direction of application, and the control to which it is applied determine the amount of force exertable.

SPEED OF MOVEMENT

Supersonic-velocity travel points up the importance of this topic. In general, the following statements hold.

Horizontal movement of the hand is faster than vertical.

Continuous curved motions are faster than ones which have abrupt direction changes.

The time it takes to start or stop a movement remains roughly constant regardless of the movement's length.

Maximum velocity is an inverse function of load moved.

Time required to reach maximum velocity varies directly with load.

For simple reactions, motor activity can be "driven" above its normal rate, with less variability, by an external "driving" stimulus.

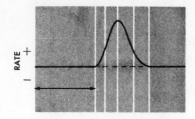

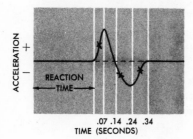

The illustration shows typical rate and acceleration components of motion in moving a control lever 9 inches in order to track a spot that jumped horizontally from one place to another on a scope.[23] Velocity is always positive (in the direction of motion) and increases for about the first 0.14 second, decreases thereafter. Acceleration in the direction of motion is positive for the first 0.14 second. It reaches a maximum at the end of the first 0.07 second, then still continues, but at a slower rate, until 0.14 second. After 0.14 second, acceleration is negative, that is, braking force is applied in a direction opposite to the motion, and this is maximal at 0.24 second. Thereafter, deceleration proceeds at a slower rate (braking force is gradually eased up) until the final position is reached at 0.34 second after the motion began. The maxima of rapid rates of change of acceleration (jerks) are marked by X's on the curve.

principles of motion economy

The ease, speed, and accuracy of manual operations may be increased by the application of motion-economy principles, some of which are listed below as presented by Barnes,[24] Hartson,[25] and the Tufts College Institute.[26]

Both hands should begin as well as complete their motion at the same instant.

The hands should not be idle except during rest periods.

Motions of the arms should be made simultaneously and in opposite and symmetrical directions.

The motion sequence that employs the fewest basic divisions of accomplishment is the best for performing a given task.

Hands should be relieved of all work that can be performed more advantageously by the feet or other parts of the body.

Where possible, work should be held by jigs or vises so that hands may be free to operate.

Tools, materials, and controls should be located in an arc around the work place and as near the worker as possible.

Tools and materials should be pre-positioned in order to eliminate searching and selecting.

Two or more tools should be combined wherever possible.

The height of the work place and the chair should preferably be so arranged that alternate sitting and standing at work are easily possible.

Continuous, curved motions are preferable to straight-line motions involving sudden and sharp changes in direction.

Ballistic movements are faster, easier, and more accurate than restricted or controlled movements.

Rhythm is essential to the smooth and automatic performance of an operation and the work should be arranged to permit easy and natural rhythm wherever possible.

Successive movements should be so interrelated that one movement passes easily into the next, each ending in a position favorable for the beginning of the next movement.

A movement is less fatiguing if it occurs in the direction in which the greatest possible use of gravity can be made.

When a forcible stroke is required, the movements and the material of the worker must be so arranged that the stroke is delivered when, as far as is practicable, it has reached its greatest momentum; momentum should be reduced to a minimum if it must be overcome by muscular effort.

Hesitation — or the temporary and often minute cessation from motion — should be analyzed; its cause should be accounted for and, if possible, eliminated.

If a definite combination of movements has been determined as economically most suitable, this method must be applied without any exception from the beginning of the learning. In other words, lay emphasis on form rather than upon accuracy, even if this involves a rather poor showing at the beginning of the apprenticeship period.

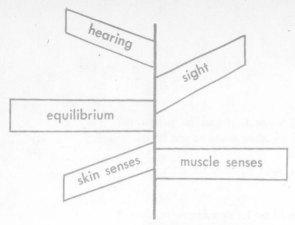

ORIENTATION

We maintain our orientation to and equilibrium in the world about us by a combination of visual and auditory information, data provided by action of the semicircular canals, information from kinesthesis and the skin senses, and other less important cues. We can accurately judge verticality, for example, when the framework of our visual field is in perfect alignment with normal gravitational forces acting upon special receptors (page 6-11) in the semicircular canals. Even under ideal conditions, however, there are certain instabilities in our makeup, as well as imperfections in our ability to sense departures from any given orientation. Abnormal or conflicting conditions make discriminations more difficult, and sometimes cause serious errors of perception.

body sway

The body is never perfectly rigid but, depending upon its position, sways to some extent in all directions; backward and forward rocking is 50 to 75 per cent greater in range than side-to-side sway. Amplitude of sway is unrelated to height or weight, but increases to some extent with increased bodily tension. There is no relation between body sway (static equilibrium) and the ability to maintain balance under unstable conditions (dynamic equilibrium). For both types of equilibrium the contribution of visual cues is emphasized by the fact that sway increases markedly when the eyes are closed.

sensitivity to motion

Thresholds for sensitivity to body motion (when an external force is the mover) depend largely on cues from the semicircular canal mechanism, which is sensitive only to acceleration; this acceleration threshold varies inversely with the length of time during which the acceleration acts. Vibration, pressure, and kinesthetic stimuli, however, are also provided by the apparatus used to move the subject, and are appreciable before labyrinthine thresholds can be reached. Thresholds for various types of accelerations follow.

LINEAR ACCELERATION

    vertical, 4-12 cm/sec^2
    horizontal, 12-20 cm/sec^2

ANGULAR ACCELERATION

    →

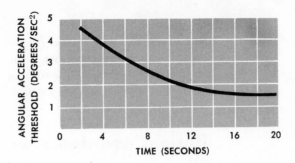

For ordinary flying conditions, threshold is about 1 to 2 degrees per second per second. Lower values than these have been reported, however.

nystagmus

One important manifestation of the interrelationship between vision and the labyrinthine apparatus is the reflex eye motion that accompanies rotation or other changes of body position. This reflex eye movement is called nystagmus, the slow phase of which is a direct outcome of labyrinthine stimulation. The nystagmus occurs regardless of whether the eyes are closed or open, and takes place in the same plane as the body's rotation. It consists of slow, drifting eye movements interrupted by rapid saccadic movements in the opposite direction. A typical course of the slow movements, keeping in mind that rapid reverse motions are interspersed between them, is as follows:

On rotation to the right, for example, until a constant rotation speed is reached and maintained, there follows in sequence:

1. Compensatory eye movements to the left, after a 50-to-80-millisecond delay from the start of the rotation.

2. Movements to the right when the preceding motions have decelerated to zero. This motion is called *post-rotational nystagmus.*

3. Movements to the left after those described in (2) have decelerated. These motions are ones of *inverse nystagmus.*[27]

These phases may not be completed until as much as 10 minutes after the start of the rotation. If the rotation is stopped before the preceding sequence has run its course, the response to deceleration is added algebraically to the orginal response, thus overriding it to greater or lesser extent depending upon the time difference between the starting and stopping of the motion. Most nystagmus studies have in fact been done in just this way, so that the third phase above is not usually identified. There is evidence that a roughly linear relationship exists between acceleration times, duration of acceleration (a labyrinthine power input) and velocity of post-rotational nystagmus (a visual output).

illusions associated with motion

It can be seen, therefore, that many of the illusions arising from body movement are, at least in part, accounted for by vestibular activation of these reflex nystagmus motions of the eye. Some illusions concomitant with body movement, including several not primarily associated with nystagmus, are tabulated below. They are not, however, universally observed by all people, nor in the same manner by those who do observe them.

CONDITION OF OBSERVER	CONDITION OF VISUAL STIMULUS OBJECT(S)	NATURE OF ILLUSION
Starts motion	Stationary	Observer sees visual stimulus moving in opposite direction, feels himself stationary
Stationary	Starts motion	Observer sees object stationary, feels self moving in direction opposite to object's motion
Accelerating rotation to 15 rpm; dark room with only target illuminated	Slow revolution around observer's head, in same direction as his acceleration	* Object loses motion, is displaced in direction opposite to its direction of movement
Above rotation continued at 15 rpm	As above	* Observer loses own sensation of motion; object appears to move in opposite direction with greater velocity than before
Strong rotation suddenly stops	Fixed	* At first, object and subject both seem to rotate. Then observer may feel self fixed while visual stimuli rotate about him in a direction opposite to that of his previous motion. This illusion is called the *oculo-gyral illusion*. After all apparent motion stops, subject still feels vaguely unpleasant sensations.

* When experiments are conducted in a lighted room the last three illusions do not occur.

perception of the vertical

Perception of the vertical — that is, the direction of action of normal gravitational forces — and of one's postural relation to that vertical are important aspects of orientation. As in the case of other percepts, their accuracy, although high, is limited, especially under unfavorable conditions. Both visual and postural vertical are largely determined by joint action of visual and gravitational forces. Visual "forces" affecting the judgment are those which spring from the alignment (or lack of it) of the visual framework or main lines of visual space with respect to the true vertical position. Gravitational (g) force on the body is the vector sum of forces imposed on it by acceleration and normal gravitation. This resultant force exerts a very powerful influence upon our orientation and/or perception of the vertical, which is in the direction of action of the resultant g.

POSTURAL TILT

The smallest degree of body tilt in any direction which can be detected has been found for a group of pilots to range from less than 1 degree all the way up to 14 degrees. The average threshold was between 2 and 3 degrees, with that of backward tilt roughly ½ degree higher than thresholds for tilt in the other quadrants. Elimination of visual cues raises these thresholds. With poor visibility, banks of 10-15 degrees in aircraft may not be recognized by an individual in flight.[28]

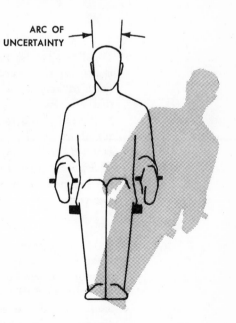

Laboratory tests,[29] using a "tilt chair" which can be operated by the experimenter or by the subject himself while seated in it, have shown greater sensitivities than those observed under conditions of flight. The postural vertical can be judged very well, even without visual cues. When blindfolded subjects were required to return themselves to the vertical from positions of tilt varying from 5 to 90 degrees to the left or right, they tended toward underestimation; that is, the vertical was judged to be at a mean position of 0.8 degree from the true vertical in the direction of the original tilt. On approaching the vertical, judgment of its true position was very uncertain. The middle 75 per cent of chair settings in the experiment described above extended over a range of 4.4 degrees. This 75 per cent range has been called the "arc of uncertainty." When the experimenter controlled the chair's motion and re-

ARC OF UNCERTAINTY

quired the subject to signal when he had reached what he thought to be the vertical position, the error — 2.40 degrees, with an arc of uncertainty of 7.4 degrees — was found to be higher than it was when the subject controlled his own chair. When a foam-rubber seat was used, with the intent to eliminate cues of pressure, the arc of uncertainty rose slightly, but the constant error of judgment in the direction of the original tilt remained the same. Accuracy of the judgment was unaffected by inclination of the head.

In flight, judgments of tilt in the lateral plane (roll) have been found more accurate than judgments in the medial plane (pitch).[30] There is a delay of 7.5 seconds before tilt is felt. Furthermore, in flight the feeling of tilt disappears before one is level again. The latter is an adaptation effect which has also been evidenced in the tilt-chair tests. In these tests, a 10-second minimum is required before any adaptation occurs. After that time, the longer one is kept at a tilted position, the less one feels himself to be tilted away from the true vertical. This phenomenon has caused considerable trouble in aviation.

VISUAL TILT

Judgment of the visual vertical (visual judgment of the gravitational vertical, by lining up a rod to the vertical position, for example) is also limited in accuracy. The main lines or framework of the visual space influences the visual perception of orientation of objects within that framework. Constant error of judgments of the visual vertical have been found to be as low as 0.2 degree.[31] Judgments of the horizontal are equally precise. The phenomenon of adaptation occurs here as it did for postural tilt — continued observation of tilted lines (except 45 degrees) causes them to appear less tilted. Adaptation to the vertical is accompanied, to a lesser exent, by adaptation to the horizontal, and vice-versa.

A striking example of the influence of the visual framework on visual orientation would be the appearance of a landing field as seen through the window of a plane just landed. If one is far enough back from the window so that its outlines form the framework of the field, the level field may be seen sloping downward, that is, in the opposite direction to the tilt of the plane window.

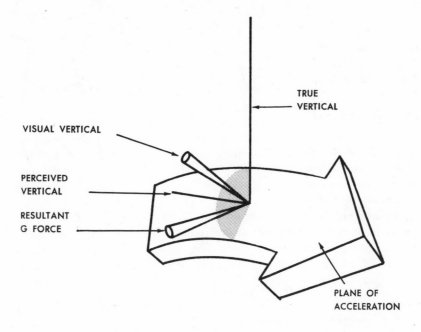

TRUE VERTICAL

VISUAL VERTICAL

PERCEIVED VERTICAL

RESULTANT G FORCE

PLANE OF ACCELERATION

VISUAL AND GRAVITATIONAL CONFLICT

Both visual and postural orientation are influenced by the visual framework. Both are likewise influenced by resultant g forces acting on the body. There is some controversy over which cues, visual or gravitational, are predominant as determinants of our orientation, but it may safely be said that our judgments, in cases of conflict between the two cues, represent a compromise. Such a conflict is present, for example, in an airplane flying in conditions of zero visibility, having an angular acceleration giving a resultant g force on the body, say 45 degrees from the vertical. The cockpit, say 90 degrees from the vertical when this force is acting, represents the whole visual field. Under this conflict of visual and gravitational cues (90 vs 45 degrees), one feels the vertical to be somewhere between them, with the bulk of the evidence indicating that the judgment is closer to the gravitational than to the visual forces. The condition illustrated, in which a pilot's orientation with respect to the earth is disturbed, is called "aviator's vertigo." Visual indicators which show the plane's true attitude to the pilot, and proper training in the use of these instruments, help suppress any actions on his part that might be taken on the basis of erroneous orientation. There are, of course, physiological effects of g perhaps more dramatic than these perceptual ones.

absence of gravity

With the advent of manned space vehicles and space stations, crew members are subject to a new environment — weightlessness! Although perceptual-motor responses are affected by this lack of gravity, the effects can be overcome quite easily.

Body movements are exaggerated in the absence of opposing gravitational forces. No serious problems occur as long as adequate visual cues and proper anchoring of the body are provided. Other minor problems, such as eating and drinking, loose objects floating about the cabin, or navigating from one point to another, can easily be overcome through adequate design.

Of more serious concern are the problems of physiological system equilibrium over long periods of weightlessness. For example, unless the metabolic balance can be maintained between food intake and energy expenditure through adequate exercise, the body systems (skeletal, muscular, chemical, etc.) tend to deteriorate. Actual shrinkage of tissue and atrophy of the bone structure can occur — much the same as during prolonged bed rest. Such conditions can change the tolerance limits of the individual so that he may not be able to withstand the sudden stress of deceleration during the re-entry phase of a return to earth.

Adequate provision of a "normal" atmospheric environment and a planned program of feeding and exercise will insure the well-being of crews having to operate under sub-gravity conditions.

Some people are more susceptible to the side effects of sub-gravity than others, and become nauseous quite readily. It is therefore necessary to select those persons with a natural immunity to such problems for space crew-members. In addition, it is possible to condition crew members to such conditions before their embarking on space missions. In general, man will be able to perform satisfactorily in the gravity-free state if the normal precautions mentioned here and elsewhere in this guide are taken.

If a man is to perform a turning or tightening task by hand, he can exert his maximum torque with a minimum of resultant body movement if he positions himself so that his body is at right angles to the axis of rotation of his turning task.

A handle should be available within the work area, so that the man can maintain himself in position.

The handhold angle should be as nearly parallel as possible to the imaginary line joining the handhold mid-point and the point of the man's force application. The handhold should never be perpendicular to this line.

Units or push buttons should not require a torque of greater than 2.5 pound feet (the force, of course, depends on the distance of the handhold from the application point of the force) if this torque is to be exerted for longer than 3 seconds.

A large-amplitude, short-time force or torque can be used in many cases to perform a task with less body reaction than that resulting from a smaller, long-time force.

Special tools which fasten to the work and do not require continual application of contact force are best for many maintenance tasks. These tools can simultaneously function as handholds.*

---

*Data on this page from Dzendolet and Rievely.[32]

VIGILANCE

Human vigilance or alertness depends upon many interacting factors. It is of importance to equipment designers principally because of the role of the human operator in a monitoring task. Assuming that the operator has not been deprived of sleep, and that he is not distracted by influences of his own making or introduced by others, it is important to create (through design) an environment which permits the least possible chance for degradation of the operator's level of alertness. The following principles are suggested by Bergum and Klein:[33]

Design the system so that operators do not work in isolation from other persons.

Create an optimum environment in terms of noise, temperature, humidity, illumination, vibration, etc.

Provide sensory signals of large magnitude — i.e., size, intensity, duration, etc.

Restrict the area in which the signal appears.

If the rate of occurrence of a signal is very infrequent — i.e., less than about 20 occurrences per hour — provide artificial signals during the longer periods of "no real signals."

Provide anticipatory auxiliary signals where possible.

Provide confirmation of signal detection so that the operator retains confidence in his judgment of existence or absence of signal.

Wherever possible, signals should persist until they have been seen or heard.

Continuous operation at a monitoring task which requires alertness to infrequent signals should be limited to no more than about 30 minutes. A short interruption, even for "reporting in," will improve the operator's level of alertness for a short time.

Wherever possible, do not create "dim-out" or darkened room conditions for situations which require extreme alertness on the part of an operator. Illumination, like any other perceptual stimulation, is important to vigilance. On the other hand, avoid introducing regular, monotonous stimulations which tend to lull the operator to sleep — e.g., a pulsing noise or vibration.

MAXIMUM RATES OF INFORMATION TRANSFER IN
VARIOUS DIMENSIONS OF SENSORY MODALITIES

MODALITY	DIMENSION	MAXIMUM RATE (BITS/STIMULUS)
Visual	Linear extent	3.25
	Area	2.7
	Direction of line	3.3
	Curvature of line	2.2
	Hue	3.1
	Brightness	3.3
Auditory	Loudness	2.3
	Pitch	2.5
Taste	Saltiness	1.9
Tactile	Intensity	2.0
	Duration	2.3
	Location on the chest	2.8
Smell	Intensity	1.53
(MULTI-DIMENSIONAL MEASUREMENTS)		
Visual	Dot in a square	4.4
	Size, brightness, and hue (all correlated)	4.1
Auditory	Pitch and loudness	3.1
	Pitch, loudness, rate of interruption, on-time fraction, duration, spatial location	7.2
Taste	Saltiness and sweetness	2.3

SOURCES: Hake and Garner,[34] Miller,[35] Ericksen, and Hake,[36] Garner,[37] Pollack,[38] Beebe-Center et al.,[39] Engen and Pfaffmann,[40] Klemmer and Frick,[41] Pollack and Fitts.[42]

SPACE MYOPIA

Empty-space myopia is a condition in which the eyes tend to accommodate for a distance of about 6 meters in front of the observer. This is owing to the lack of something definite on which to focus. Objects beyond this distance are consequently out of focus and may not be seen. This phenomenon occurs at very high altitudes and can be a serious problem if the pilot or astronaut is being depended upon to detect other objects or vehicles. Within the earth's atmosphere the astronaut normally accommodates to a succession of objects or clouds, but in space he has no way to determine whether his eyes are focusing at 6 meters or at infinity.[43]

Distant objects must be detected by electronic methods while they are at great distances; after they have been located, it will be possible to utilize human vision — first through optical systems and finally by direct viewing.

SPACE VISIBILITY

In addition to space myopia, the environment in space creates one more difficult visibility problem — extreme brightness-contrast owing to the absence of light-scattering atmosphere. The only parts of objects which will be seen in deep space are those which reflect the sun's light rays directly. Any portion of the object which is in shadow will not appear at all as far as the observer is concerned. Searchlights will be a necessary requirement of seeing objects when they are in the shadow of the earth or other planet nearby. Space vehicles which are expected to rendezvous or operate in close proximity to each other require external position lights much the same as does an aircraft.

references

1. Boring, E.G. *et al. Foundations of Psychology* Wiley, 1948, p. 361.

2. Fulton, J.F. *Physiology of the Nervous System* Oxford University Press, 1938, p. 8.

3. Boring, E.G. *et al. Introduction to Psychology* Wiley, 1939, pp. 622-623.

4. Breeze, R.K. *Space Vehicle Environmental Control Requirements Based on Equipment and Physiological Criteria* (North American Aviation, Inc., Aerospace Systems Division, Technical Report no. 61-161, pt. 1) December 1961.

5. Morgan, C.T. *Physiological Psychology* McGraw-Hill, 1943, p. 48.

6. Fitts, P.M., and Crannell, C. *Location Discrimination. II. Accuracy of Reaching Movements to Twenty-four Different Areas* (Air Force, Air Materiel Command, Technical Report no. 5833) 1950.

7. Chapanis, A. *et al. Applied Experimental Psychology* Wiley, 1949, (a) p. 281; (b) p. 286.

8. Fitts, P.M. "Engineering Psychology and Equipment Design" Chapter 35 in Stevens, S.S. (ed.) *Handbook of Experimental Psychology* Wiley, 1951, (a), p. 1330; (b), p. 1325.

9. Elkind, J.I. *Characteristics of Simple Manual Control Systems* (Massachusetts Institute of Technology, Lincoln Laboratory, Technical Report no. 111) April 1956.

10. Raggazini, J.R. "Engineering Aspects of the Human Being as a Servo-Mechanism," Unpublished paper presented at American Psychological Association meeting, 1948.

11. Searle, L.V., and Taylor, F.V. "Studies of Tracking Behavior. I. Rate and Time Characteristics of Simple Corrective Movements" *Journal of Experimental Psychology* vol. 38, 1948, pp. 615-631.

12. Craik, K.J.W. "Theory of the Human Operator in Control Systems. I. The Operator as an Engineering System" *British Journal of Psychology* vol. 38, 1947.

13. Hick, W.E. "The Discontinuous Functioning of the Human Operator in Pursuit Tasks" *Quarterly Journal of Experimental Psychology* vol. 1, 1948, pp. 36-51.

14. Tustin, A. "The Nature of the Operator's Response in Manual Control and Its Implications for Controller Design" *Journal of the Institute of Electrical Engineers* (British) vol. 94 (II-A), 1947.

15. Senders, J.W. *Survey of Human Dynamics Data and a Sample Application* (Air Force. Wright Air Development Center, Technical Report no. 59-712) November 1959.

16. Diamantides, N.D. "Man as a Link in the Control Loop" *Electro-Technology* January 1962.

17. Bekey, G.A. *An Investigation of Sampled Data Models of the Human Operator in a Control System* (Air Force. Flight Controls Laboratory, Air Force Systems Command, Technical Documentary Report no. ASD-TDR 62-36) February 1962.

18. McRuer, D., and Krendel, E. *Dynamic Response of Human Operators* (Air Force. Wright Air Development Center, Technical Report no. 56-524) October 1957.

19. Westheimer, G., and Conover, D. "Smooth Eye Movements in the Absence of a Moving Visual Stimulus" *Journal of Experimental Psychology* vol. 47, no. 4, April 1954.

20. Noble, M. *et al.* "The Frequency Response of Skilled Subjects in a Pursuit Tracking Task" *Journal of Experimental Psychology* vol. 49, 1955.

21. Chernikoff, R. *et al.* "A Comparison of Pursuit and Compensatory Tracking under Conditions of Aiding and No Aiding" *Journal of Experimental Psychology* vol. 49, 1955.

22. Briggs, G.E. *Pursuit and Compensatory Modes of Information Display: A Review* (Air Force. Air Materiel Command, Aero Medical Research Laboratory Technical Documentary Report no. 62-93) August 1962.

23. Taylor, F.V., and Birmingham, H.P. "Studies of Tracking Behavior. II. The Acceleration Pattern of Quick Manual Corrective Responses" *Journal of Experimental Psychology* vol. 38, no. 6, December 1948, p. 786.

24. Barnes, R.M. *Motion and Time Study* 3d ed., Wiley, 1949, p. 144.

25. Hartson, L.D. "Contrasting Approaches to the Analysis of Skilled Movements" *Journal of General Psychology* vol. 20, 1939, pp. 265, 268, 269.

26. Tufts College Institute for Applied Experimental Psychology *Handbook of Human Engineering Data for Design Engineers* (Technical Report no. SDC 199-1-1) 1 December 1949, pt. 6, Chapter 4, sec. 1, p. 1.

27. Wendt, G.R. "Vestibular Functions" Chapter 31 in Stevens, S.S. (ed.) *Handbook of Experimental Psychology* Wiley, 1951, pp. 1199-1200.

28. McFarland, R.A. *Human Factors in Air Transport Design* McGraw-Hill, 1946, pp. 360-362.

29. Mann, C.W. *et al.* "The Perception of the Vertical. I. Visual and Non-Labyrinthine Cues" *Journal of Experimental Psychology* vol. 39, no. 4, August 1949, pp. 538-547.

30. Jones, R.E. *et al. Investigation of Errors Made by Pilots in Judging the Attitude of an Aircraft without the Aid of Vision* (Air Force. Air Materiel Command, Aero Medical Laboratory Memorandum Report no. TSEAA-694-13) 1947.

31. Passey, G.E. *Perception of the Vertical. VI. Adjustment to the Vertical with Normal and Tilted Visual Frames of Reference* U. S. Naval School of Aviation Medicine Research and Tulane University, Joint Report no. 10, 1949.

32. Dzendolet, E., and Rievley, J.F. *Man's Ability to Apply Certain Torques while Weightless* (Air Force. Wright Air Development Center, Technical Report no. 59-94) April 1959.

33. Bergum, B.O., and Klein, I.C. *A Survey and Analysis of Vigilance Research* Unpublished working paper, U.S. Army Air Defense Human Research Unit, Fort Bliss, Texas, December 1960.

34. Hake, W.W., and Garner, W.R. "The Effect of Presenting Various Numbers of Discrete Steps on Scale and Scale Reading Accuracy" *Journal of Experimental Psychology* vol. 41, 1951, pp. 358-366.

35. Miller, G.A. "The Magical Number Seven, Plus or Minus Two: Some Limits on Our Capacity for Processing Information" *Psychological Review* vol. 63, 1956, pp. 81-97.

36. Eriksen, C.W., and Hake, H.W., "Multidimensional Stimulus Differences and Accuracy of Discrimination" *Journal of Experimental Psychology* vol. 50, 1955, pp. 153-160.

37. Garner, W.R. "An Informational Analysis of Absolute Judgment of Loudness" *Journal of Experimental Psychology* vol. 46, 1953, pp. 373-380.

38. Pollack, I. "The Information of Elementary Auditory Displays" *Journal of the Acoustical Society of America* vol. 14, 1952.

39. Beebe-Center, J.G. *et al.* "Transmission of Information about Sucrose and Saline Solution through the Sense of Taste" *Journal of Psychology* vol. 39, 1955, pp. 157-160.

40. Engen, T., and Pfaffmann, C. "Absolute Judgment of Odor Intensity" *Journal of Experimental Psychology* vol. 58, 1959, pp. 23-36.

41. Klemmer, E.T., and Frick, F.C. "Assimilation of Information from Dot and Matrix Patterns" *Journal of Experimental Psychology* vol. 45, 1953, pp. 15-19.

42. Pollack, I., and Fitts, L. "Information of Multidimensional Auditory Displays" *Journal of the Acoustical Society of America* vol. 26, 1954, pp. 155-158.

43. *The Time Course of Night and Space Myopia*, Aerospace Medical Division, 6570th Aerospace Medical Research Laboratories, Report no. AMRL-TDR-62-80 (Final Report), August 1962.

recommended human engineering basic reference shelf

BOOKS

Benson, O.O., and Strughold, H. (eds.) *Physics and Medicine of the Atmosphere and Space* John Wiley & Sons, Inc., New York, 1960.

Borko, H. *Computer Applications in the Behavioral Sciences* Prentice-Hall, Inc., Englewood Cliffs, N.J., 1962.

Chapanis, A. *Research Techniques in Human Engineering* Johns Hopkins Press, Baltimore, 1959.

Dreyfuss, H. *The Measure of Man: Human Factors in Design* Whitney Library of Design, 18 E. 50th St., New York 22, 1960.

Eckman, D.P. *Systems: Research and Design* John Wiley & Sons, Inc., New York, 1961.

Flaherty, B.E. *Psychophysicological Aspects of Space Flight*, Columbia University Press, New York, 1961.

Fogel, L. J. *Biotechnology: Concepts and Applications* Prentice-Hall Inc., Englewood Cliffs, N.J., 1963.

Gagne, R.M., and Melton, A.W. (eds.) *Psychological Principles in System Development* Holt, Rinehart and Winston Inc., New York, 1962.

Gantz, K.F. *Man in Space* Duell, Sloan and Pearce, New York, 1959.

Gauer, O.H., and Suidema, G.D. *Gravitational Stress in Aerospace Medicine* Little, Brown and Co., Boston, 1961.

I.E.S. Lighting Handbook 3d ed, Illuminating Engineering Society, 1860 Broadway, New York 23, 1959.

Koelle, H.H. ed. *Handbook of Astronautical Engineering* McGraw-Hill Book Co., Inc., New York, 1961.

McCormick, E.J. *Human Engineering* McGraw-Hill Book Co., Inc., New York, 1957.

Morgan, C.T. et al. (ed.) *Human Engineering Guide to Equipment Design* McGraw-Hill Book Co. Inc., New York, 1963.

Paul Webb Associates *NASA Life Sciences Data Book* National Aeronautics and Space Administration, Office of Manned Space Flight, Washington, D.C., 1962.

Pierce, J.R. *Symbols, Signals and Noise: The Nature and Process of Communication* Harper & Brothers, New York, 1961.

Sells, S.B., and Berry, C.A. *Human Factors in Jet and Space Travel* Ronald Press, New York, 1961.

Shilling, C.W. *The Human Machine* United States Naval Institute, Annapolis, Md., 1955.

Stevens, S.S. (ed.) *Handbook of Experimental Psychology* John Wiley & Sons, Inc., New York, 1951.

Thompson, G.V.E. *Space Research and Technology* Gordon & Breach Science Publishers, 150 Fifth Ave., New York 11, 1962.

Tufts College Institute for Applied Experimental Psychology *Handbook of Human Engineering Data for Design Engineers* (Technical Report no. SDC 199-1-2) 2d ed.

Van Doren, H. *Industrial Design* 2d ed. McGraw-Hill Book Co., Inc., New York, 1954.

Wiener, N. *Cybernetics, or Control and Communication in the Animal and the Machine* 2d ed. Massachusetts Institute of Technology Press and John Wiley and Sons, Inc., New York, 1961.

REPORTS

Brody, A.L., and Weinstock, S. *Mathematical Theories in Performance, Decision Making and Learning: A Literature Review* 6570th Aerospace Medical Research Laboratory, Aerospace Medical Division, Aerospace Systems Division (Report no. MRL-TDR-62-76) July 1962.

Demaree, R.G., and Marks, M.R. *Development of Qualitative and Quantitative Personnel Requirements Information* 6570th Aerospace Medical Research Laboratory Wright-Patterson Air Force Base (Report no. MRL-TDR-62,4) December 1962.

Federal Electric Corp. *Maintainability Design Criteria Handbook for Designers of Shipboard Electronic Equipment* (NAVSHIPS 94324) Government Printing Office, Washington, D.C., 1962.

Fitts, P.M. "Functions of Man in Complex Systems" *Aerospace Engineering* January 1962.

Losee, J.E. et al, *Methods for Computing Manpower Requirements for Weapon Systems under Development* Aerospace Systems Division, Wright-Patterson Air Force Base (Technical Report no. 61-361) August 1961.

Miller, R.B. *Manual for Man-Machine Job-Task Description* American Institute for Research, Pittsburgh, Penna., June, 1955.

North American Aviation, Inc. *Environmental Control Systems Selection for Manned Space Vehicles* Part I, vol. 1, Aerospace Systems Division, Wright-Patterson Air Force Base (Technical Report no. 61-240) December 1961.

Wulfeck, J.W. et al. *Vision in Military Aviation* (Air Force. Wright Air Development Center, Technical Report no. 58-399) November 1958.

UNITED STATES GOVERNMENT REGULATORY DOCUMENTS

MIL STD 203—*Cockpit Controls; Location and Actuation of, for Fixed Wing Aircraft.* Standardization Division, Office of the Assistant Secretary of Defense (Supply and Logistics), Washington 25, D. C.

MIL STD 250—*Cockpit Controls; Location and Actuation of, for Helicopters.* Standardization Division, Office of the Assistant Secretary of Defense (Supply and Logistics), Washington 25, D. C.

MIL STD 411—*Aircrew Station Signals.* Standardization Division, Armed Forces Supply Support Center, Washington 25, D. C.

MIL STD 803—*Human Engineering Criteria for Aircraft, Missile and Space Systems, Ground Support Equipment.* Director of Administrative Services, Hq. Space Systems Division, Air Force Systems Command, Air Force Unit Post Office, Los Angeles 45, California.

FED STD 595—*Colors.* Standardization Division, Federal Supply Service, General Services Administration, 7th & D Street, S. W., Washington, D. C.

AFR 30-8—*Planning and Programming for System Personnel.* Director of Administrative Services, Hq. United States Air Force, The Pentagon, Washington 25, D. C.

MIL-H-27894(USAF)—*Human Engineering Requirements for Aerospace Systems and Equipment.* Director of Administrative Services, Hq. United States Air Force, The Pentagon, Washington 25, D. C.

MIL-D-26239(USAF)—*Data, Qualitative and Quantitative Personnel Requirements Information (QQPRI).* Director of Administrative Services, Hq. United States Air Force, The Pentagon, Washington 25, D. C.

MIL-H-22174(AER)—*Human Factors Data for Aircraft and Missile Systems.* Commanding Officer, Naval Aviation Supply Depot, 5801 Tabor Avenue, Philadelphia 20, Pa., Attn: Code CDS.

NAVEXOS P-643—*Handbook of Human Engineering Data for Design Engineers.* Commanding Officer, Naval Aviation Supply Depot, 5801 Tabor Avenue, Philadelphia 20, Pa., Attn: Code CDS.

OCTI 200-1-59—*Human Factors Engineering in Ordnance Materiel Research, Development, and Evaluation.* U. S. Army Ordnance, Human Engineering Laboratories, Aberdeen Proving Ground, Md.

SCL-1787—*Human Factors Engineering for Signal Corps Systems and Equipment.* U. S. Army Signal Corps Laboratories, Fort Monmouth, N. J., Attn: The Adjutant.

U.S. Army TM 21-62—*Manual of Standard Practice for Human Factors in Military Vehicle Design.* R. E. Hedgcock, J. W. Lewis, and F. M. McIntyre, U. S. Army Human Engineering Laboratories, Aberdeen Proving Ground, Md., August 1962.

subject index